The
Human Body
Identification Manual

The Human Body
Identification Manual

**YOUR
BODY
&
HOW
IT
WORKS**

QUAD BOOKS

Quarto is the authority on a wide range of topics.

Quarto educates, entertains and enriches the lives of our readers—enthusiasts and lovers of hands-on living.

www.QuartoKnows.com

First published in 2010 by
Global Book Publishing Pty Ltd
10.2 Level 10, 8 West Street,
North Sydney, 2060, Australia

ISBN 978-0-85762-471-0

Copyright © Global Book Publishing Pty Ltd 2016

Printed and Bound in China

Conceived, designed and produced by Global Book Publishing Pty Ltd

Latin terminology consultant: Professor Ian Whitmore

Chief consultant on 2010 edition: Ken W. S. Ashwell

Design: Kate Haynes, Stan Lamond, Kylie Mulquin

Illustrations:
David Carroll, Peter Child, Deborah Clarke, Geoff Cook, Marcus Cremonese, Beth Croce, Hans De Haas, Wendy de Paauw, Levant Efe, Mike Golding, Mike Gorman, Jeff Lang, Alex Lavroff, Ulrich Lehmann, Ruth Lindsay, Richard McKenna, Annabel Milne, Tony Pyrzakowski, Oliver Rennert, Caroline Rodrigues, Otto Schmidinger, Bob Seal, Vicky Short, Graeme Tavendale, Jonathan Tidball, Paul Tresnan, Valentin Varetsa, Glen Vause, Spike Wademan, Trevor Weekes, Paul Williams, David Wood

c o n t

How This Book Works

The Human Body Identification Manual is a stunning pictorial handbook that reveals the marvels of the human body. By concentrating on graphic elements, this comprehensive book allows people learning about human anatomy to visualize the various parts of the body and their special links to each other quickly and easily.

Divided into 15 chapters, the book begins with an overview of the body systems and regions, followed by an introduction to cells and tissues. Subsequent chapters identify the structures and functions of the major body systems, from the skeletal and muscular to the endocrine and reproductive.

The book features over 500 anatomically correct illustrations with clear and informative labels showing both the English and formal medical terminology. Short but instructive captions explain physiological processes, microscopic structures, and other difficult anatomical concepts. As well as showing the location and name of hundreds of body parts, the color illustrations also reveal the unique composition of the human form.

In some instances, the illustrator has removed one part of the body so that another may be viewed more clearly: for example, in some of the illustrations of the abdominal organs, the liver has been peeled back to show the gallbladder. This is also true of some of the lung illustrations.

Many illustrations are supplemented by a locator diagram, which indicates where the organ is in relation to the rest of the body or shows the position and orientation of a cross-section illustration. The appearance of an organ often depends on the angle from which it is viewed, and for this reason some of the illustration names include an orientation such as Front View, Side View, or Rear View.

For ready reference, each chapter features an individually colored border along the side margins of its pages. The chapter name appears within the colored border on the left-hand page, while the body region or part appears within the colored border on the right-hand page. This helps readers to find the body system and region or part that they are looking for with ease.

Illustration headings
Illustration headings give the name of the body part. The orientation is included if necessary, and right or left limbs are also identified here.

Locator diagrams
Locator diagrams are included to show where in the body the particular organ or part is found, or to establish the body region from which a cross-section illustration has been drawn.

Chapter name

Subject title

~
A [~] means there is no direct Latin translation for this label

Illustrations
Illustrations may show a whole body system, a single organ or body part, or the microstructure of a body part.

Labels
The labels on each illustration name the important parts of the body system, organ, or microstructure. Illustrations showing physiological elements may include labels that identify the processes occurring within the image, and the order in which they happen.

Captions
Captions have been added to illustrations showing physiological or microscopic elements of the body, to make it easier to understand what the illustration is showing.

Body Overview

Overview of the Body Systems

THE SKIN

MUSCULAR SYSTEM

SKELETAL SYSTEM

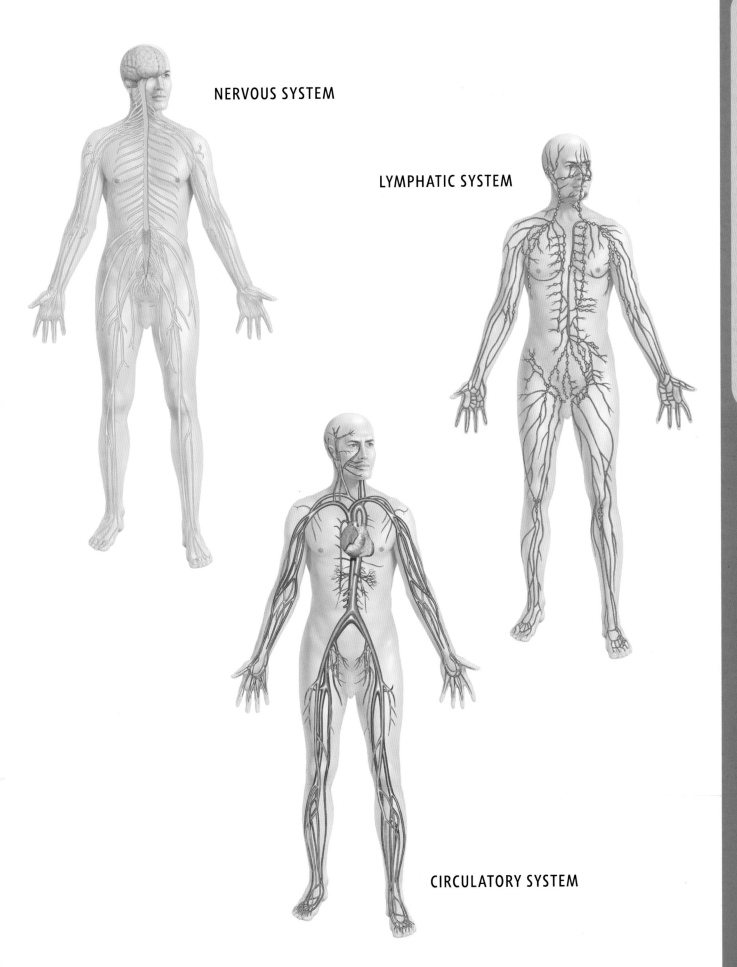

NERVOUS SYSTEM

LYMPHATIC SYSTEM

CIRCULATORY SYSTEM

Overview of the Body Systems

RESPIRATORY SYSTEM

DIGESTIVE SYSTEM

URINARY SYSTEM

ENDOCRINE SYSTEM

REPRODUCTIVE SYSTEM

Body Regions

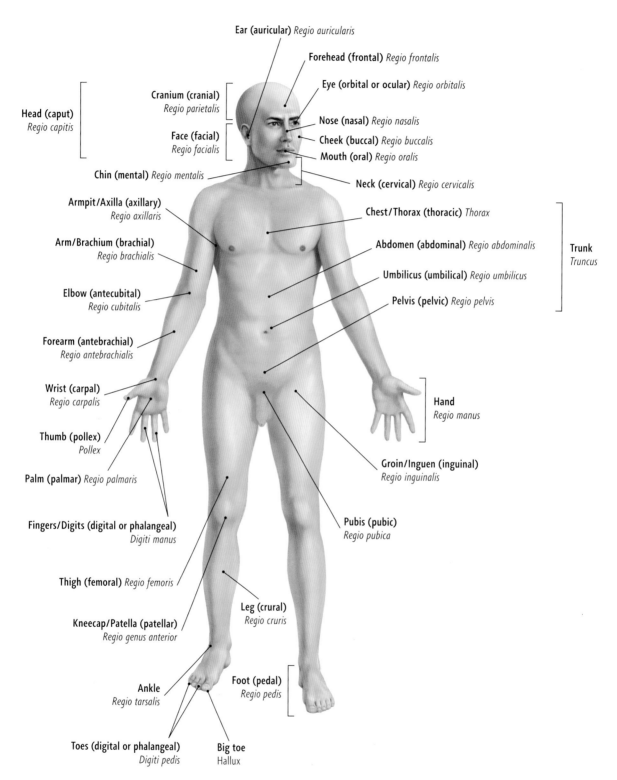

Ear (auricular) *Regio auricularis*

Forehead (frontal) *Regio frontalis*

Eye (orbital or ocular) *Regio orbitalis*

Head (caput)
Regio capitis

Cranium (cranial)
Regio parietalis

Nose (nasal) *Regio nasalis*

Cheek (buccal) *Regio buccalis*

Face (facial)
Regio facialis

Mouth (oral) *Regio oralis*

Chin (mental) *Regio mentalis*

Neck (cervical) *Regio cervicalis*

Armpit/Axilla (axillary)
Regio axillaris

Chest/Thorax (thoracic) *Thorax*

Arm/Brachium (brachial)
Regio brachialis

Abdomen (abdominal) *Regio abdominalis*

Umbilicus (umbilical) *Regio umbilicus*

Trunk
Truncus

Elbow (antecubital)
Regio cubitalis

Pelvis (pelvic) *Regio pelvis*

Forearm (antebrachial)
Regio antebrachialis

Wrist (carpal)
Regio carpalis

Hand
Regio manus

Thumb (pollex)
Pollex

Palm (palmar) *Regio palmaris*

Groin/Inguen (inguinal)
Regio inguinalis

Fingers/Digits (digital or phalangeal)
Digiti manus

Pubis (pubic)
Regio pubica

Thigh (femoral) *Regio femoris*

Leg (crural)
Regio cruris

Kneecap/Patella (patellar)
Regio genus anterior

Foot (pedal)
Regio pedis

Ankle
Regio tarsalis

Toes (digital or phalangeal)
Digiti pedis

Big toe
Hallux

FRONT VIEW

18

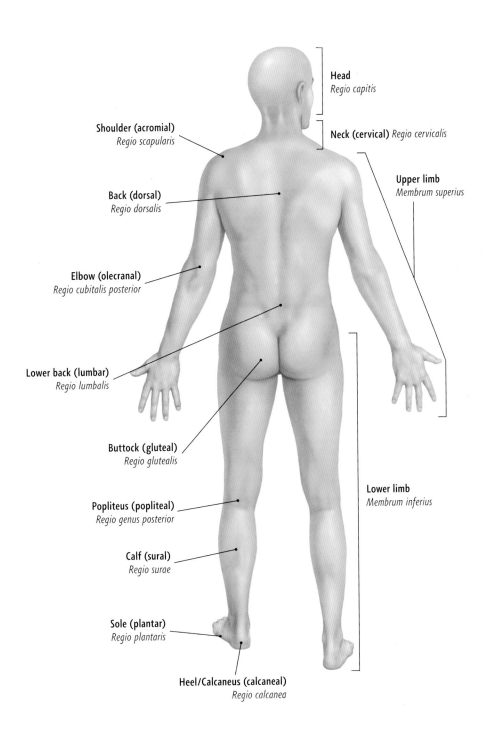

Head
Regio capitis

Shoulder (acromial)
Regio scapularis

Neck (cervical) *Regio cervicalis*

Upper limb
Membrum superius

Back (dorsal)
Regio dorsalis

Elbow (olecranal)
Regio cubitalis posterior

Lower back (lumbar)
Regio lumbalis

Buttock (gluteal)
Regio glutealis

Lower limb
Membrum inferius

Popliteus (popliteal)
Regio genus posterior

Calf (sural)
Regio surae

Sole (plantar)
Regio plantaris

Heel/Calcaneus (calcaneal)
Regio calcanea

REAR VIEW

Body Regions

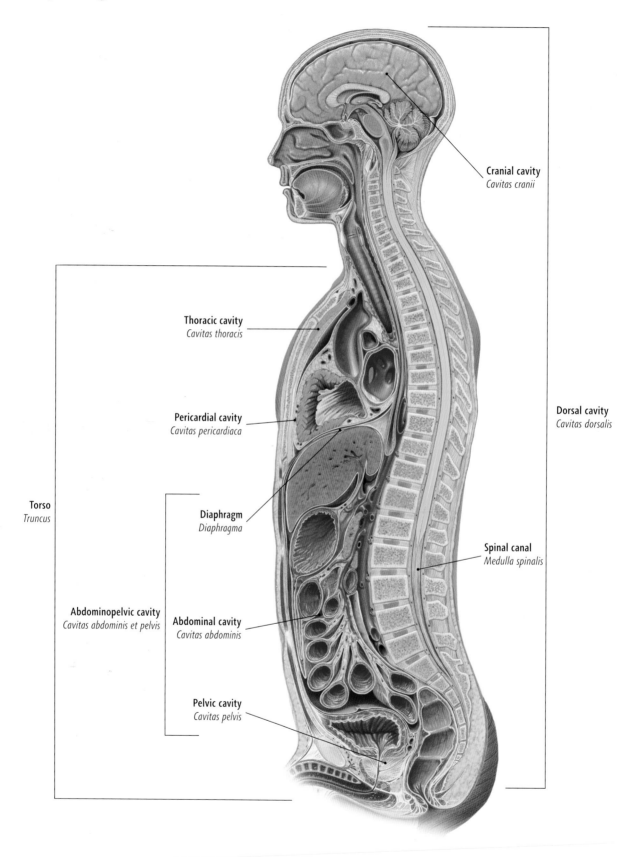

Cranial cavity
Cavitas cranii

Thoracic cavity
Cavitas thoracis

Dorsal cavity
Cavitas dorsalis

Pericardial cavity
Cavitas pericardiaca

Torso
Truncus

Diaphragm
Diaphragma

Spinal canal
Medulla spinalis

Abdominopelvic cavity
Cavitas abdominis et pelvis

Abdominal cavity
Cavitas abdominis

Pelvic cavity
Cavitas pelvis

BODY CAVITIES—CROSS-SECTIONAL VIEW

Body Shapes

ECTOMORPH FEMALE

MESOMORPH FEMALE

ENDOMORPH FEMALE

ECTOMORPH MALE

MESOMORPH MALE

ENDOMORPH MALE

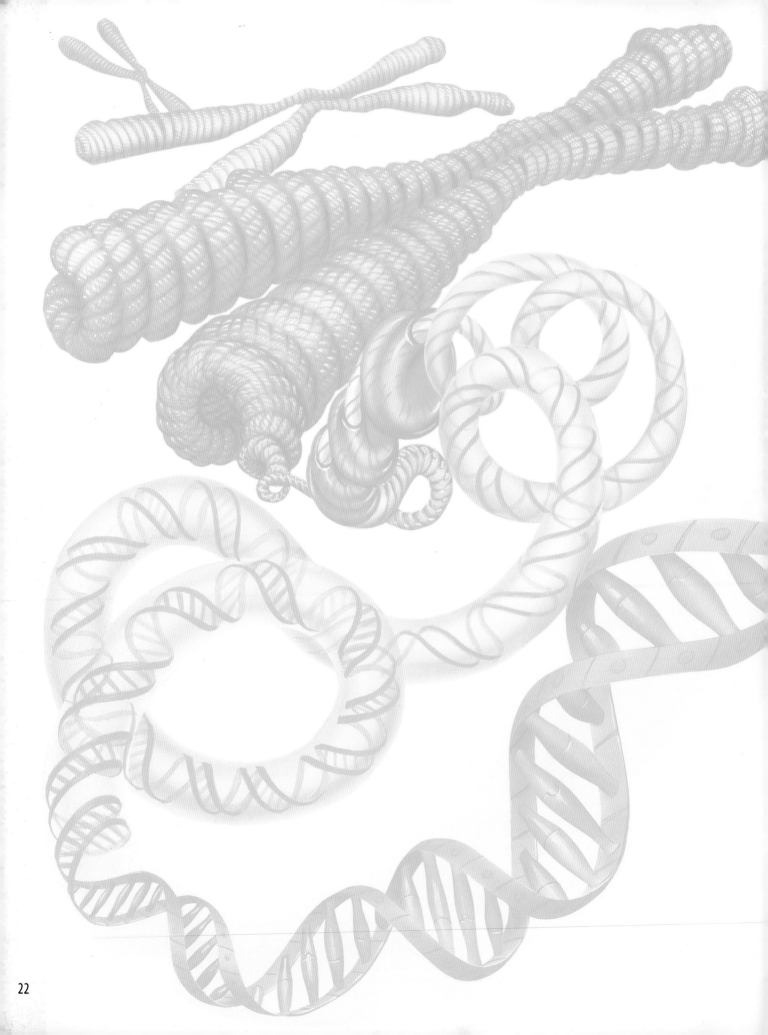

Cells and Tissues

Cell Structure and Major Cell Types

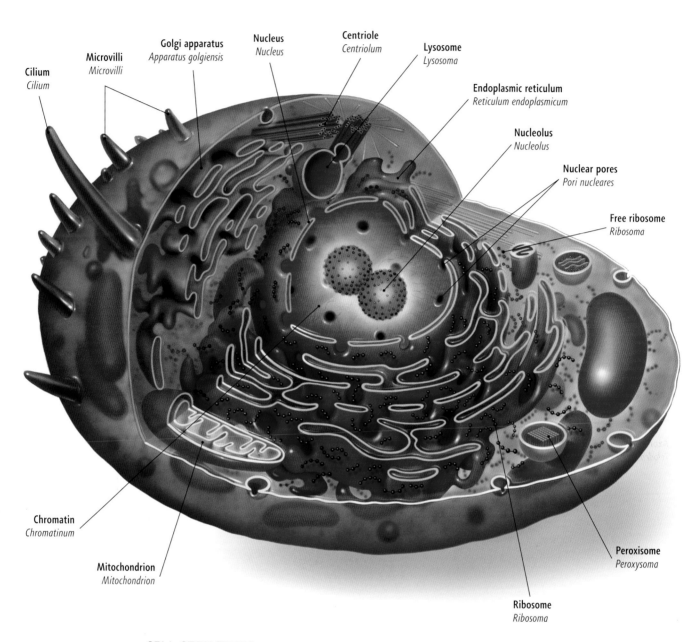

Cilium
Cilium

Microvilli
Microvilli

Golgi apparatus
Apparatus golgiensis

Nucleus
Nucleus

Centriole
Centriolum

Lysosome
Lysosoma

Endoplasmic reticulum
Reticulum endoplasmicum

Nucleolus
Nucleolus

Nuclear pores
Pori nucleares

Free ribosome
Ribosoma

Chromatin
Chromatinum

Mitochondrion
Mitochondrion

Peroxisome
Peroxysoma

Ribosome
Ribosoma

CELL STRUCTURE

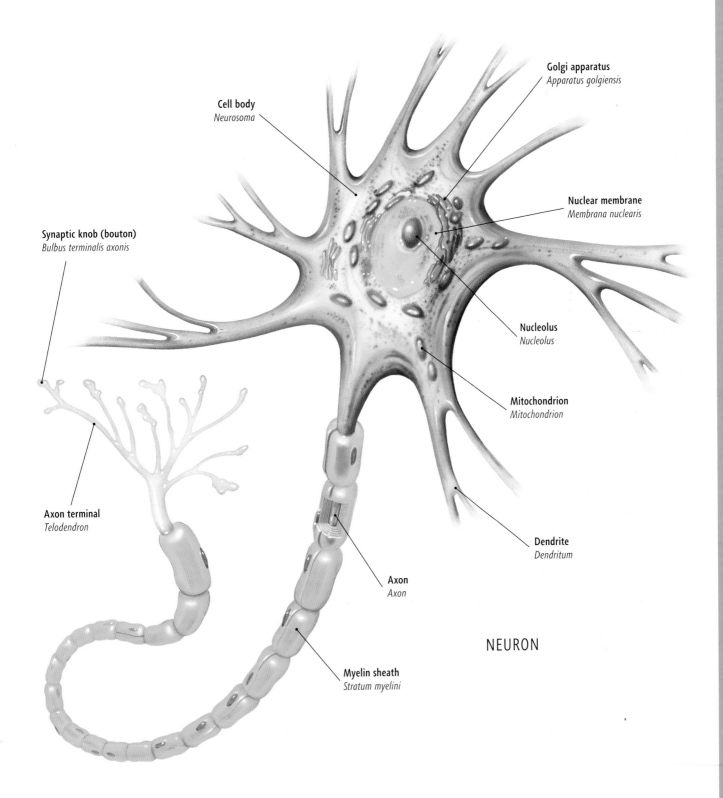

Golgi apparatus
Apparatus golgiensis

Cell body
Neurosoma

Nuclear membrane
Membrana nuclearis

Synaptic knob (bouton)
Bulbus terminalis axonis

Nucleolus
Nucleolus

Mitochondrion
Mitochondrion

Axon terminal
Telodendron

Dendrite
Dendritum

Axon
Axon

NEURON

Myelin sheath
Stratum myelini

Blood Cells

COMPONENTS
OF BLOOD

White blood cell (eosinophil)
Leucocytus (eosinophilus)

Nucleus of endothelial cell
Nucleus endotheliocyti

White blood cell (lymphocyte)
Leucocytus (lymphocytus)

White blood cell (neutrophil)
Leucocytus (neutrophilus)

Platelets
Thrombocyti

Red blood cells
Erythrocyti

White blood cell (basophil)
Leucocytus (basophilus)

White blood cell (monocyte)
Leucocytus (monocytus)

Basal lamina
Lamina basalis

Heme
~

Globin protein strand
~

RED BLOOD CELL

Iron ion
~

RED BLOOD CELL CONTENT

[~] = no direct Latin equivalent

Monocyte
Monocytus

Macrophage
Macrophagocytus

Neutrophil
Neutrophilus

Basophil
Basophilus

Eosinophil
Eosinophilus

Lymphocyte
Lymphocytus

WHITE BLOOD CELLS

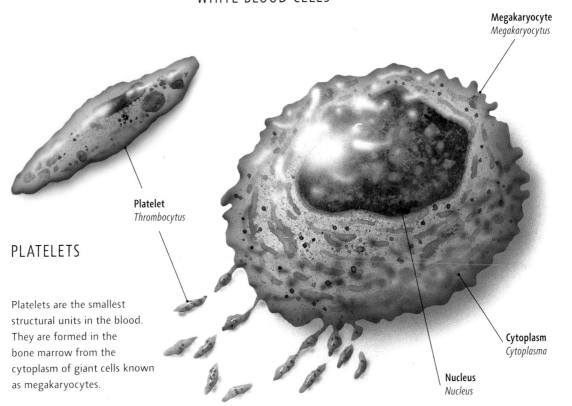

Megakaryocyte
Megakaryocytus

Platelet
Thrombocytus

Cytoplasm
Cytoplasma

Nucleus
Nucleus

PLATELETS

Platelets are the smallest structural units in the blood. They are formed in the bone marrow from the cytoplasm of giant cells known as megakaryocytes.

Healing

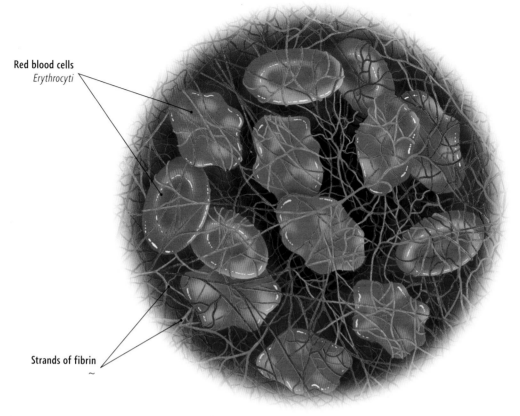

Red blood cells
Erythrocyti

Strands of fibrin
~

BLOOD CLOT

Scar tissue
~

Normal epidermis
Epidermis solitus

Fibrous scar tissue
Textus fibrosus

Normal dermis
Dermis solitus

SCAR

[~] = no direct Latin equivalent

BLOOD CLOTTING

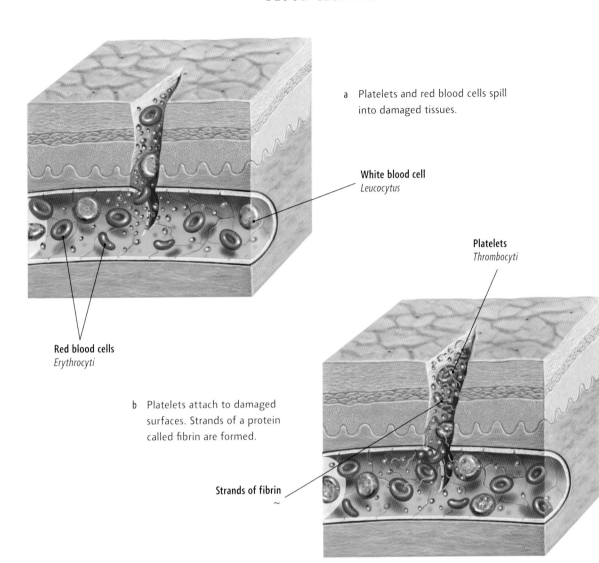

a   Platelets and red blood cells spill into damaged tissues.

White blood cell
Leucocytus

Platelets
Thrombocyti

Red blood cells
Erythrocyti

b   Platelets attach to damaged surfaces. Strands of a protein called fibrin are formed.

Strands of fibrin
~

Clot
Concretus sanguis

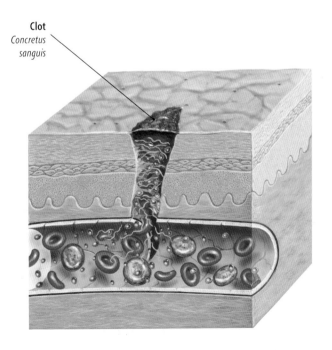

c   Blood cells, platelets, and fibrin strands become entangled and form a clot.

[~] = no direct Latin equivalent

DNA

Chromosome
Chromosoma

Chromosome strand
Chromatid

**Codon: sequence
for one amino acid
(three pairs of bases)**
*Codon: sequence
for one amino acid
(three pairs of bases)*
*Codon: sequence
for one amino acid
(three pairs of bases)*

Base pairs
~

**Sugar and
phosphate units**
~

DNA REPLICATION

DNA passes on its genetic information to protein factories
(ribosomes) within cells by creating a messenger acid (mRNA).

a   To make mRNA, the DNA ladder separates lengthwise.

b   One of the separated DNA strands is used as a template
    to make an mRNA strand.

c   The mRNA leaves the cell and passes into the cytoplasm, where
    it gives the ribosomes the information needed to produce proteins.

d   The two chains of DNA now join back together into a spiral ladder.

[~] = no direct Latin equivalent

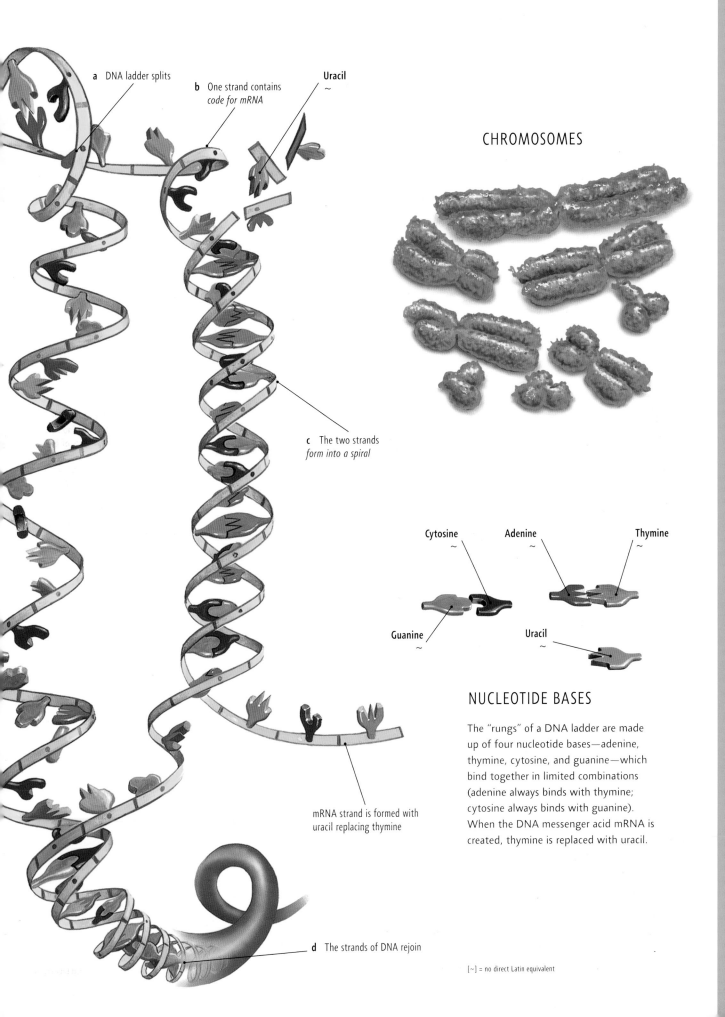

a DNA ladder splits

b One strand contains *code for mRNA*

Uracil ~

c The two strands *form into a spiral*

mRNA strand is formed with uracil replacing thymine

d The strands of DNA rejoin

CHROMOSOMES

Cytosine ~

Adenine ~

Thymine ~

Guanine ~

Uracil ~

NUCLEOTIDE BASES

The "rungs" of a DNA ladder are made up of four nucleotide bases—adenine, thymine, cytosine, and guanine—which bind together in limited combinations (adenine always binds with thymine; cytosine always binds with guanine). When the DNA messenger acid mRNA is created, thymine is replaced with uracil.

[~] = no direct Latin equivalent

Genes and Heredity

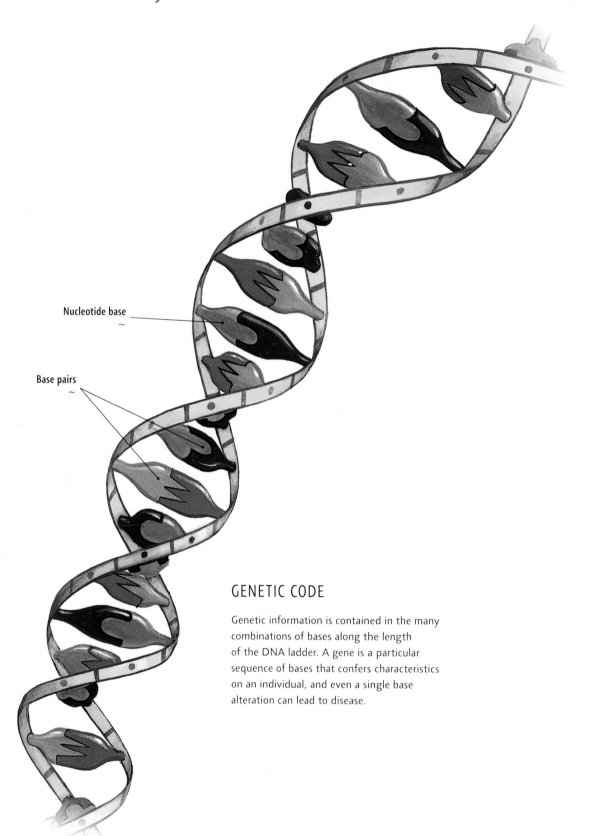

Nucleotide base
~

Base pairs
~

GENETIC CODE

Genetic information is contained in the many combinations of bases along the length of the DNA ladder. A gene is a particular sequence of bases that confers characteristics on an individual, and even a single base alteration can lead to disease.

[~] = no direct Latin equivalent

a · Mother · Father · Children

DOMINANT AND RECESSIVE GENES

Some features, such as eye color, are determined by a single gene. The gene for brown eyes is dominant over the gene for blue eyes. Two parents with brown eyes can only have a blue-eyed child if the child inherits a recessive blue gene from both parents (a). If one parent with brown eyes has two dominant brown-eye genes, all children will inherit at least one dominant gene and will have brown eyes (b).

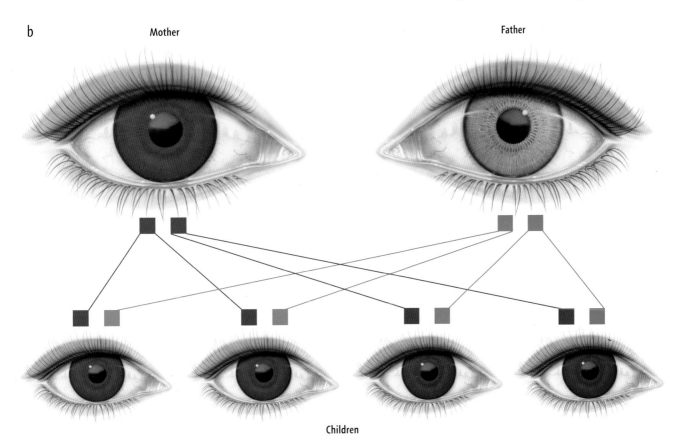

b · Mother · Father · Children

Bacteria

Bacteria are simple organisms of microscopic size. Many are beneficial and live in harmony with humans. Some are harmful and can cause and spread infections such as cholera, syphilis, and food poisoning.

**TREPONEMA PALLIDUM
(SYPHILIS)**

**BORRELIA BURGDORFERI
(LYME DISEASE)**

**CLOSTRIDIUM TETANI
(TETANUS)**

**SALMONELLA
(FOOD POISONING)**

**E. COLI
(FOOD POISONING)**

STREPTOCOCCUS
(INFECTION)

NEISSERIA MENINGITIDIS
(MENINGOCOCCAL DISEASE)

NEISSERIA GONORRHOEAE
(GONORRHEA)

VIBRIO CHOLERAE
(CHOLERA)

CHLAMYDIA TRACHOMATIS
(CHLAMYDIA)

Viruses

These tiny organisms are much smaller than bacteria and vary considerably in shape and structure. Some viruses cause acute disease lasting for only a short time and others cause recurring or chronic disease, while others do not cause any disease.

POLIO VIRUS

INFLUENZA VIRUS

HERPES VIRUS

EBOLA VIRUS

ROTAVIRUS (GASTROENTERITIS)

HEPATITIS VIRUS

COLD VIRUS

WART VIRUS

SMALLPOX VIRUS

Capsid (outer protein shell of virus)
Capsa virus

Strands of DNA
~

Viral envelope
Involucrum viri

a Virus enters cell and
discards its viral envelope

Host cell
Cellula hospitalis

c DNA is used to manufacture more DNA,
capsid proteins, and viral proteins

e Some viruses destroy the cell
membrane as they burst out

b Virus separates into capsid
proteins and DNA

Nucleus
Nucleus

e Some viruses leave the cell membrane
intact when they emerge

Cell membrane
Membrana cellularis

d New viral particles form

VIRUS REPLICATION

A virus reproduces by using parts
of a healthy host cell to create clones
of itself. These copies then invade the
body, causing illness.

[~] = no direct Latin equivalent

Immunity

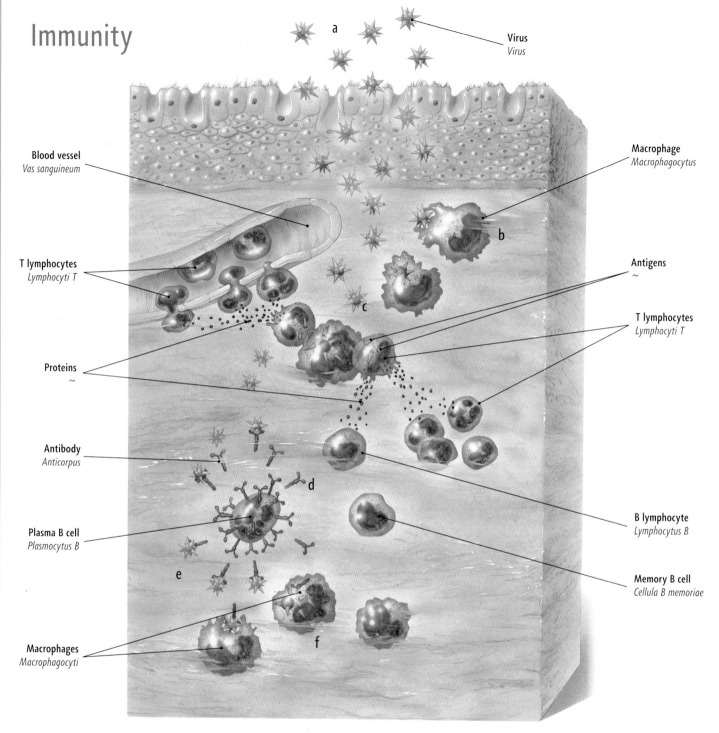

a

Virus
Virus

Blood vessel
Vas sanguineum

Macrophage
Macrophagocytus

T lymphocytes
Lymphocyti T

b

Antigens
~

T lymphocytes
Lymphocyti T

Proteins
~

c

Antibody
Anticorpus

B lymphocyte
Lymphocytus B

d

Plasma B cell
Plasmocytus B

Memory B cell
Cellula B memoriae

e

Macrophages
Macrophagocyti

f

HUMORAL IMMUNE RESPONSE

B lymphocytes (white blood cells) produce antibodies to help identify and eliminate invading antigens (carried by bacteria or viruses). They are helped in the body's defenses by circulating T lymphocytes and macrophages (scavenging white blood cells).

a   Virus particles invade tissue through surface cells and multiply.

b   Virus particles are consumed by macrophages.

c   Macrophages break down the virus and present antigens to circulating T lymphocytes, which release proteins that attract more T and B lymphocytes.

d   B lymphocytes divide into memory B cells (which remember the virus for future attacks) and plasma B cells (which make virus-specific antibodies).

e   Circulating antibodies attach to the virus particles.

f   Macrophages primed to recognize the antibody consume the virus and break it down, saving the body from infection.

[~] = no direct Latin equivalent

ALLERGIC REACTION

The body's exposure to allergens leads to the release of histamine, which causes symptoms such as sneezing and rash.

a On first exposure to allergens, plasma B cells produce antibodies.

b Antibodies attach to mast cells in the body's tissues.

c Subsequent exposure sees allergens captured by antibodies.

d Mast cells respond by releasing histamine.

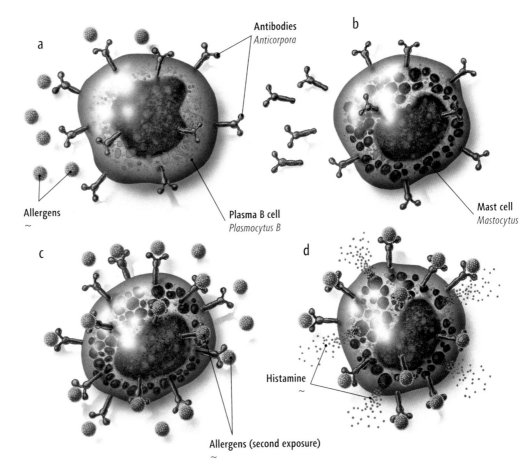

a

Antibodies
Anticorpora

b

Allergens
~

Plasma B cell
Plasmocytus B

Mast cell
Mastocytus

c

d

Histamine
~

Allergens (second exposure)
~

CELL-MEDIATED IMMUNE RESPONSE

T lymphocytes (a type of white blood cell) are responsible for the delayed action of the cell-mediated immune response.

a Circulating macrophages ingest the invading virus.

b Macrophages process the virus and present antigens to T cells.

c T cells produce clones that each play a special role in the immune response: memory T cells remember the invading antigen for future attacks; helper T cells recruit B and T cells to the site of the antigen attack; suppressor T cells inhibit the action of B and T cells; and killer T cells attach to invading antigens and destroy them.

Virus entering macrophage
Virus intrans macrophagocytus

a

b

Antigens
~

c

T cell
Lymphocytus T

Macrophage
Macrophagocytus

Killer T cell
Cellula T cytotoxica

Memory T cell
Cellula T memoriae

Helper T cell
Cellula T adjuvans

Suppressor T cell
Cellula T supprimens

[~] = no direct Latin equivalent

39

Tissues

LOOSE CONNECTIVE TISSUE

Connective tissue is the framework that supports, connects, and fills out body structures.

BONE TISSUE

Spongy or cancellous bone consists of a lattice-work system of bony spikes called trabeculae, arranged in different directions.

ADIPOSE TISSUE

Adipose tissue is a specialized connective tissue that stores fat.

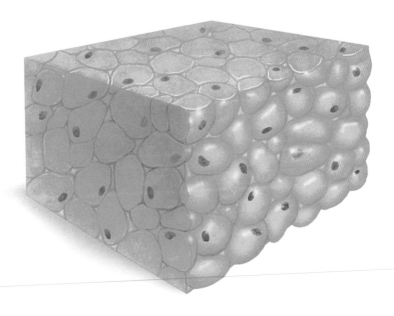

EPITHELIAL TISSUE

Formed from cells that are packed closely together, epithelial tissue is found in the outermost layer of the skin and in some internal organs.

NEURAL TISSUE

The nervous system is made up of neural tissue, which transmits messages to and from the brain.

LYMPHATIC TISSUE

Found at the entrances to the respiratory system and in the digestive and urogenital tracts, lymphatic tissue acts as a first line of defense against infection.

Tissues

MUSCLE TISSUE: SKELETAL MUSCLE

Featuring long, cylindrical muscle fibers, skeletal muscle is usually attached to bones via tendons.

MUSCLE TISSUE: SMOOTH MUSCLE

Smooth muscle is found in the walls of blood vessels, in airways, and inside the eye.

MUSCLE TISSUE: CARDIAC MUSCLE

Found only in the heart, cardiac muscle cannot regenerate after being destroyed.

TENDON TISSUE (RELAXED)

Tendons are constructed primarily of collagen fibers arranged in a regular formation, which provide the strength to attach muscles to bones.

CARTILAGE TISSUE: HYALINE CARTILAGE

Found in many places in the body, hyaline cartilage forms the skeleton in the embryo, the end of the nose and ribs, and the rings around the windpipe.

CARTILAGE TISSUE: FIBROCARTILAGE

Resilient and able to withstand compression, fibrocartilage is located between the bones of the spinal column, hip, and pelvis.

CARTILAGE TISSUE: ELASTIC CARTILAGE

Elastic cartilage is strong but supple, and makes up the epiglottis and the springy part of the outer ear.

LIGAMENT TISSUE (TIGHT)

Ligaments are tough, white, fibrous, slightly elastic tissues that mainly support and strengthen joints.

The Skin, Nails, and Hair

The Skin

Ruffini endings
Corpusculi sensorii fusiformia

Free nerve ending
Terminationes nervorum liberum

Meissner corpuscles
Corpusculi tactile

Hair
Pilus

Horny layer
Stratum corneum

Epidermis
Epidermis

Stratum granulosum
Stratum granulosum

Stratum spinosum
Stratum spinosum

Dermis
Dermis

Sebaceous gland
Glandula sebacea

Subcutaneous fat
Panniculus adiposus

Deep fascia
Fascia profunda

Subcutaneous fat
Panniculus adiposus

Sweat gland
Glandula sudorifera

Nerve endings
Terminationes nervorum

Pacinian corpuscle
Corpusculum lamellosum

Krause bulb
C. bulboideum

Hair follicle
Folliculus pili

Dermal papilla
Papilla dermis

SKIN—CROSS-SECTIONAL VIEW

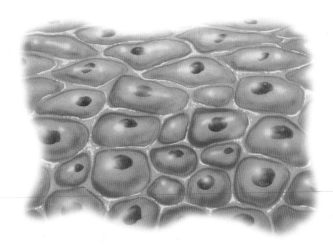

STRATIFIED SQUAMOUS SKIN CELLS

Near the surface of the skin (the horny layer), cells are flattened. The arrangement of cell layers provides a protective shield and prevents dehydration.

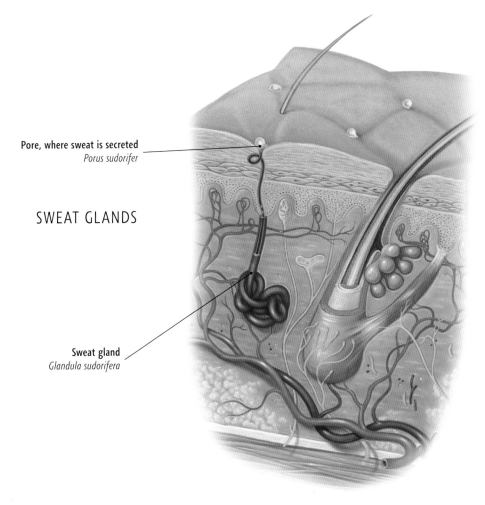

Pore, where sweat is secreted
Porus sudorifer

SWEAT GLANDS

Sweat gland
Glandula sudorifera

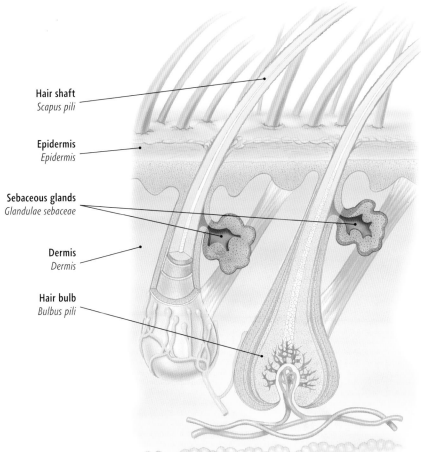

Hair shaft
Scapus pili

Epidermis
Epidermis

Sebaceous glands
Glandulae sebaceae

Dermis
Dermis

Hair bulb
Bulbus pili

SEBACEOUS GLANDS

[~] = no direct Latin equivalent

Skin and Temperature

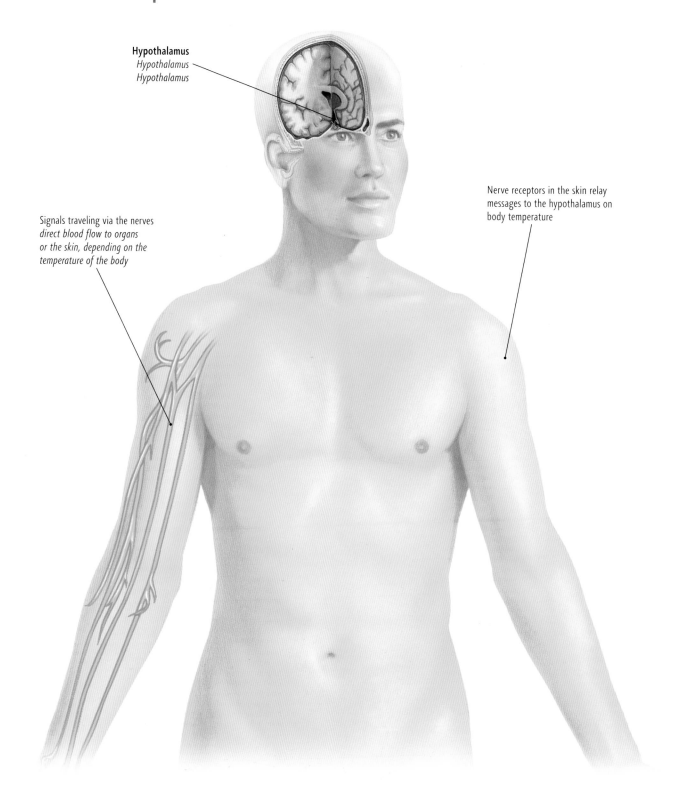

Hypothalamus
Hypothalamus
Hypothalamus

Nerve receptors in the skin relay messages to the hypothalamus on body temperature

Signals traveling via the nerves *direct blood flow to organs or the skin, depending on the temperature of the body*

TEMPERATURE REGULATION

The body has a built-in mechanism regulated by the hypothalamus for maintaining a stable temperature. Nerve endings in the skin relay temperature changes to the hypothalamus. If the body is cold, the hypothalamus increases heat production in the body by increasing the metabolic rate. If the body is hot, the hypothalamus sends blood to the skin, where heat can be lost through radiation, conduction, convection, and evaporation.

SKIN REACTION TO COLD

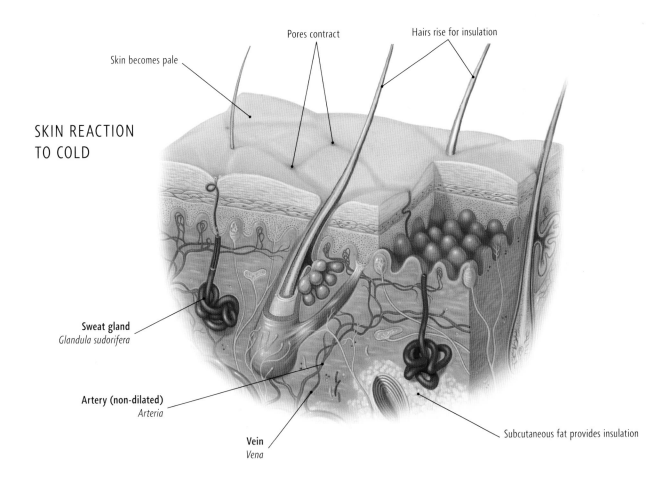

Skin becomes pale

Pores contract

Hairs rise for insulation

Sweat gland
Glandula sudorifera

Artery (non-dilated)
Arteria

Vein
Vena

Subcutaneous fat provides insulation

SKIN REACTION TO HEAT

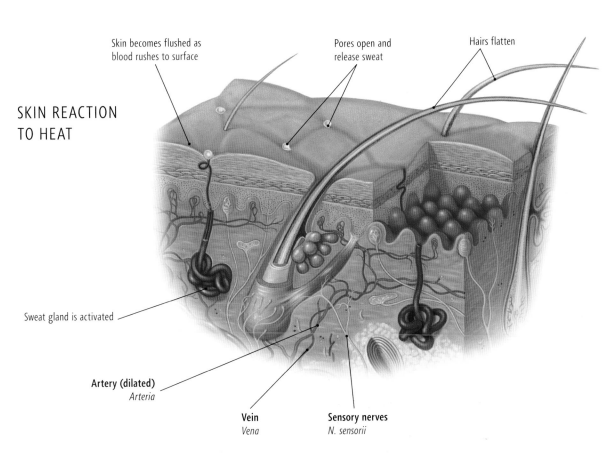

Skin becomes flushed as blood rushes to surface

Pores open and release sweat

Hairs flatten

Sweat gland is activated

Artery (dilated)
Arteria

Vein
Vena

Sensory nerves
N. sensorii

The Hair and Nails

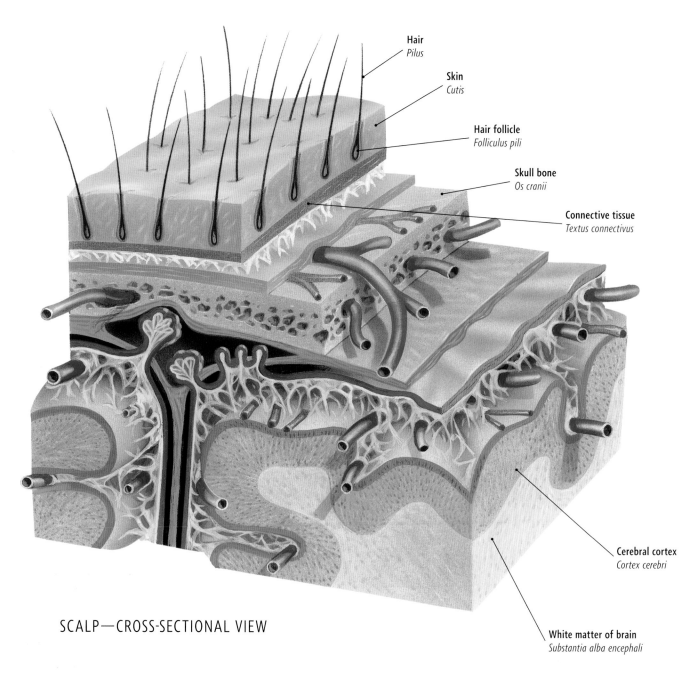

Hair
Pilus

Skin
Cutis

Hair follicle
Folliculus pili

Skull bone
Os cranii

Connective tissue
Textus connectivus

Cerebral cortex
Cortex cerebri

White matter of brain
Substantia alba encephali

SCALP—CROSS-SECTIONAL VIEW

Root of nail
Radix unguis

Cuticle
Cuticula

Lunule
Lunula

Nail
Unguis

NAIL

HAIR FOLLICLE

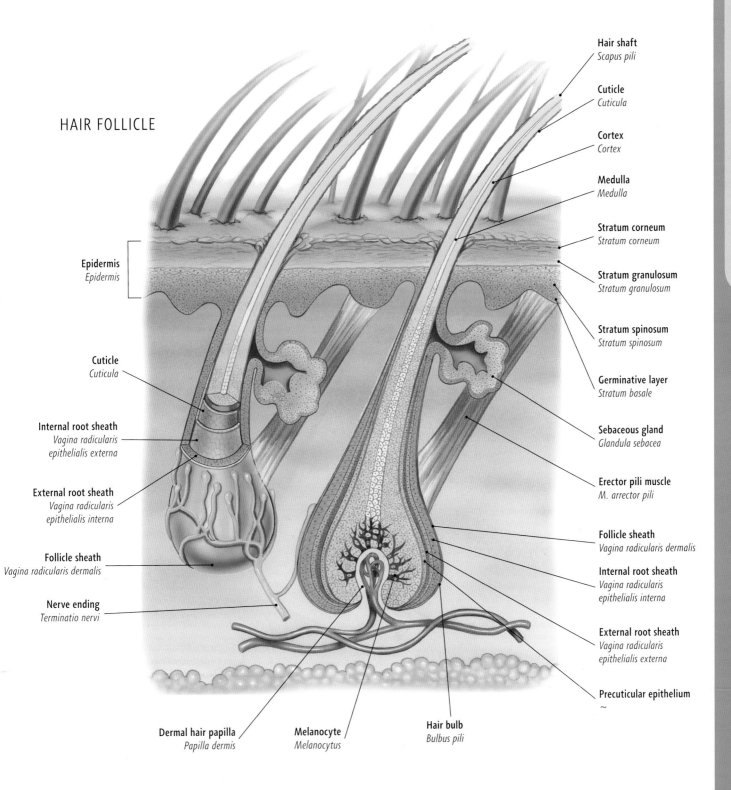

Hair shaft
Scapus pili

Cuticle
Cuticula

Cortex
Cortex

Medulla
Medulla

Stratum corneum
Stratum corneum

Stratum granulosum
Stratum granulosum

Stratum spinosum
Stratum spinosum

Germinative layer
Stratum basale

Sebaceous gland
Glandula sebacea

Erector pili muscle
M. arrector pili

Follicle sheath
Vagina radicularis dermalis

Internal root sheath
Vagina radicularis epithelialis interna

External root sheath
Vagina radicularis epithelialis externa

Precuticular epithelium
~

Epidermis
Epidermis

Cuticle
Cuticula

Internal root sheath
Vagina radicularis epithelialis externa

External root sheath
Vagina radicularis epithelialis interna

Follicle sheath
Vagina radicularis dermalis

Nerve ending
Terminatio nervi

Dermal hair papilla
Papilla dermis

Melanocyte
Melanocytus

Hair bulb
Bulbus pili

[~] = no direct Latin equivalent

51

The Skeletal System

Bones of the Body

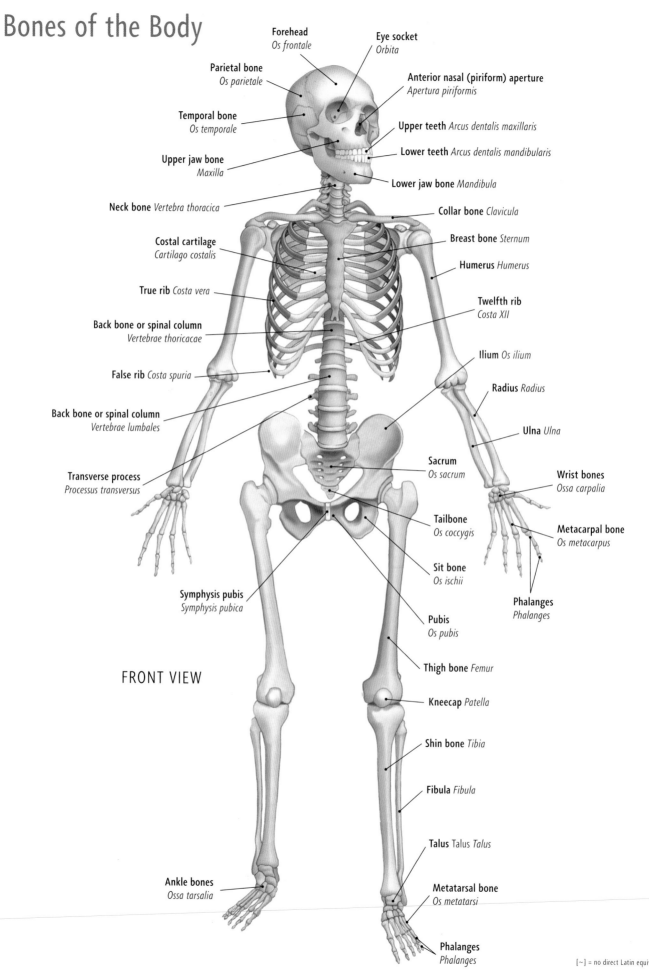

Forehead
Os frontale

Eye socket
Orbita

Parietal bone
Os parietale

Anterior nasal (piriform) aperture
Apertura piriformis

Temporal bone
Os temporale

Upper teeth *Arcus dentalis maxillaris*

Lower teeth *Arcus dentalis mandibularis*

Upper jaw bone
Maxilla

Lower jaw bone *Mandibula*

Neck bone *Vertebra thoracica*

Collar bone *Clavicula*

Breast bone *Sternum*

Costal cartilage
Cartilago costalis

Humerus *Humerus*

True rib *Costa vera*

Twelfth rib
Costa XII

Back bone or spinal column
Vertebrae thoricacae

Ilium *Os ilium*

Radius *Radius*

False rib *Costa spuria*

Ulna *Ulna*

Back bone or spinal column
Vertebrae lumbales

Sacrum
Os sacrum

Wrist bones
Ossa carpalia

Transverse process
Processus transversus

Tailbone
Os coccygis

Metacarpal bone
Os metacarpus

Sit bone
Os ischii

Symphysis pubis
Symphysis pubica

Phalanges
Phalanges

Pubis
Os pubis

FRONT VIEW

Thigh bone *Femur*

Kneecap *Patella*

Shin bone *Tibia*

Fibula *Fibula*

Talus *Talus Talus*

Ankle bones
Ossa tarsalia

Metatarsal bone
Os metatarsi

Phalanges
Phalanges

[~] = no direct Latin equivalent

Parietal bone
Os parietale

Occipital bone
Os occipitale

Cheek bone
Os zygomaticum

Atlas (C1) *Atlas (C1)*

Lower jaw bone *Mandibula*

Axis (C2) *Axis (C2)*

Collar bone
Clavicula

Acromion *Acromion*

Spinous process of thoracic vertebra
Processus spinosus vertebrae thoricacae

Spine of scapula *Spina scapulae*

Back bone or spinal column
Vertebra thoracica

Shoulder blade *Scapula*

Humerus *Humerus*

True rib *Costa vera*

Floating ribs (11 & 12)
Costae fluctuantes (XI et XII)

False rib *Costa spuria*

Ilium *Os ilium*

Back bone or spinal column
Vertebrae lumbales

Radius *Radius*

Ulna *Ulna*

Sacrum
Os sacrum

Wrist bones
Ossa carpalia

Tail bone
Os coccygis

Ischial
tuberosity
*Tuber
ischiadicum*

Metacarpal bones
Ossa metacarpalia

Phalanges
Phalanges

Symphysis pubis
Symphysis pubica

Thigh bone
Femur

REAR VIEW

Lateral condyle
Condylus lateralis femoris

Shin bone
Tibia

Fibula
Fibula

Phalanges
Phalanges

Talus
Talus

Metatarsal bone
Os metatarsi

Heel bone
Calcaneus

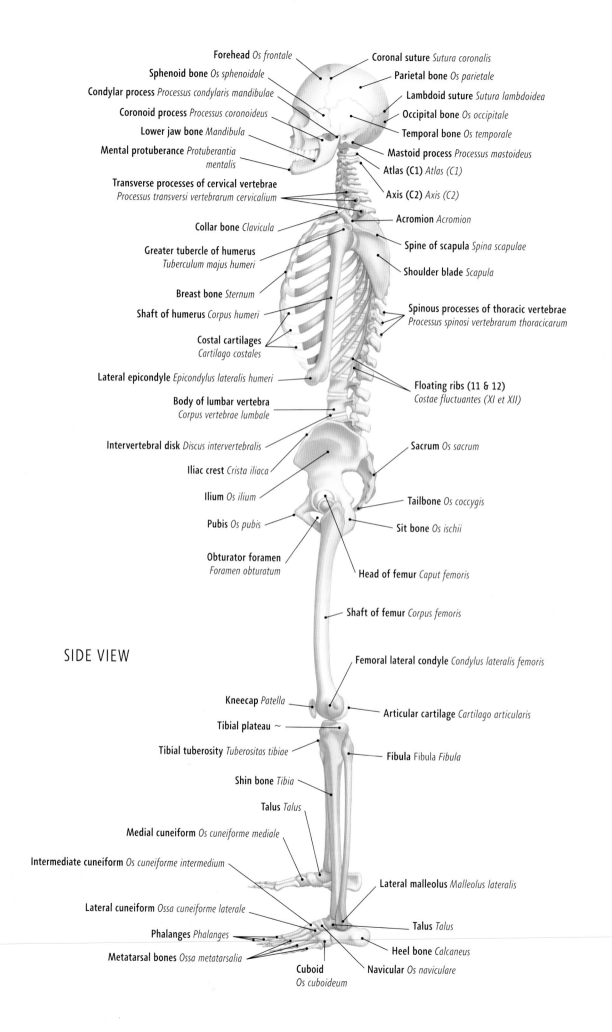

Forehead *Os frontale*

Coronal suture *Sutura coronalis*

Sphenoid bone *Os sphenoidale*

Parietal bone *Os parietale*

Condylar process *Processus condylaris mandibulae*

Lambdoid suture *Sutura lambdoidea*

Coronoid process *Processus coronoideus*

Occipital bone *Os occipitale*

Lower jaw bone *Mandibula*

Temporal bone *Os temporale*

Mental protuberance *Protuberantia mentalis*

Mastoid process *Processus mastoideus*

Atlas (C1) *Atlas (C1)*

Transverse processes of cervical vertebrae *Processus transversi vertebrarum cervicalium*

Axis (C2) *Axis (C2)*

Acromion *Acromion*

Collar bone *Clavicula*

Spine of scapula *Spina scapulae*

Greater tubercle of humerus *Tuberculum majus humeri*

Shoulder blade *Scapula*

Breast bone *Sternum*

Shaft of humerus *Corpus humeri*

Spinous processes of thoracic vertebrae *Processus spinosi vertebrarum thoracicarum*

Costal cartilages *Cartilago costales*

Lateral epicondyle *Epicondylus lateralis humeri*

Floating ribs (11 & 12) *Costae fluctuantes (XI et XII)*

Body of lumbar vertebra *Corpus vertebrae lumbale*

Intervertebral disk *Discus intervertebralis*

Sacrum *Os sacrum*

Iliac crest *Crista iliaca*

Ilium *Os ilium*

Tailbone *Os coccygis*

Pubis *Os pubis*

Sit bone *Os ischii*

Obturator foramen *Foramen obturatum*

Head of femur *Caput femoris*

Shaft of femur *Corpus femoris*

SIDE VIEW

Femoral lateral condyle *Condylus lateralis femoris*

Kneecap *Patella*

Articular cartilage *Cartilago articularis*

Tibial plateau ~

Tibial tuberosity *Tuberositas tibiae*

Fibula Fibula *Fibula*

Shin bone *Tibia*

Talus *Talus*

Medial cuneiform *Os cuneiforme mediale*

Intermediate cuneiform *Os cuneiforme intermedium*

Lateral malleolus *Malleolus lateralis*

Lateral cuneiform *Ossa cuneiforme laterale*

Talus *Talus*

Phalanges *Phalanges*

Heel bone *Calcaneus*

Metatarsal bones *Ossa metatarsalia*

Navicular *Os naviculare*

Cuboid *Os cuboideum*

Bone

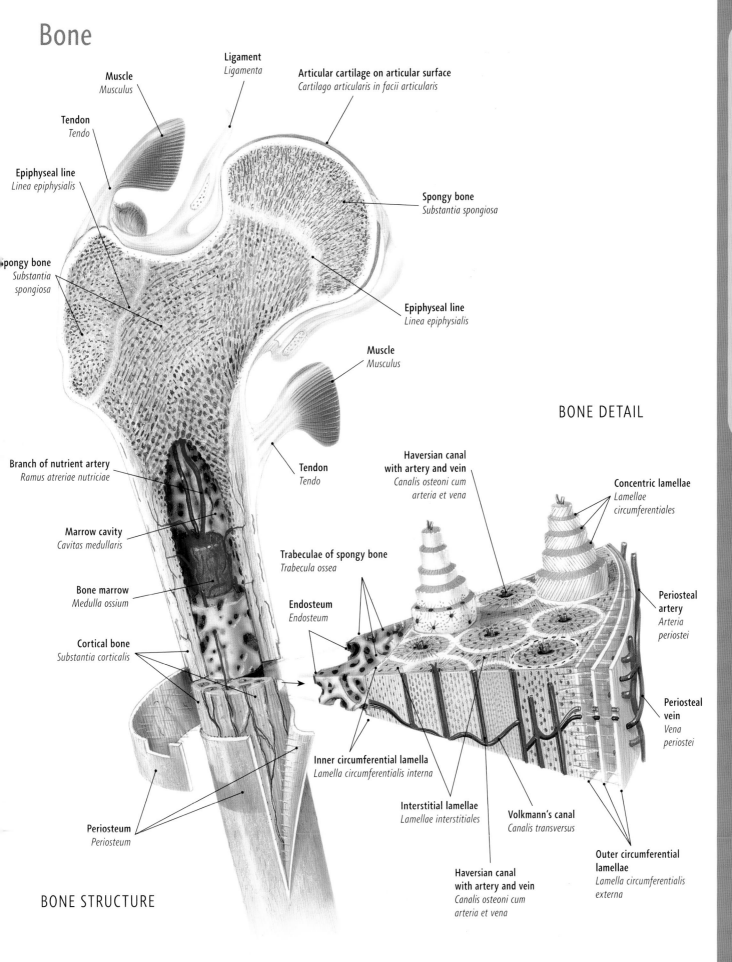

Muscle
Musculus

Tendon
Tendo

Ligament
Ligamenta

Articular cartilage on articular surface
Cartilago articularis in facii articularis

Epiphyseal line
Linea epiphysialis

Spongy bone
Substantia spongiosa

Spongy bone
Substantia spongiosa

Epiphyseal line
Linea epiphysialis

Muscle
Musculus

Branch of nutrient artery
Ramus atreriae nutriciae

Tendon
Tendo

Marrow cavity
Cavitas medullaris

Bone marrow
Medulla ossium

Cortical bone
Substantia corticalis

Trabeculae of spongy bone
Trabecula ossea

Endosteum
Endosteum

Haversian canal with artery and vein
Canalis osteoni cum arteria et vena

Concentric lamellae
Lamellae circumferentiales

Periosteal artery
Arteria periostei

Periosteal vein
Vena periostei

Periosteum
Periosteum

Inner circumferential lamella
Lamella circumferentialis interna

Interstitial lamellae
Lamellae interstitiales

Volkmann's canal
Canalis transversus

Haversian canal with artery and vein
Canalis osteoni cum arteria et vena

Outer circumferential lamellae
Lamella circumferentialis externa

BONE DETAIL

BONE STRUCTURE

Bones of the Skull

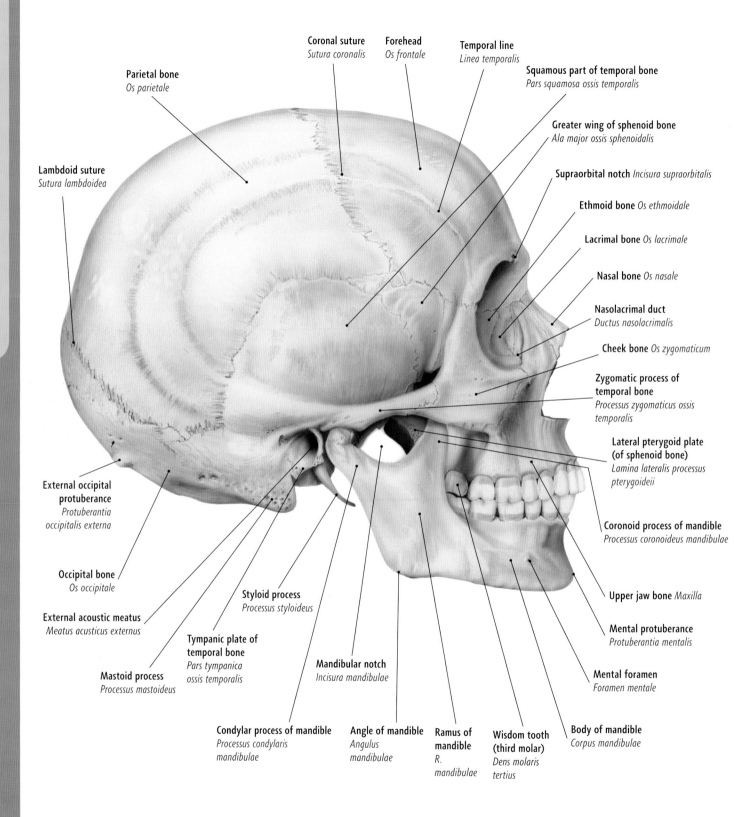

Coronal suture
Sutura coronalis

Forehead
Os frontale

Temporal line
Linea temporalis

Parietal bone
Os parietale

Squamous part of temporal bone
Pars squamosa ossis temporalis

Greater wing of sphenoid bone
Ala major ossis sphenoidalis

Supraorbital notch *Incisura supraorbitalis*

Lambdoid suture
Sutura lambdoidea

Ethmoid bone *Os ethmoidale*

Lacrimal bone *Os lacrimale*

Nasal bone *Os nasale*

Nasolacrimal duct
Ductus nasolacrimalis

Cheek bone *Os zygomaticum*

Zygomatic process of
temporal bone
Processus zygomaticus ossis temporalis

External occipital
protuberance
Protuberantia occipitalis externa

Lateral pterygoid plate
(of sphenoid bone)
Lamina lateralis processus pterygoideii

Coronoid process of mandible
Processus coronoideus mandibulae

Occipital bone
Os occipitale

Upper jaw bone *Maxilla*

External acoustic meatus
Meatus acusticus externus

Styloid process
Processus styloideus

Mental protuberance
Protuberantia mentalis

Tympanic plate of
temporal bone
Pars tympanica ossis temporalis

Mandibular notch
Incisura mandibulae

Mental foramen
Foramen mentale

Mastoid process
Processus mastoideus

Condylar process of mandible
Processus condylaris mandibulae

Angle of mandible
Angulus mandibulae

Ramus of
mandible
R. mandibulae

Wisdom tooth
(third molar)
Dens molaris tertius

Body of mandible
Corpus mandibulae

SIDE VIEW

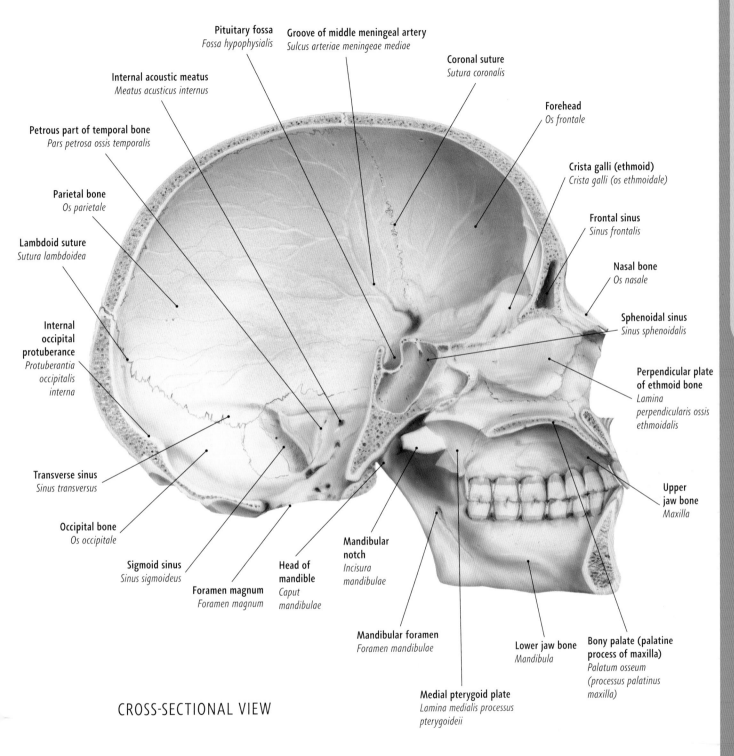

Pituitary fossa
Fossa hypophysialis

Groove of middle meningeal artery
Sulcus arteriae meningeae mediae

Internal acoustic meatus
Meatus acusticus internus

Coronal suture
Sutura coronalis

Petrous part of temporal bone
Pars petrosa ossis temporalis

Forehead
Os frontale

Parietal bone
Os parietale

Crista galli (ethmoid)
Crista galli (os ethmoidale)

Lambdoid suture
Sutura lambdoidea

Frontal sinus
Sinus frontalis

Nasal bone
Os nasale

Internal occipital protuberance
Protuberantia occipitalis interna

Sphenoidal sinus
Sinus sphenoidalis

Perpendicular plate of ethmoid bone
Lamina perpendicularis ossis ethmoidalis

Transverse sinus
Sinus transversus

Upper jaw bone
Maxilla

Occipital bone
Os occipitale

Mandibular notch
Incisura mandibulae

Sigmoid sinus
Sinus sigmoideus

Head of mandible
Caput mandibulae

Foramen magnum
Foramen magnum

Mandibular foramen
Foramen mandibulae

Lower jaw bone
Mandibula

Bony palate (palatine process of maxilla)
Palatum osseum (processus palatinus maxilla)

Medial pterygoid plate
Lamina medialis processus pterygoideii

CROSS-SECTIONAL VIEW

59

Bones of the Skull

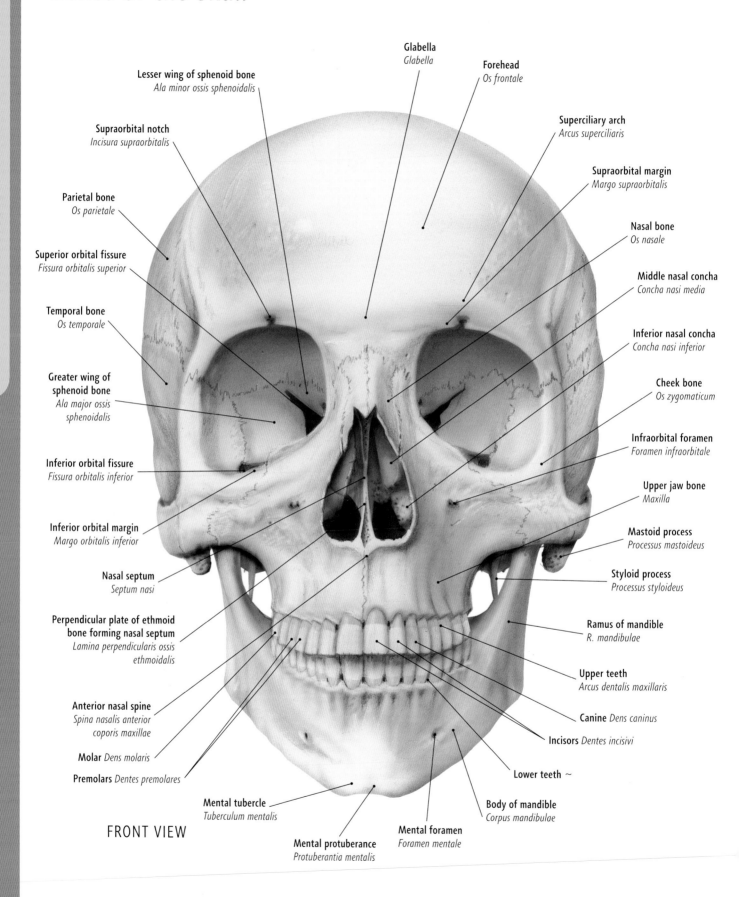

Glabella
Glabella

Forehead
Os frontale

Lesser wing of sphenoid bone
Ala minor ossis sphenoidalis

Superciliary arch
Arcus superciliaris

Supraorbital notch
Incisura supraorbitalis

Supraorbital margin
Margo supraorbitalis

Parietal bone
Os parietale

Nasal bone
Os nasale

Superior orbital fissure
Fissura orbitalis superior

Middle nasal concha
Concha nasi media

Temporal bone
Os temporale

Inferior nasal concha
Concha nasi inferior

Greater wing of
sphenoid bone
*Ala major ossis
sphenoidalis*

Cheek bone
Os zygomaticum

Infraorbital foramen
Foramen infraorbitale

Inferior orbital fissure
Fissura orbitalis inferior

Upper jaw bone
Maxilla

Inferior orbital margin
Margo orbitalis inferior

Mastoid process
Processus mastoideus

Styloid process
Processus styloideus

Nasal septum
Septum nasi

Ramus of mandible
R. mandibulae

Perpendicular plate of ethmoid
bone forming nasal septum
*Lamina perpendicularis ossis
ethmoidalis*

Upper teeth
Arcus dentalis maxillaris

Canine *Dens caninus*

Anterior nasal spine
*Spina nasalis anterior
coporis maxillae*

Incisors *Dentes incisivi*

Molar *Dens molaris*

Lower teeth ~

Premolars *Dentes premolares*

Body of mandible
Corpus mandibulae

Mental tubercle
Tuberculum mentalis

FRONT VIEW

Mental protuberance
Protuberantia mentalis

Mental foramen
Foramen mentale

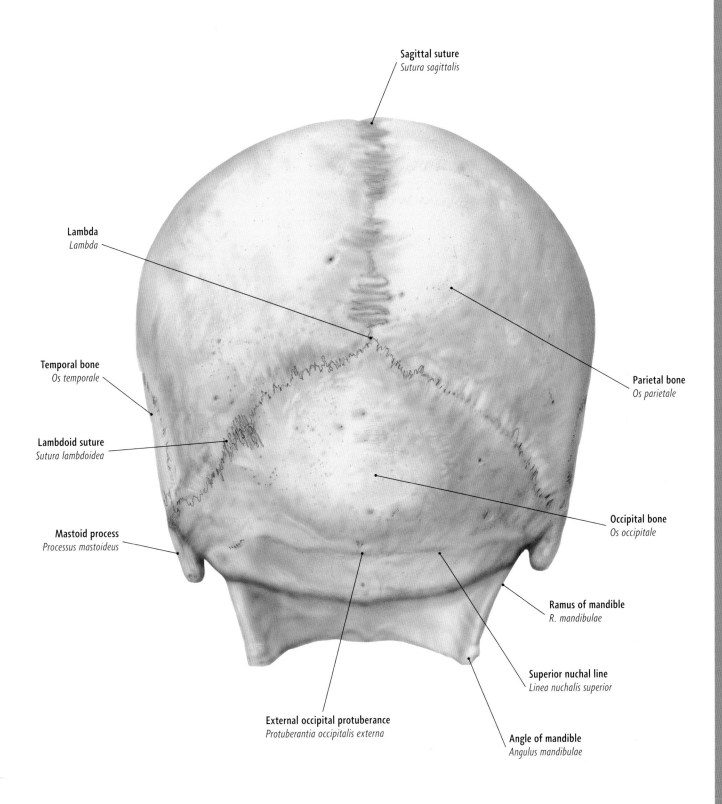

Sagittal suture
Sutura sagittalis

Lambda
Lambda

Temporal bone
Os temporale

Lambdoid suture
Sutura lambdoidea

Mastoid process
Processus mastoideus

Parietal bone
Os parietale

Occipital bone
Os occipitale

Ramus of mandible
R. mandibulae

Superior nuchal line
Linea nuchalis superior

External occipital protuberance
Protuberantia occipitalis externa

Angle of mandible
Angulus mandibulae

REAR VIEW

Bones of the Skull

Incisor
Dens incisivus

Incisive foramen
Fossa incisiva

Canine
Dens caninus

Palatine process (maxilla)
Processus palatinus maxillae

Premolars
Dentes premolares

Palatine bone
Os palatinum

Molars
Dentes molares

Posterior nasal aperture
Choana

Cheek bone
Os zygomaticum

Wisdom tooth (third molar)
Dens molaris tertius

Greater wing of sphenoid bone
Ala major ossis sphenoidalis

Medial pterygoid plate
Lamina medialis processus pterygoideii

Vomer *Vomer*

Zygomatic arch
Arcus zygomaticus

Foramen lacerum
Foramen lacerum

Lateral pterygoid plate
Lamina lateralis processus pterygoideii

Carotid canal
Canalis caroticus

Mandibular fossa
Fossa mandibularis

Jugular foramen
Foramen jugulare

Foramen ovale
Foramen ovale

Occipital condyle
Condylus occipitalis

Foramen spinosum
Foramen spinosum

Foramen magnum
Foramen magnum

Styloid process
Processus styloideus

Occipital bone
Os occipitale

Tympanic plate
Pars tympanica ossis temporalis

External occipital crest
Crista occipitalis externa

Mastoid process
Processus mastoideus

Inferior nuchal line
Linea nuchalis inferior

Superior nuchal line
Linea nuchalis superior

BASE

External occipital protuberance
Protuberantia occipitalis externa

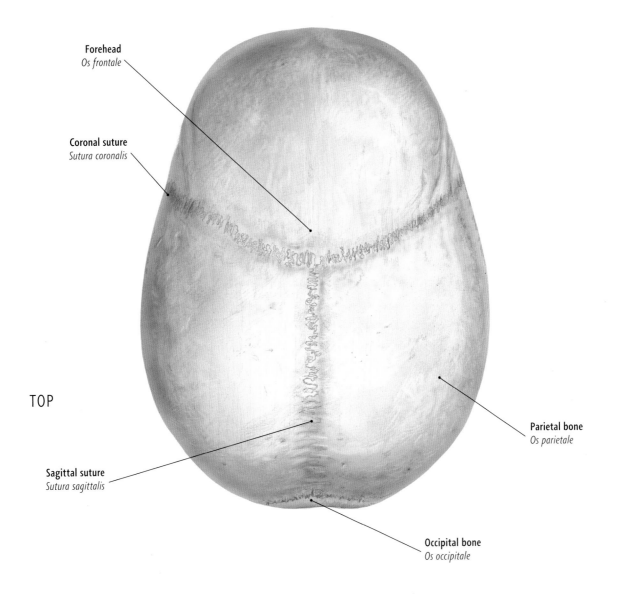

Forehead
Os frontale

Coronal suture
Sutura coronalis

TOP

Sagittal suture
Sutura sagittalis

Parietal bone
Os parietale

Occipital bone
Os occipitale

BONE FORMATION

Periosteum
Periosteum

Ridge
Crista

Artery
Arteria

New osteon
Osteonum

a   b   c   d

Bone grows in width as new bone is laid down in ridges (a) either side of a blood vessel. The ridges grow together around the vessel (b). More bone is laid down, diminishing the space around the vessel (c) and eventually forming an osteon. The process continues with parallel blood vessels (d).

Bones of the Head and Face

ORBITAL CAVITY—VIEW FROM ABOVE

Eyeball
Bulbus oculi

Cribriform plate of ethmoid bone
Lamina cribrosa ossis ethmoidalis

Ethmoid bone
Os ethmoidale

Frontal sinus
Sinus frontalis

Forehead
Os frontale

Temporal bone
Os temporale

Frontal sinus
Sinus frontalis

Sphenoidal sinus
Sinus sphenoidalis

Ethmoid air cells
Cellulae ethmoidales

Maxillary sinus
Sinus maxillaris

PARANASAL SINUSES

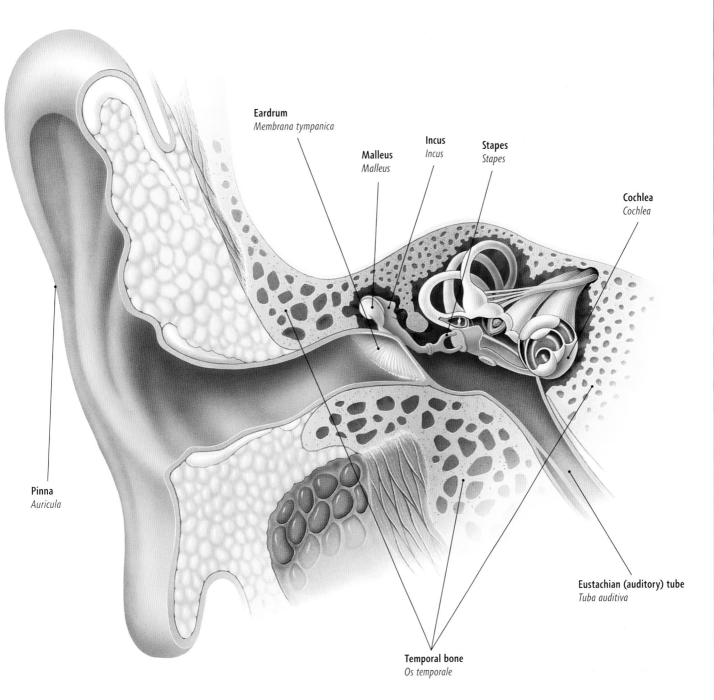

Eardrum
Membrana tympanica

Malleus
Malleus

Incus
Incus

Stapes
Stapes

Cochlea
Cochlea

Pinna
Auricula

Eustachian (auditory) tube
Tuba auditiva

Temporal bone
Os temporale

BONES OF THE EAR

Spine

Atlas (C1)
Atlas (CI)

Axis (C2)
Axis (C2)

Transverse processes
of cervical vertebrae
*Processus transversi
vertebrarum
cervicalium*

Spinous
processes
of thoracic
vertebrae
*Processus spinosi
vertebrarum
thoracicarum*

Bodies of lumbar
vertebrae
*Corpora vertebrarum
lumbalium*

Intervertebral disk
Discus intervertebralis

Cervical
Cervicalis

Thoracic
Thoracica

Lumbar
Lumbalis

Sacral
Sacralis

Coccygeal
Coccyx

SPINE IN SITU—SIDE VIEW

SPINE IN SITU—REAR VIEW

[~] = no direct Latin equivalent

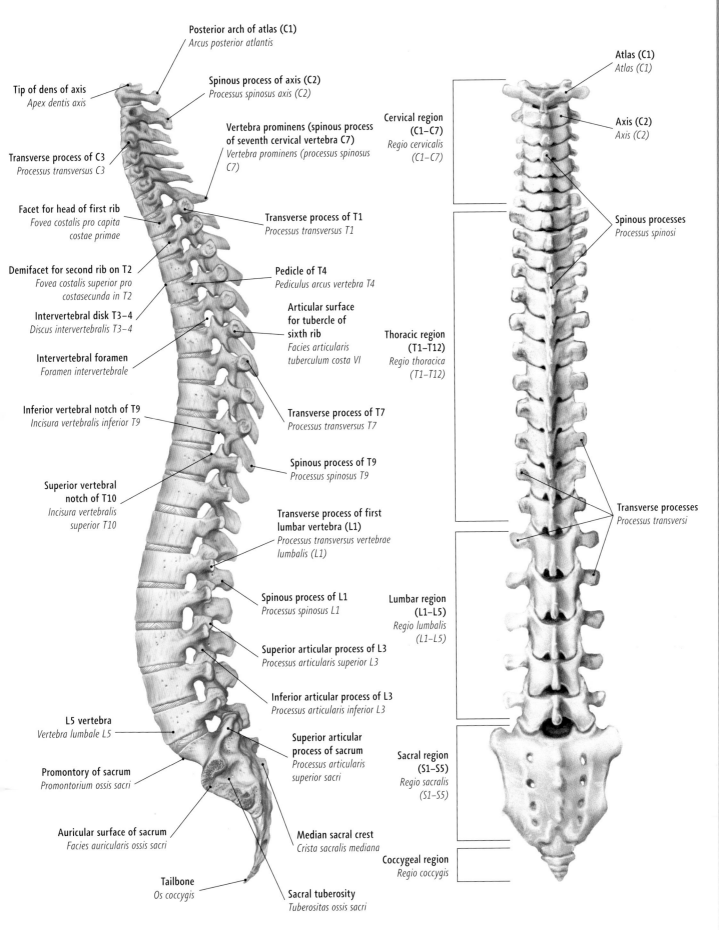

Posterior arch of atlas (C1)
Arcus posterior atlantis

Spinous process of axis (C2)
Processus spinosus axis (C2)

Tip of dens of axis
Apex dentis axis

Vertebra prominens (spinous process of seventh cervical vertebra C7)
Vertebra prominens (processus spinosus C7)

Transverse process of C3
Processus transversus C3

Facet for head of first rib
Fovea costalis pro capita costae primae

Transverse process of T1
Processus transversus T1

Demifacet for second rib on T2
Fovea costalis superior pro costasecunda in T2

Pedicle of T4
Pediculus arcus vertebra T4

Intervertebral disk T3–4
Discus intervertebralis T3–4

Articular surface for tubercle of sixth rib
Facies articularis tuberculum costa VI

Intervertebral foramen
Foramen intervertebrale

Inferior vertebral notch of T9
Incisura vertebralis inferior T9

Transverse process of T7
Processus transversus T7

Superior vertebral notch of T10
Incisura vertebralis superior T10

Spinous process of T9
Processus spinosus T9

Transverse process of first lumbar vertebra (L1)
Processus transversus vertebrae lumbalis (L1)

Spinous process of L1
Processus spinosus L1

Superior articular process of L3
Processus articularis superior L3

Inferior articular process of L3
Processus articularis inferior L3

L5 vertebra
Vertebra lumbale L5

Superior articular process of sacrum
Processus articularis superior sacri

Promontory of sacrum
Promontorium ossis sacri

Auricular surface of sacrum
Facies auricularis ossis sacri

Median sacral crest
Crista sacralis mediana

Tailbone
Os coccygis

Sacral tuberosity
Tuberositas ossis sacri

Atlas (C1)
Atlas (C1)

Axis (C2)
Axis (C2)

Cervical region (C1–C7)
Regio cervicalis (C1–C7)

Spinous processes
Processus spinosi

Thoracic region (T1–T12)
Regio thoracica (T1–T12)

Transverse processes
Processus transversi

Lumbar region (L1–L5)
Regio lumbalis (L1–L5)

Sacral region (S1–S5)
Regio sacralis (S1–S5)

Coccygeal region
Regio coccygis

[~] = no direct Latin equivalent

SPINE—SIDE VIEW

SPINE—REAR VIEW

Vertebrae

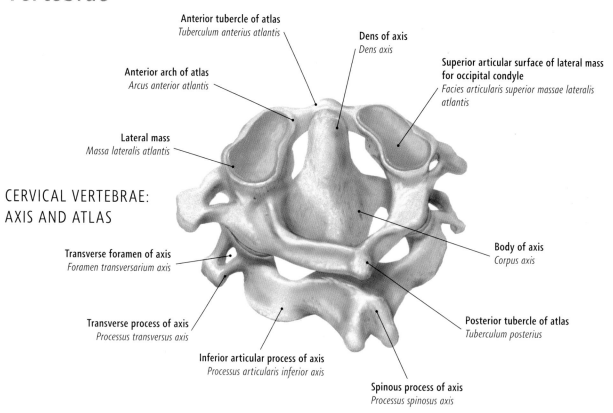

Anterior tubercle of atlas
Tuberculum anterius atlantis

Dens of axis
Dens axis

Superior articular surface of lateral mass
for occipital condyle
*Facies articularis superior massae lateralis
atlantis*

Anterior arch of atlas
Arcus anterior atlantis

Lateral mass
Massa lateralis atlantis

CERVICAL VERTEBRAE: AXIS AND ATLAS

Transverse foramen of axis
Foramen transversarium axis

Body of axis
Corpus axis

Transverse process of axis
Processus transversus axis

Posterior tubercle of atlas
Tuberculum posterius

Inferior articular process of axis
Processus articularis inferior axis

Spinous process of axis
Processus spinosus axis

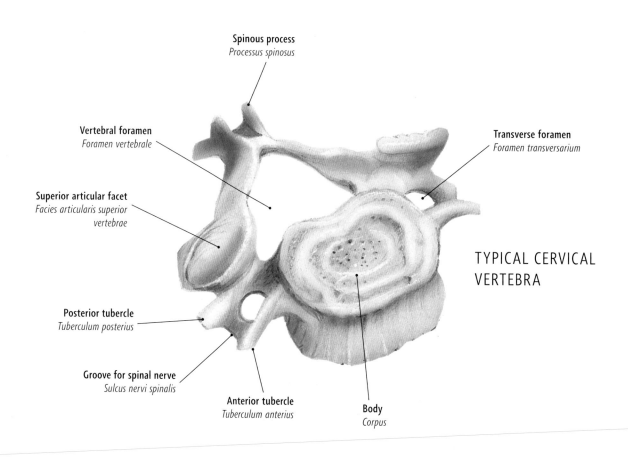

Spinous process
Processus spinosus

Vertebral foramen
Foramen vertebrale

Transverse foramen
Foramen transversarium

Superior articular facet
*Facies articularis superior
vertebrae*

TYPICAL CERVICAL VERTEBRA

Posterior tubercle
Tuberculum posterius

Groove for spinal nerve
Sulcus nervi spinalis

Anterior tubercle
Tuberculum anterius

Body
Corpus

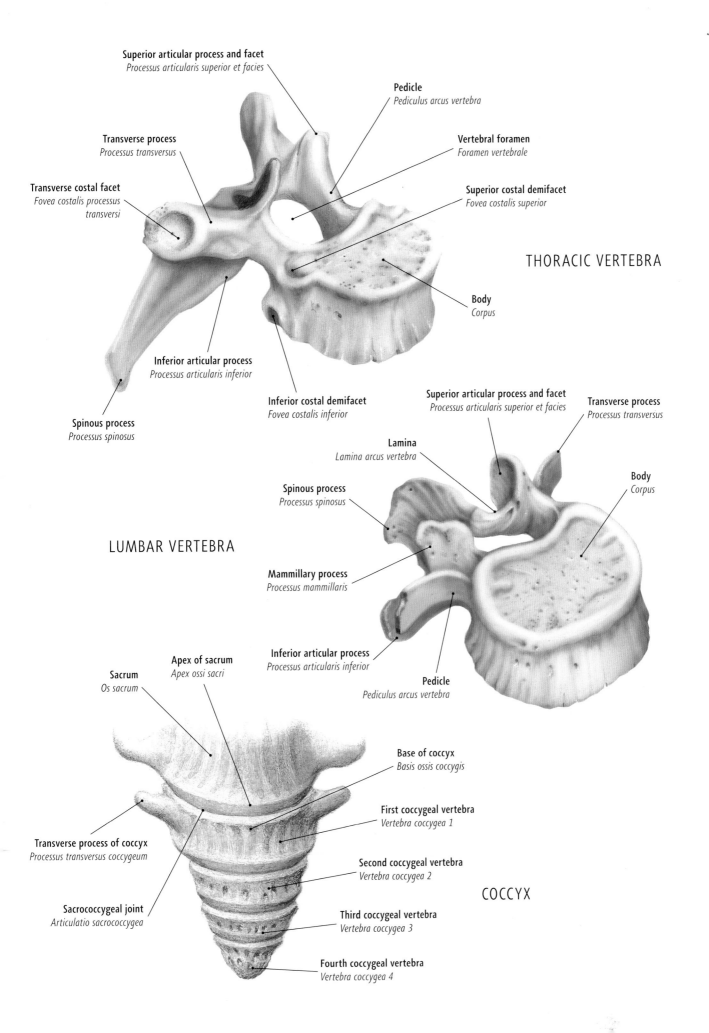

Superior articular process and facet
Processus articularis superior et facies

Pedicle
Pediculus arcus vertebra

Transverse process
Processus transversus

Vertebral foramen
Foramen vertebrale

Transverse costal facet
Fovea costalis processus transversi

Superior costal demifacet
Fovea costalis superior

THORACIC VERTEBRA

Body
Corpus

Inferior articular process
Processus articularis inferior

Spinous process
Processus spinosus

Inferior costal demifacet
Fovea costalis inferior

Superior articular process and facet
Processus articularis superior et facies

Transverse process
Processus transversus

Lamina
Lamina arcus vertebra

Body
Corpus

Spinous process
Processus spinosus

LUMBAR VERTEBRA

Mammillary process
Processus mammillaris

Inferior articular process
Processus articularis inferior

Pedicle
Pediculus arcus vertebra

Apex of sacrum
Apex ossi sacri

Sacrum
Os sacrum

Base of coccyx
Basis ossis coccygis

First coccygeal vertebra
Vertebra coccygea 1

Transverse process of coccyx
Processus transversus coccygeum

Second coccygeal vertebra
Vertebra coccygea 2

COCCYX

Sacrococcygeal joint
Articulatio sacrococcygea

Third coccygeal vertebra
Vertebra coccygea 3

Fourth coccygeal vertebra
Vertebra coccygea 4

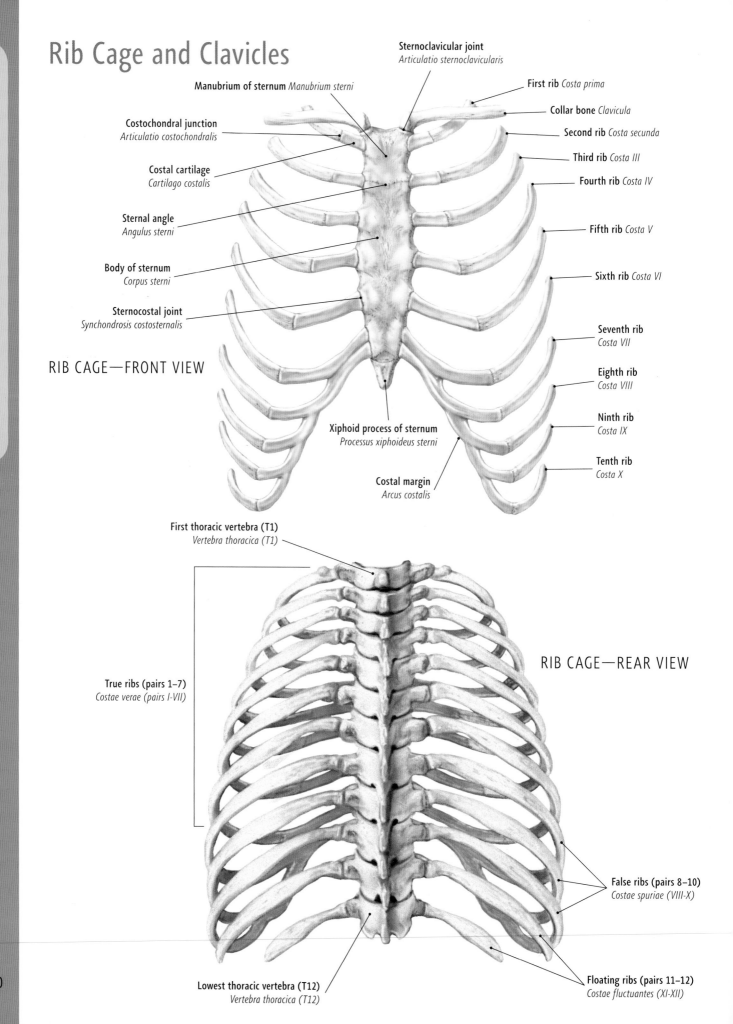

Rib Cage and Clavicles

Sternoclavicular joint *Articulatio sternoclavicularis*

Manubrium of sternum *Manubrium sterni*

First rib *Costa prima*

Collar bone *Clavicula*

Costochondral junction *Articulatio costochondralis*

Second rib *Costa secunda*

Third rib *Costa III*

Costal cartilage *Cartilago costalis*

Fourth rib *Costa IV*

Sternal angle *Angulus sterni*

Fifth rib *Costa V*

Body of sternum *Corpus sterni*

Sixth rib *Costa VI*

Sternocostal joint *Synchondrosis costosternalis*

Seventh rib *Costa VII*

Eighth rib *Costa VIII*

RIB CAGE—FRONT VIEW

Ninth rib *Costa IX*

Xiphoid process of sternum *Processus xiphoideus sterni*

Tenth rib *Costa X*

Costal margin *Arcus costalis*

First thoracic vertebra (T1) *Vertebra thoracica (T1)*

RIB CAGE—REAR VIEW

True ribs (pairs 1–7) *Costae verae (pairs I-VII)*

False ribs (pairs 8–10) *Costae spuriae (VIII-X)*

Floating ribs (pairs 11–12) *Costae fluctuantes (XI-XII)*

Lowest thoracic vertebra (T12) *Vertebra thoracica (T12)*

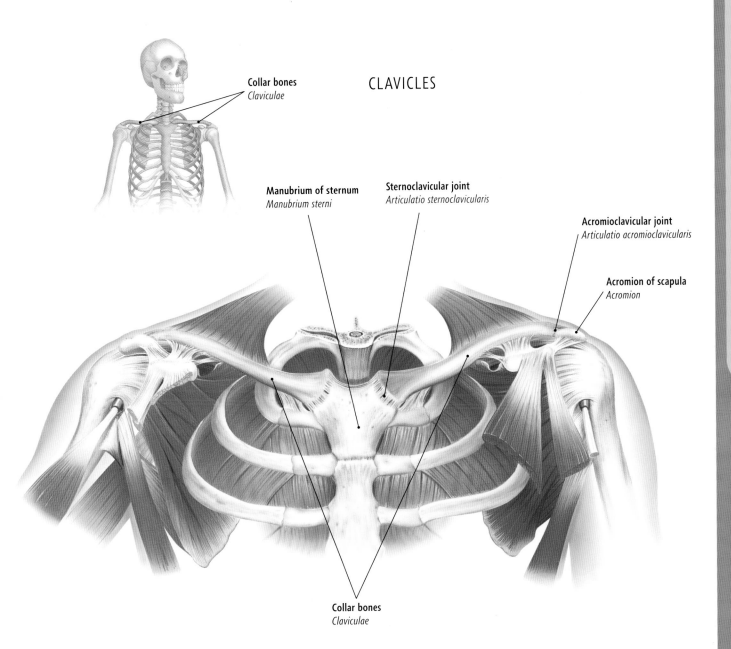

Collar bones
Claviculae

CLAVICLES

Manubrium of sternum
Manubrium sterni

Sternoclavicular joint
Articulatio sternoclavicularis

Acromioclavicular joint
Articulatio acromioclavicularis

Acromion of scapula
Acromion

Collar bones
Claviculae

Bones of the Arm

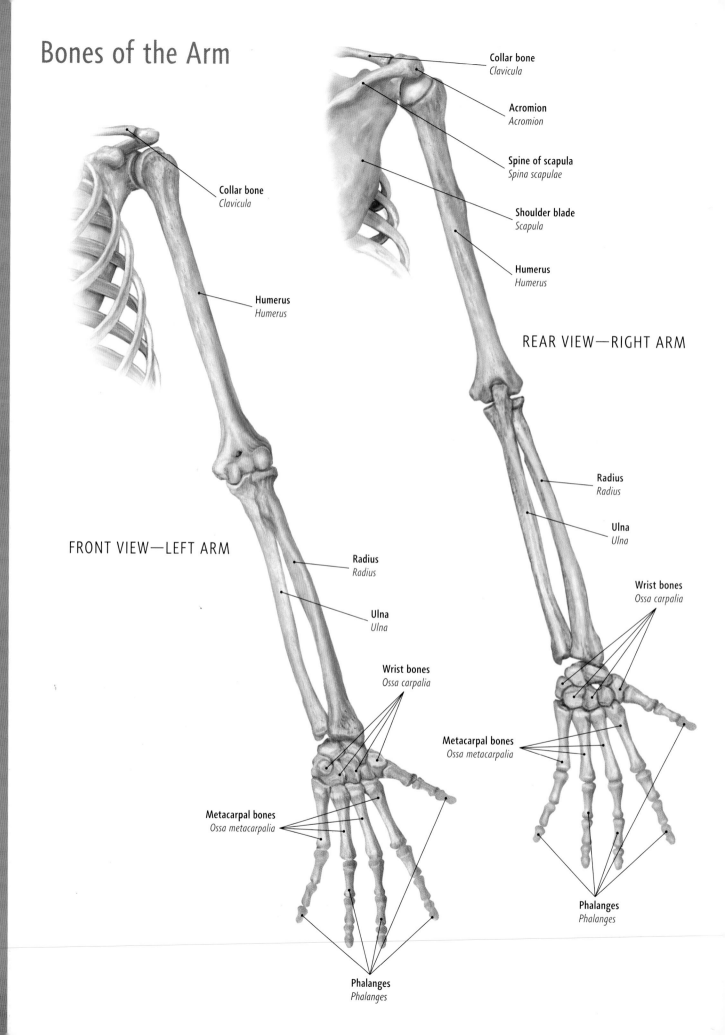

Collar bone
Clavicula

Acromion
Acromion

Spine of scapula
Spina scapulae

Shoulder blade
Scapula

Humerus
Humerus

REAR VIEW—RIGHT ARM

Collar bone
Clavicula

Humerus
Humerus

Radius
Radius

Ulna
Ulna

FRONT VIEW—LEFT ARM

Radius
Radius

Ulna
Ulna

Wrist bones
Ossa carpalia

Wrist bones
Ossa carpalia

Metacarpal bones
Ossa metacarpalia

Metacarpal bones
Ossa metacarpalia

Phalanges
Phalanges

Phalanges
Phalanges

Coracoid process
Processus coracoideus

Collar bone *Clavicula*

Acromion
Acromion

Superior border of scapula
Margo superior scapula

Greater tubercle
Tuberculum majus

Lesser tubercle
Tuberculum minus

Head of humerus
Caput humeri

Glenoid
cavity
*Cavitas
glenoidalis*

Subscapular fossa
Fossa subscapularis

Humerus
Humerus

Medial border of scapula
Margo medialis scapulae

Lateral border of
scapula
*Margo lateralis
scapulae*

Coracoid process
Processus coracoideus

Acromioclavicular joint
Articulatio acromioclavicularis

Acromion
Acromion

Collar bone
Clavicula

Head of humerus
Caput humeri

Spine of scapula
Spina scapulae

Glenoid fossa
Cavitas glenoidalis

Humerus
Humerus

Medial border of scapula
Margo medialis scapula

Lateral border of scapula
Margo lateralis scapulae

SHOULDER JOINT—
REAR VIEW

Bones of the Upper Arm

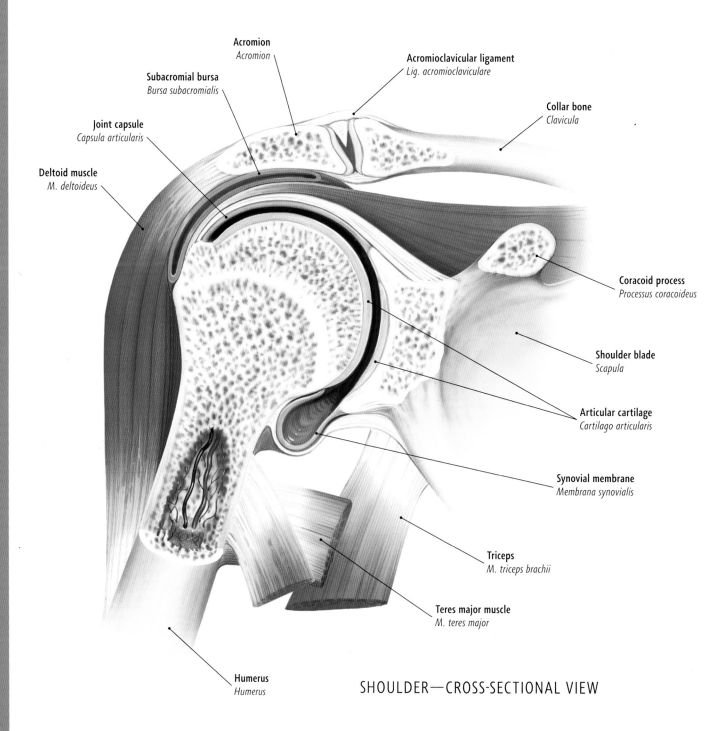

Acromion
Acromion

Acromioclavicular ligament
Lig. acromioclaviculare

Subacromial bursa
Bursa subacromialis

Collar bone
Clavicula

Joint capsule
Capsula articularis

Deltoid muscle
M. deltoideus

Coracoid process
Processus coracoideus

Shoulder blade
Scapula

Articular cartilage
Cartilago articularis

Synovial membrane
Membrana synovialis

Triceps
M. triceps brachii

Teres major muscle
M. teres major

Humerus
Humerus

SHOULDER—CROSS-SECTIONAL VIEW

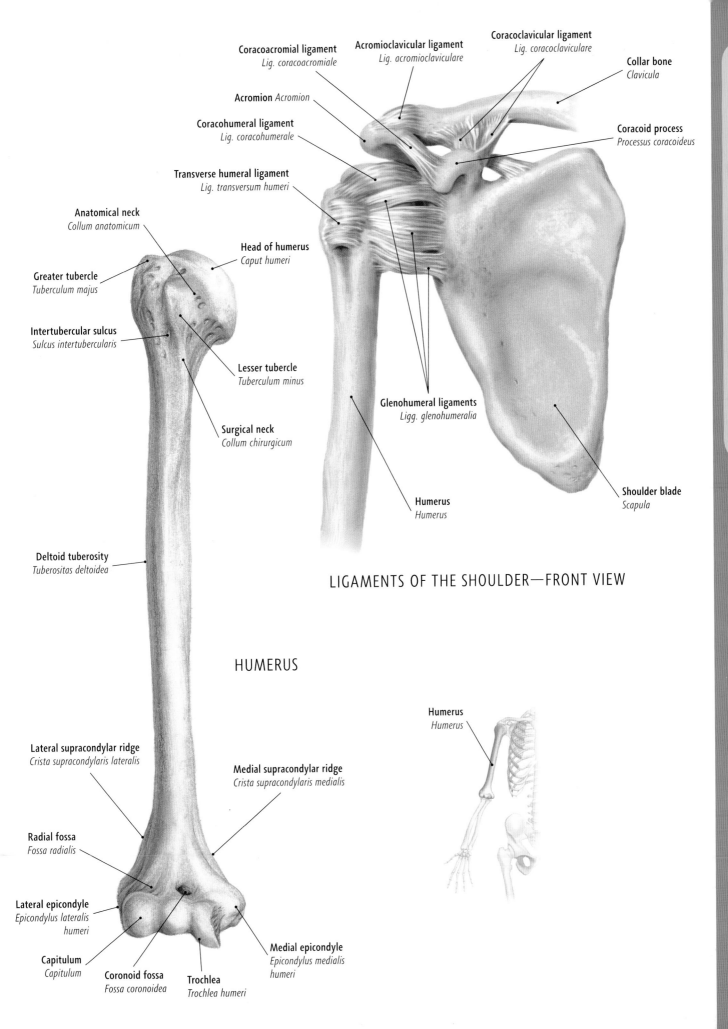

Coracoacromial ligament
Lig. coracoacromiale

Acromioclavicular ligament
Lig. acromioclaviculare

Coracoclavicular ligament
Lig. coracoclaviculare

Collar bone
Clavicula

Acromion *Acromion*

Coracohumeral ligament
Lig. coracohumerale

Coracoid process
Processus coracoideus

Transverse humeral ligament
Lig. transversum humeri

Anatomical neck
Collum anatomicum

Head of humerus
Caput humeri

Greater tubercle
Tuberculum majus

Intertubercular sulcus
Sulcus intertubercularis

Lesser tubercle
Tuberculum minus

Surgical neck
Collum chirurgicum

Glenohumeral ligaments
Ligg. glenohumeralia

Shoulder blade
Scapula

Humerus
Humerus

Deltoid tuberosity
Tuberositas deltoidea

LIGAMENTS OF THE SHOULDER—FRONT VIEW

HUMERUS

Humerus
Humerus

Lateral supracondylar ridge
Crista supracondylaris lateralis

Medial supracondylar ridge
Crista supracondylaris medialis

Radial fossa
Fossa radialis

Lateral epicondyle
Epicondylus lateralis humeri

Capitulum
Capitulum

Coronoid fossa
Fossa coronoidea

Trochlea
Trochlea humeri

Medial epicondyle
Epicondylus medialis humeri

Bones of the Lower Arm

ELBOW JOINT

Humerus
Humerus

Head of radius
Caput radii

Neck of radius
Collum radii

Radius
Radius

Medial epicondyle of humerus
Epicondylus medialis humeri

Trochlea of humerus
Trochlea humeri

Olecranon
Olecranon

Coronoid process of ulna
Processus coronoideus ulnae

Ulna
Ulna

Radius
Radius

Oblique cord
Chorda obliqua membranae interossei antebrachii

Anular ligament of radius
Lig. anulare radii

Humerus
Humerus

Ulna
Ulna

Ulnar collateral ligament
Lig. collaterale ulnare

Olecranon
Olecranon

LIGAMENTS OF THE ELBOW

Olecranon
Olecranon

Trochlear notch
Incisura trochlearis

Coronoid process
Processus coronoideus

Radial notch of ulna
Incisura radialis

Ulnar tuberosity
(for brachialis)
Tuberositas ulnae (M. brachialis)

Ulnar tuberosity (on coronoid process)
Tuberositas ulnae (processus coronoideus)

Ulna
Ulna

Head of radius
Caput radii

Neck of radius
Collum radii

Radial tuberosity
Tuberositas radii

Anterior surface
Facies anterior

Interosseous border
Margo interosseous

RADIUS

ULNA

Radius
Radius

Head of ulna
Caput ulnae

Styloid process of ulna
Processus styloideus ulnae

Distal radioulnar joint
Articulatio radioulnaris distalis

Styloid process of radius
Processus styloideus radii

Bones of the Wrist and Hand

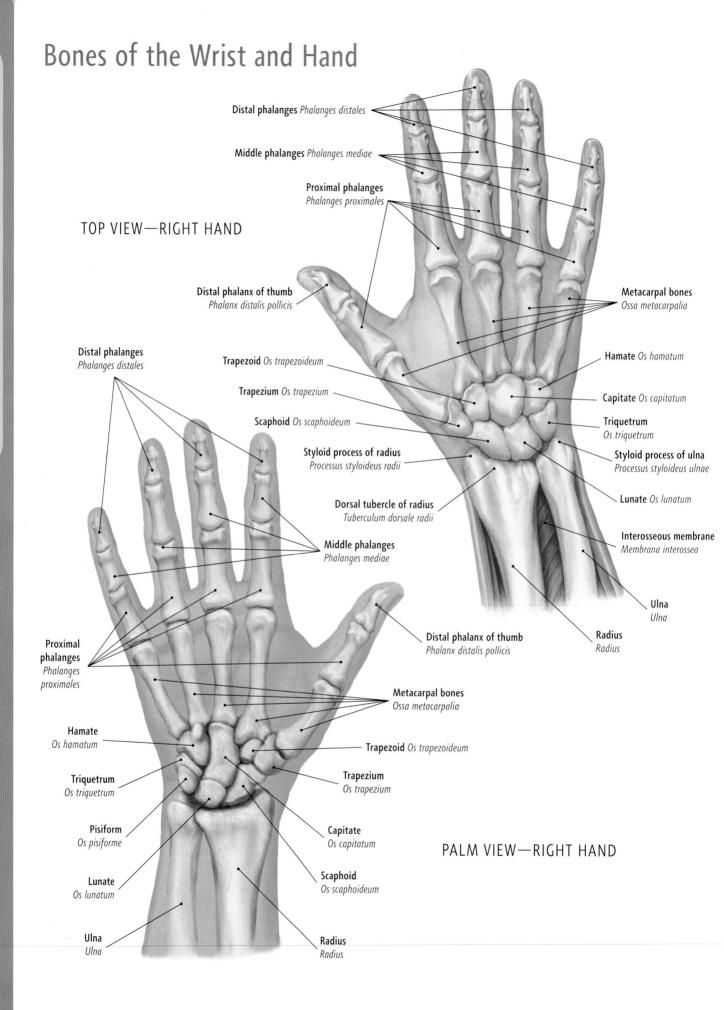

TOP VIEW—RIGHT HAND

Distal phalanges *Phalanges distales*

Middle phalanges *Phalanges mediae*

Proximal phalanges *Phalanges proximales*

Distal phalanx of thumb *Phalanx distalis pollicis*

Distal phalanges *Phalanges distales*

Trapezoid *Os trapezoideum*

Trapezium *Os trapezium*

Scaphoid *Os scaphoideum*

Styloid process of radius *Processus styloideus radii*

Dorsal tubercle of radius *Tuberculum dorsale radii*

Middle phalanges *Phalanges mediae*

Metacarpal bones *Ossa metacarpalia*

Hamate *Os hamatum*

Capitate *Os capitatum*

Triquetrum *Os triquetrum*

Styloid process of ulna *Processus styloideus ulnae*

Lunate *Os lunatum*

Interosseous membrane *Membrana interossea*

Ulna *Ulna*

Radius *Radius*

Proximal phalanges *Phalanges proximales*

Distal phalanx of thumb *Phalanx distalis pollicis*

Metacarpal bones *Ossa metacarpalia*

Trapezoid *Os trapezoideum*

Trapezium *Os trapezium*

Hamate *Os hamatum*

Triquetrum *Os triquetrum*

Pisiform *Os pisiforme*

Capitate *Os capitatum*

Scaphoid *Os scaphoideum*

Lunate *Os lunatum*

Ulna *Ulna*

Radius *Radius*

PALM VIEW—RIGHT HAND

78

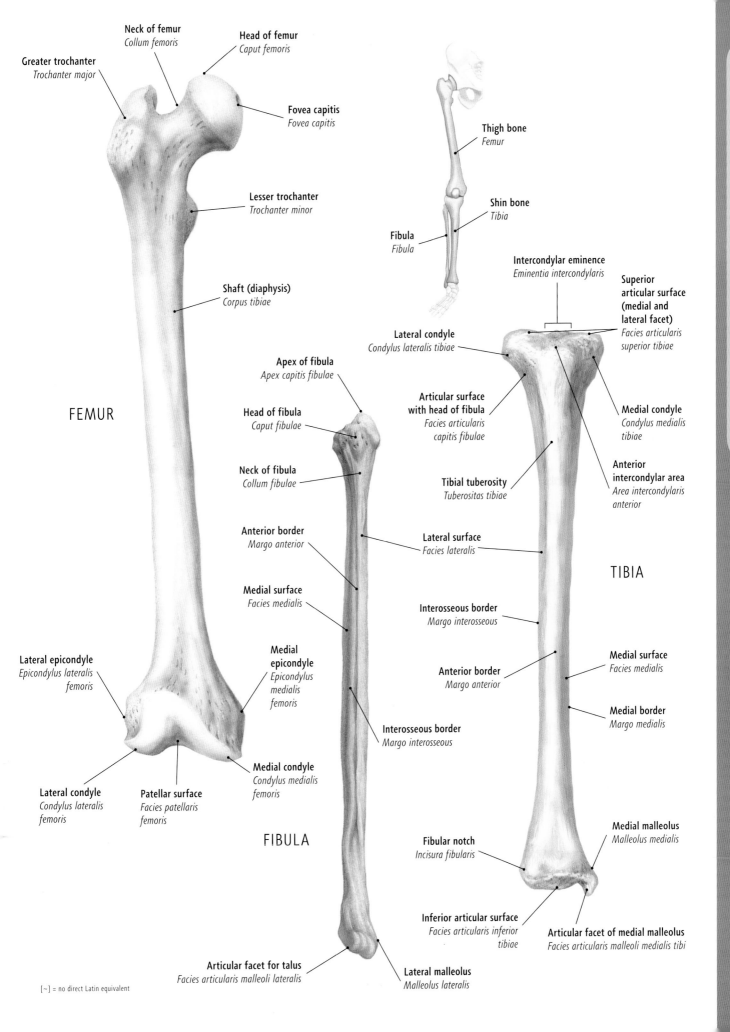

Neck of femur
Collum femoris

Head of femur
Caput femoris

Greater trochanter
Trochanter major

Fovea capitis
Fovea capitis

Lesser trochanter
Trochanter minor

Thigh bone
Femur

Shin bone
Tibia

Fibula
Fibula

Shaft (diaphysis)
Corpus tibiae

Intercondylar eminence
Eminentia intercondylaris

Superior articular surface (medial and lateral facet)
Facies articularis superior tibiae

Lateral condyle
Condylus lateralis tibiae

Apex of fibula
Apex capitis fibulae

Head of fibula
Caput fibulae

Articular surface with head of fibula
Facies articularis capitis fibulae

Medial condyle
Condylus medialis tibiae

FEMUR

Neck of fibula
Collum fibulae

Tibial tuberosity
Tuberositas tibiae

Anterior intercondylar area
Area intercondylaris anterior

Anterior border
Margo anterior

Lateral surface
Facies lateralis

Medial surface
Facies medialis

TIBIA

Interosseous border
Margo interosseous

Medial epicondyle
Epicondylus medialis femoris

Anterior border
Margo anterior

Medial surface
Facies medialis

Lateral epicondyle
Epicondylus lateralis femoris

Medial border
Margo medialis

Interosseous border
Margo interosseous

Medial condyle
Condylus medialis femoris

Lateral condyle
Condylus lateralis femoris

Patellar surface
Facies patellaris femoris

FIBULA

Medial malleolus
Malleolus medialis

Fibular notch
Incisura fibularis

Inferior articular surface
Facies articularis inferior tibiae

Articular facet of medial malleolus
Facies articularis malleoli medialis tibi

Articular facet for talus
Facies articularis malleoli lateralis

Lateral malleolus
Malleolus lateralis

[~] = no direct Latin equivalent

Bones of the Knee

Thigh bone
Femur

Lateral condyle of femur
Condylus lateralis femoris

Fibular collateral ligament
Lig. collaterale fibulare

Lateral meniscus
Meniscus lateralis

Patellar ligament
Lig. patellae

Kneecap (reflected)
Patella (reflected)

Posterior cruciate ligament
Lig. cruciatum posterius

Anterior cruciate ligament
Lig. cruciatum anterius

Medial condyle of femur
Condylus medialis femoris

Medial meniscus
Meniscus medialis

Tibial collateral ligament
Lig. collaterale tibiale

Shin bone
Tibia

BONES AND LIGAMENTS OF THE KNEE—FRONT VIEW

Shaft of femur
Corpus femoris

Femoral lateral condyle
Condylus lateralis femoris

Kneecap
Patella

Tibial plateau *Tibial plateau*

Articular cartilage
Cartilago articularis

Shin bone
Tibia

Fibula
Fibula

BONES OF THE KNEE—
SIDE VIEW

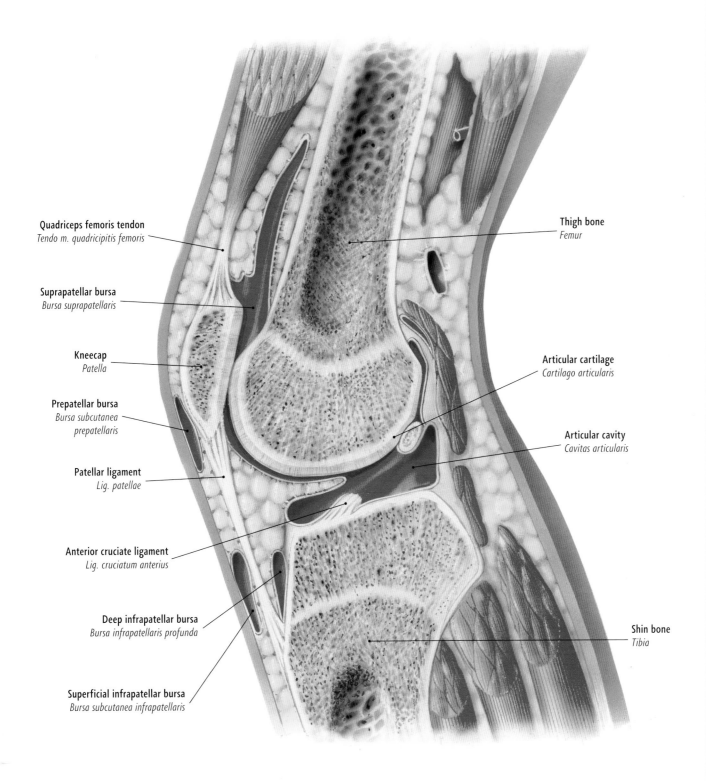

Quadriceps femoris tendon
Tendo m. quadricipitis femoris

Suprapatellar bursa
Bursa suprapatellaris

Kneecap
Patella

Prepatellar bursa
Bursa subcutanea prepatellaris

Patellar ligament
Lig. patellae

Anterior cruciate ligament
Lig. cruciatum anterius

Deep infrapatellar bursa
Bursa infrapatellaris profunda

Superficial infrapatellar bursa
Bursa subcutanea infrapatellaris

Thigh bone
Femur

Articular cartilage
Cartilago articularis

Articular cavity
Cavitas articularis

Shin bone
Tibia

KNEE JOINT—CROSS-SECTIONAL VIEW

Bones of the Ankle and Foot

Talus
Talus

Lateral
Laterale

Intermediate
Intermedium

Cuneiform bones
Ossa cuneiformia

Medial
Mediale

Proximal phalanges
Phalanges proximales

Middle phalanges
Phalanges mediae

Heel bone
Calcaneus

Cuboid
Os cuboideum

Metatarsal bones
Ossa metatarsalia

Distal phalanges
Phalanges distales

BONES OF THE FOOT—SIDE VIEW

THE ANKLE—REAR VIEW

Shin bone
Tibia

Interosseous membrane
Membrana interossea

Fibula
Fibula

Medial malleolus
Malleolus medialis

Posterior tibiofibular ligament
Lig. talofibulare posterius

Deltoid (medial) ligament
*Lig. collaterale mediale
(deltoideum)*

Lateral malleolus
Malleolus lateralis

Posterior talocalcaneal ligament
Lig. talocalcaneum posterius

Posterior talofibular ligament
Lig. talofibulare posterius

Calcaneofibular ligament
Lig. calcaneofibulare

Talus
Talus

Heel bone
Calcaneus

Fibula
Fibula

Shin bone
Tibia

Anterior tibiofibular ligament
Lig. tibiofibulare anterius

Anterior talofibular ligament
Lig. talofibulare anterius

Dorsal cuboideonavicular ligament
Lig. cuboideonaviculare dorsale

Dorsal cuneonavicular ligaments
Lig. cuneonavicularia dorsalia

Posterior tibiofibular ligament
Lig. tibiofibulare posterius

Dorsal intercuneiform ligament
Lig. intercuneiformia dorsalia

Calcaneofibular ligament
Lig. calcaneofibulare

Dorsal tarsometatarsal ligaments
Ligg. tarsometatarsalia dorsalia

Heel bone
Calcaneus

Talocalcaneal ligaments
Ligg. talocalcanei

Dorsal metatarsal ligaments
Ligg. metatarsalia dorsalia

Dorsal calcaneocuboid ligament
Lig. calcaneocuboideum dorsale

Bifurcate ligament
Lig. bifurcatum

Dorsal cuneocuboid ligament
Lig. cuneocuboideum dorsale

LIGAMENTS OF THE ANKLE
AND FOOT—SIDE VIEW

Body Movement

Movements of the Body

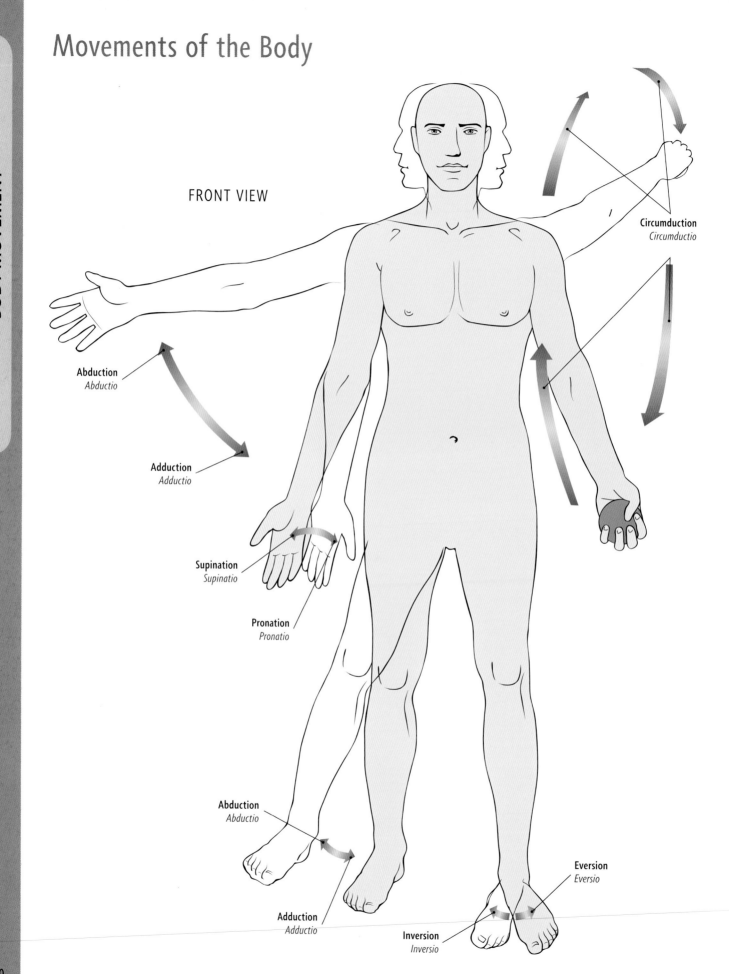

FRONT VIEW

Circumduction
Circumductio

Abduction
Abductio

Adduction
Adductio

Supination
Supinatio

Pronation
Pronatio

Abduction
Abductio

Adduction
Adductio

Eversion
Eversio

Inversion
Inversio

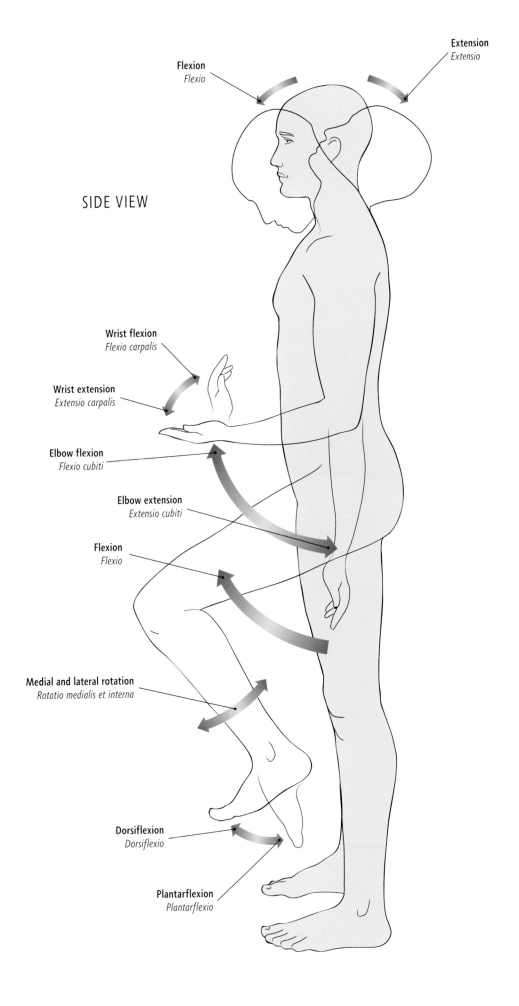

Flexion
Flexio

Extension
Extensio

SIDE VIEW

Wrist flexion
Flexio carpalis

Wrist extension
Extensio carpalis

Elbow flexion
Flexio cubiti

Elbow extension
Extensio cubiti

Flexion
Flexio

Medial and lateral rotation
Rotatio medialis et interna

Dorsiflexion
Dorsiflexio

Plantarflexion
Plantarflexio

Types of Joints

GLIDING JOINT

Gliding joints
Articulationes planae

Wrist bones
Ossa carpalia

Ulna
Ulna

Radius
Radius

Metacarpal
bone of thumb
*Os metacarpi
pollicis*

Saddle joint
Articulatio sellaris

Trapezium
Os trapezium

SADDLE JOINT

Ellipsoidal joint
Articulatio ellipsoidea

Ulna
Ulna

ELLIPSOIDAL JOINT

Scaphoid
Os scaphoideum

Radius
Radius

PIVOT JOINT

Atlas
Atlas

Pivot joint
Articulatio trochoidea

Axis
Axis

Humerus
Humerus

HINGE JOINT

Trochlea
of humerus
*Trochlea
humeri*

Ulna
Ulna

Olecranon
Olecranon

Hinge joint
Ginglymus

Radius
Radius

BALL-AND-SOCKET JOINT

Head of femur
Caput femoris

Acetabular fossa
Fossa acetabuli

Ligament of head of femur
Lig. capitis femoris

Joints

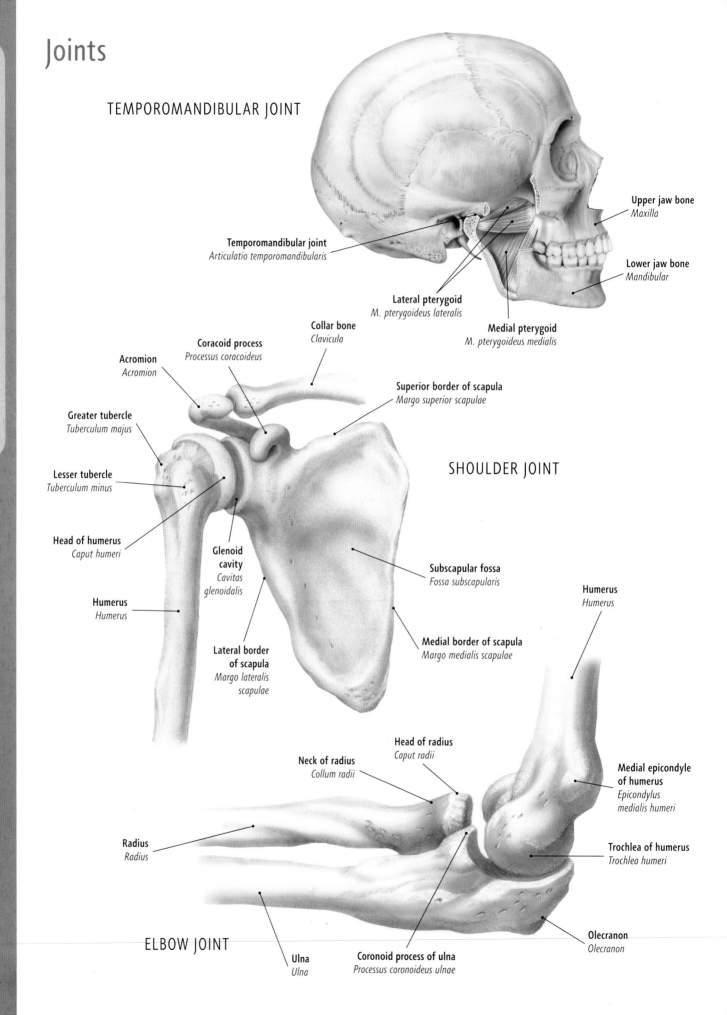

TEMPOROMANDIBULAR JOINT

Upper jaw bone
Maxilla

Temporomandibular joint
Articulatio temporomandibularis

Lower jaw bone
Mandibular

Lateral pterygoid
M. pterygoideus lateralis

Medial pterygoid
M. pterygoideus medialis

Coracoid process
Processus coracoideus

Collar bone
Clavicula

Acromion
Acromion

Superior border of scapula
Margo superior scapulae

Greater tubercle
Tuberculum majus

SHOULDER JOINT

Lesser tubercle
Tuberculum minus

Head of humerus
Caput humeri

Glenoid
cavity
*Cavitas
glenoidalis*

Subscapular fossa
Fossa subscapularis

Humerus
Humerus

Humerus
Humerus

Medial border of scapula
Margo medialis scapulae

Lateral border
of scapula
*Margo lateralis
scapulae*

Head of radius
Caput radii

Neck of radius
Collum radii

Medial epicondyle
of humerus
*Epicondylus
medialis humeri*

Radius
Radius

Trochlea of humerus
Trochlea humeri

Olecranon
Olecranon

ELBOW JOINT

Ulna
Ulna

Coronoid process of ulna
Processus coronoideus ulnae

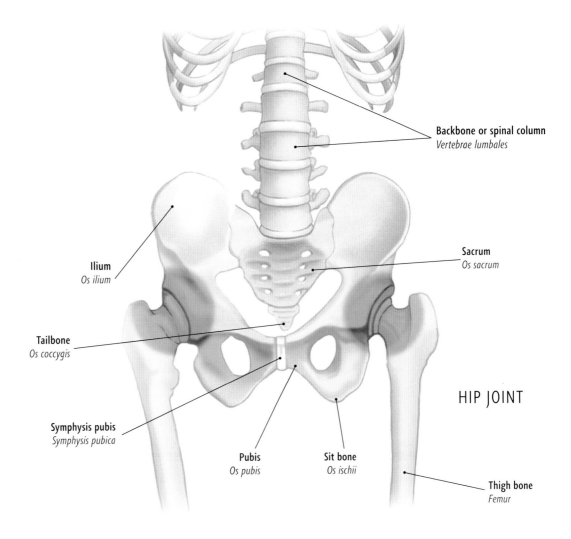

Backbone or spinal column
Vertebrae lumbales

Ilium
Os ilium

Sacrum
Os sacrum

Tailbone
Os coccygis

HIP JOINT

Symphysis pubis
Symphysis pubica

Pubis
Os pubis

Sit bone
Os ischii

Thigh bone
Femur

KNEE JOINT

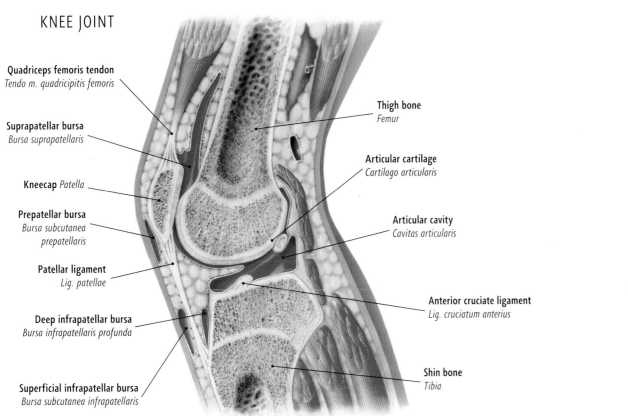

Quadriceps femoris tendon
Tendo m. quadricipitis femoris

Suprapatellar bursa
Bursa suprapatellaris

Kneecap *Patella*

Prepatellar bursa
*Bursa subcutanea
prepatellaris*

Patellar ligament
Lig. patellae

Deep infrapatellar bursa
Bursa infrapatellaris profunda

Superficial infrapatellar bursa
Bursa subcutanea infrapatellaris

Thigh bone
Femur

Articular cartilage
Cartilago articularis

Articular cavity
Cavitas articularis

Anterior cruciate ligament
Lig. cruciatum anterius

Shin bone
Tibia

The Muscular System

Muscles of the Body

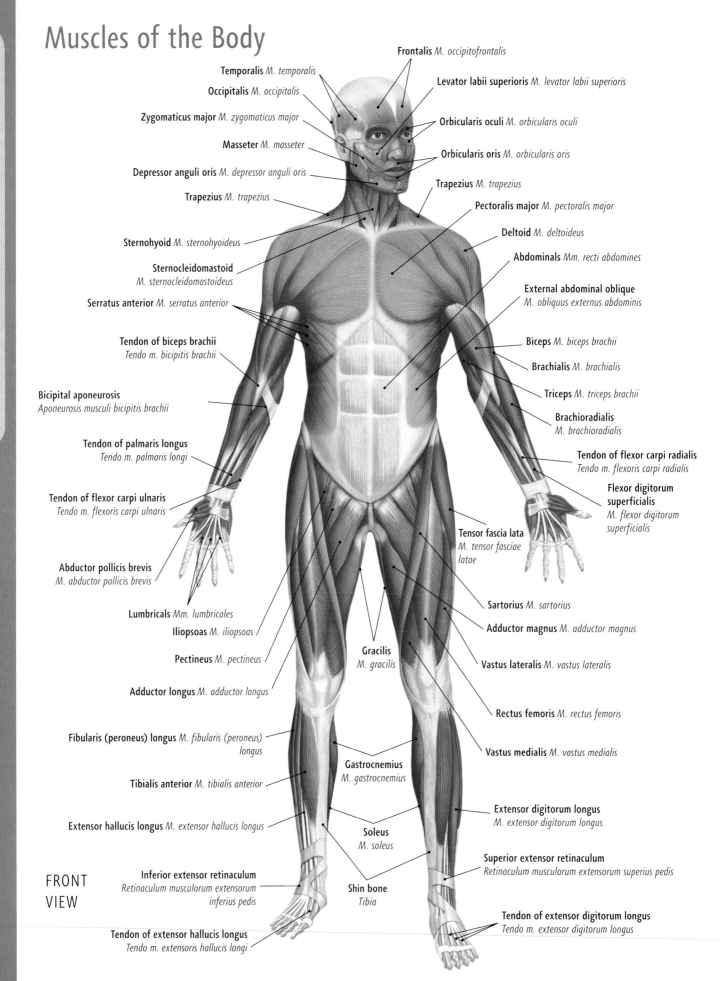

Frontalis *M. occipitofrontalis*

Temporalis *M. temporalis*

Occipitalis *M. occipitalis*

Levator labii superioris *M. levator labii superioris*

Zygomaticus major *M. zygomaticus major*

Orbicularis oculi *M. orbicularis oculi*

Masseter *M. masseter*

Orbicularis oris *M. orbicularis oris*

Depressor anguli oris *M. depressor anguli oris*

Trapezius *M. trapezius*

Trapezius *M. trapezius*

Pectoralis major *M. pectoralis major*

Sternohyoid *M. sternohyoideus*

Deltoid *M. deltoideus*

Sternocleidomastoid
M. sternocleidomastoideus

Abdominals *Mm. recti abdomines*

Serratus anterior *M. serratus anterior*

External abdominal oblique
M. obliquus externus abdominis

Tendon of biceps brachii
Tendo m. bicipitis brachii

Biceps *M. biceps brachii*

Brachialis *M. brachialis*

Bicipital aponeurosis
Aponeurosis musculi bicipitis brachii

Triceps *M. triceps brachii*

Brachioradialis
M. brachioradialis

Tendon of palmaris longus
Tendo m. palmaris longi

Tendon of flexor carpi radialis
Tendo m. flexoris carpi radialis

Tendon of flexor carpi ulnaris
Tendo m. flexoris carpi ulnaris

Flexor digitorum
superficialis
*M. flexor digitorum
superficialis*

Abductor pollicis brevis
M. abductor pollicis brevis

Lumbricals *Mm. lumbricales*

Tensor fascia lata
*M. tensor fasciae
latae*

Iliopsoas *M. iliopsoas*

Sartorius *M. sartorius*

Pectineus *M. pectineus*

Gracilis
M. gracilis

Adductor magnus *M. adductor magnus*

Adductor longus *M. adductor longus*

Vastus lateralis *M. vastus lateralis*

Fibularis (peroneus) longus *M. fibularis (peroneus)
longus*

Rectus femoris *M. rectus femoris*

Tibialis anterior *M. tibialis anterior*

Gastrocnemius
M. gastrocnemius

Vastus medialis *M. vastus medialis*

Extensor hallucis longus *M. extensor hallucis longus*

Extensor digitorum longus
M. extensor digitorum longus

Soleus
M. soleus

Superior extensor retinaculum
Retinaculum musculorum extensorum superius pedis

**FRONT
VIEW**

Inferior extensor retinaculum
*Retinaculum musculorum extensorum
inferius pedis*

Shin bone
Tibia

Tendon of extensor hallucis longus
Tendo m. extensoris hallucis longi

Tendon of extensor digitorum longus
Tendo m. extensor digitorum longus

Occipitalis *M. occipitalis*

Temporalis
M. temporalis

Trapezius
M. trapezius

Sternocleidomastoid
M. sternocleidomastoideus

Spine of scapula
Spina scapulae

Teres minor *M. teres minor*

Deltoid *M. deltoideus*

Teres major *M. teres major*

Latissimus dorsi
M. latissimus dorsi

Triceps *M. triceps brachii*

Tendon of triceps brachii
Tendo m. tricipitis brachii

Brachioradialis *M. brachioradialis*

External abdominal oblique
M. obliquus externus abdominis

Olecranon *Olecranon*

Extensor digitorum
M. extensor digitorum

Abductor pollicis longus
M. abductor pollicis longus

Flexor carpi
ulnaris
*M. flexor carpi
ulnaris*

Iliac crest
Crista iliaca

Extensor retinaculum
*Retinaculum musculorum
extensorum manus*

Extensor pollicis brevis *M. extensor pollicis brevis*

Gluteus maximus *M. gluteus maximus*

Adductor
magnus
*M. adductor
magnus*

Long head of biceps femoris
Caput longum musculi bicipitis femoris

Thoracolumbar fascia
Fascia thoracolumbalis

Semitendinosus
M. semitendinosus

Vastus lateralis
M. vastus lateralis

Gracilis
M. gracilis

Semimembranosus
M. semimembranosus

REAR VIEW

Medial head of gastrocnemius
Caput mediale musculi gastrocnemii

Soleus
M. soleus

Achilles tendon
Tendo calcaneus

Fibularis (peroneus) longus
M. fibularis (peroneus) longus

Muscles of the Body

Frontalis
M. occipitofrontalis

Orbicularis oculi
M. orbicularis oculi

Temporalis *M. temporalis*

Zygomaticus major
M. zygomaticus major

Occipitalis *M. occipitalis*

Trapezius *M. trapezius*

Orbicularis oris
M. orbicularis oris

Levator scapulae *M. levator scapulae*

Scalenus anterior and medius
Mm. scaleni anterior et medius

Depressor anguli oris
M. depressor anguli oris

Deltoid *M. deltoideus*

Lateral head of triceps brachii
Caput laterale musculi tricipitis brachii

Sternocleidomastoid
M. sternocleidomastoideus

Brachialis *M. brachialis*

Biceps *M. biceps brachii*

Brachioradialis
M. brachioradialis

Pectoralis major *M. pectoralis major*

Extensor carpi radialis longus
M. extensor carpi radialis longus

Serratus anterior *M. serratus anterior*

Extensor digitorum
M. extensor digitorum

External abdominal oblique
M. obliquus externus abdominis

Flexor carpi ulnaris
M. flexor carpi ulnaris

Latissimus dorsi
M. latissimus dorsi

Extensor carpi ulnaris
M. extensor carpi ulnaris

Sartorius
M. sartorius

Gluteus maximus *M. gluteus maximus*

SIDE VIEW

**Quadriceps femoris
(vastus lateralis)**
*M. quadriceps femoris
(m. vastus lateralis)*

Iliotibial tract
Tractus iliotibialis

Lateral head of gastrocnemius
Caput laterale musculi gastrocnemius

Tibialis anterior
M. tibialis anterior

Fibularis (peroneus) longus
M. fibularis (peroneus) longus

Soleus *M. soleus*

Extensor digitorum longus
M. extensor digitorum longus

Superior extensor retinaculum
*Retinaculum musculorum extensorum superius
pedis*

Inferior extensor retinaculum
*Retinaculum musculorum extensorum
inferius pedis*

Superior peroneal retinaculum
Retinaculum musculorum peroneorum superius

Achilles tendon
Tendo calcaneus

Muscle Types

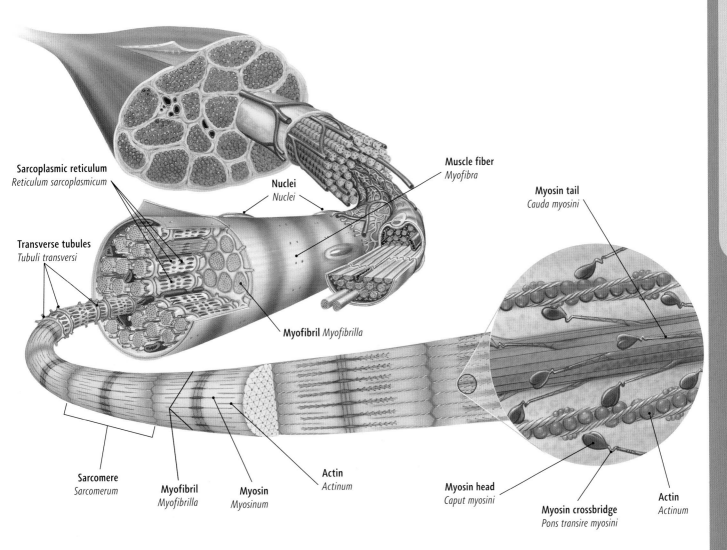

Sarcoplasmic reticulum
Reticulum sarcoplasmicum

Transverse tubules
Tubuli transversi

Nuclei
Nuclei

Muscle fiber
Myofibra

Myosin tail
Cauda myosini

Myofibril *Myofibrilla*

Sarcomere
Sarcomerum

Myofibril
Myofibrilla

Myosin
Myosinum

Actin
Actinum

Myosin head
Caput myosini

Myosin crossbridge
Pons transire myosini

Actin
Actinum

MUSCLE FIBER—MICROSTRUCTURE

Muscle fibers are elongated cells containing fine threads made of myofibrils. Myofibrils consist of contractile protein myofilaments, arranged in regular arrays. Contraction of the muscle is produced by the interaction of myosin heads with actin.

[~] = no direct Latin equivalent

MUSCLE SHAPES

Muscles are classified based on their general shape—some muscles have mainly parallel fibers, and others have oblique fibers. The shape and arrangement of muscle fibers reflects the function of the muscle (for example, muscle fibers that support organs are criss-crossed).

Unipennate
M. unipennatus

Bipennate
M. bipennatus

Multipennate
M. multipennatus

Spiral
M. spiralis

Spiral
M. spiralis

Radial
M. radialis

Circular
M. orbicularis

Multicaudal
M. multicaudalis

Quadrilateral
M. quadratus

Strap
M. habenalis

Strap (with tendinous intersections)
M. habenalis (cum intersectiones tendineae)

Cruciate
M. cruciatus

Triangular
M. triangularis

Fusiform
M. fusiformis

Bicipital
M. biceps

Tricipital
M. triceps

Quadricipital
M. quadriceps

Digastric
M. biventer

Muscle Action

EXERCISING MUSCLES

Muscles are arranged in antagonistic pairs to allow opposing movements such as flexion of a joint in one direction and extension in another. For example, biceps brachii controls flexion of the elbow, while triceps brachii controls elbow extension.

MOVEMENT AND SUPPORT

The muscles of the shoulder joint, known as the rotator cuff muscles, provide important support for the joint, while allowing a wide range of movement.

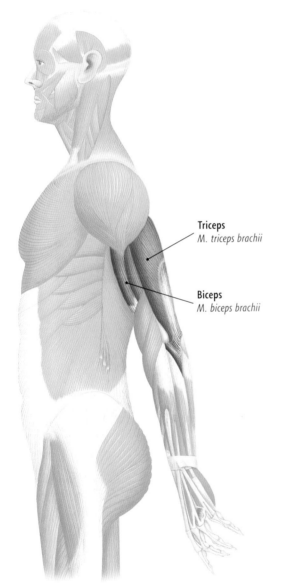

Triceps
M. triceps brachii

Biceps
M. biceps brachii

Supraspinatus
M. supraspinatus

Teres minor
M. teres minor

Infraspinatus
M. infraspinatus

Tibialis anterior
M. tibialis anterior

Tendon sheath
Vagina tendinis

MUSCLE CONTRACTION

When a muscle contracts, it shortens and pulls the muscle attachment. The muscle's action depends on its position in relation to the joint it works on. The tibialis anterior, for example, crosses in front of the ankle and moves the foot upward (dorsiflexion).

Muscles of the Head

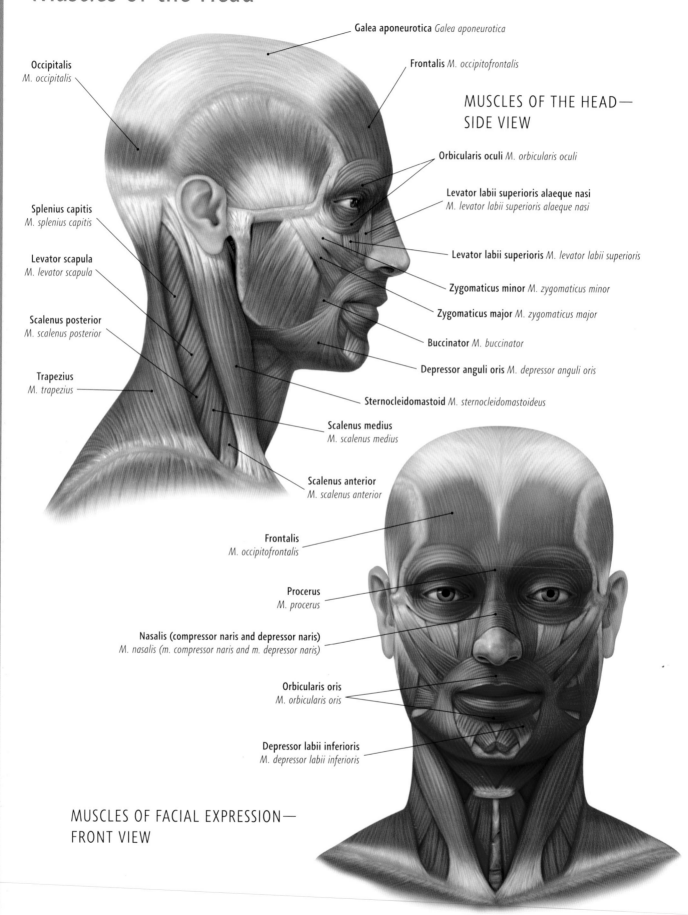

Galea aponeurotica *Galea aponeurotica*

Frontalis *M. occipitofrontalis*

Occipitalis
M. occipitalis

MUSCLES OF THE HEAD— SIDE VIEW

Orbicularis oculi *M. orbicularis oculi*

Levator labii superioris alaeque nasi
M. levator labii superioris alaeque nasi

Splenius capitis
M. splenius capitis

Levator labii superioris *M. levator labii superioris*

Levator scapula
M. levator scapula

Zygomaticus minor *M. zygomaticus minor*

Zygomaticus major *M. zygomaticus major*

Scalenus posterior
M. scalenus posterior

Buccinator *M. buccinator*

Depressor anguli oris *M. depressor anguli oris*

Trapezius
M. trapezius

Sternocleidomastoid *M. sternocleidomastoideus*

Scalenus medius
M. scalenus medius

Scalenus anterior
M. scalenus anterior

Frontalis
M. occipitofrontalis

Procerus
M. procerus

Nasalis (compressor naris and depressor naris)
M. nasalis (m. compressor naris and m. depressor naris)

Orbicularis oris
M. orbicularis oris

Depressor labii inferioris
M. depressor labii inferioris

MUSCLES OF FACIAL EXPRESSION— FRONT VIEW

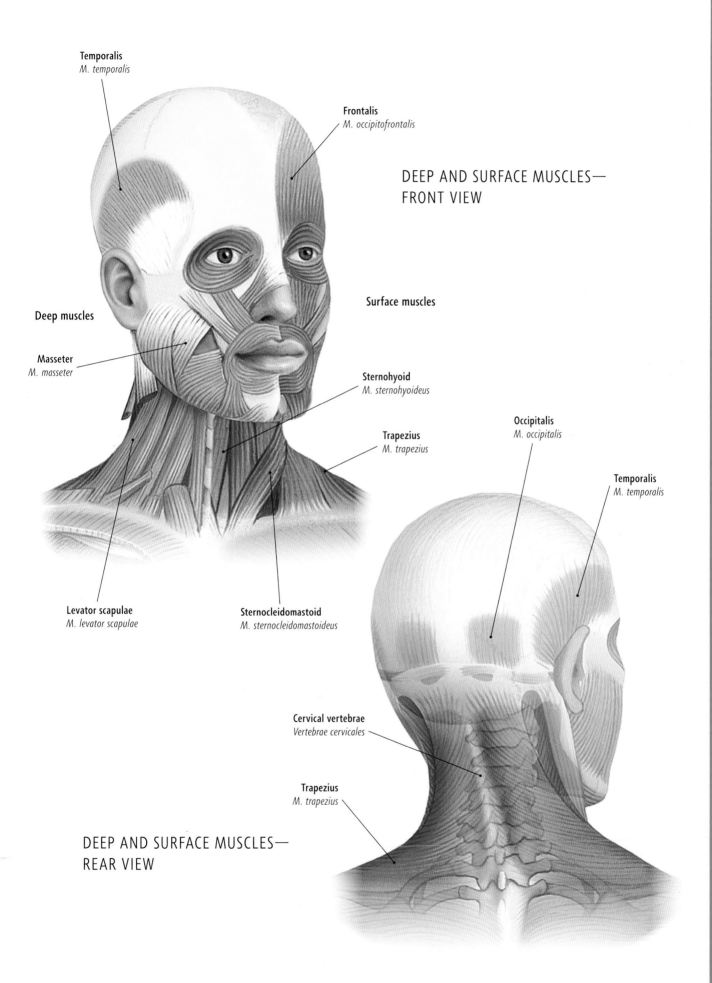

Temporalis
M. temporalis

Frontalis
M. occipitofrontalis

DEEP AND SURFACE MUSCLES—
FRONT VIEW

Surface muscles

Deep muscles

Masseter
M. masseter

Sternohyoid
M. sternohyoideus

Trapezius
M. trapezius

Occipitalis
M. occipitalis

Temporalis
M. temporalis

Levator scapulae
M. levator scapulae

Sternocleidomastoid
M. sternocleidomastoideus

Cervical vertebrae
Vertebrae cervicales

Trapezius
M. trapezius

DEEP AND SURFACE MUSCLES—
REAR VIEW

Muscles of the Eye and Neck

Superior oblique
M. obliquus superior

Superior rectus
M. rectus superior

Levator palpebrae superioris (cut)
M. levator palpebrae superioris

Medial rectus
M. rectus medialis

Tear gland
Glandula lacrimalis

Trochlea
Trochlea

Optic nerve
N. opticus (II)

MUSCLES OF THE EYE—
SIDE VIEW

Inferior oblique
M. obliquus inferior

Inferior rectus
M. rectus inferior

Lateral rectus (cut)
M. rectus lateralis

Lateral rectus
M. rectus lateralis

Optic nerve
Nervus opticus

Superior rectus (cut)
M. rectus superior

Medial rectus
M. rectus medialis

Superior oblique
M. obliquus superior

MUSCLES OF THE EYE—
VIEW FROM ABOVE

Levator palpebrae superioris (cut)
M. levator palpebrae superioris

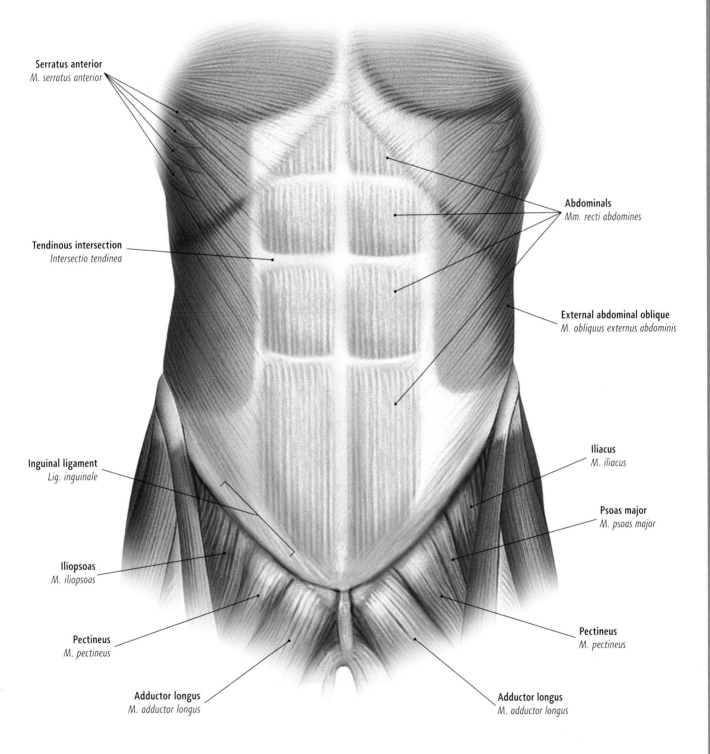

Serratus anterior
M. serratus anterior

Tendinous intersection
Intersectio tendinea

Inguinal ligament
Lig. inguinale

Iliopsoas
M. iliopsoas

Pectineus
M. pectineus

Adductor longus
M. adductor longus

Abdominals
Mm. recti abdomines

External abdominal oblique
M. obliquus externus abdominis

Iliacus
M. iliacus

Psoas major
M. psoas major

Pectineus
M. pectineus

Adductor longus
M. adductor longus

MUSCLES OF THE ABDOMEN

Muscles of Breathing and the Pelvis

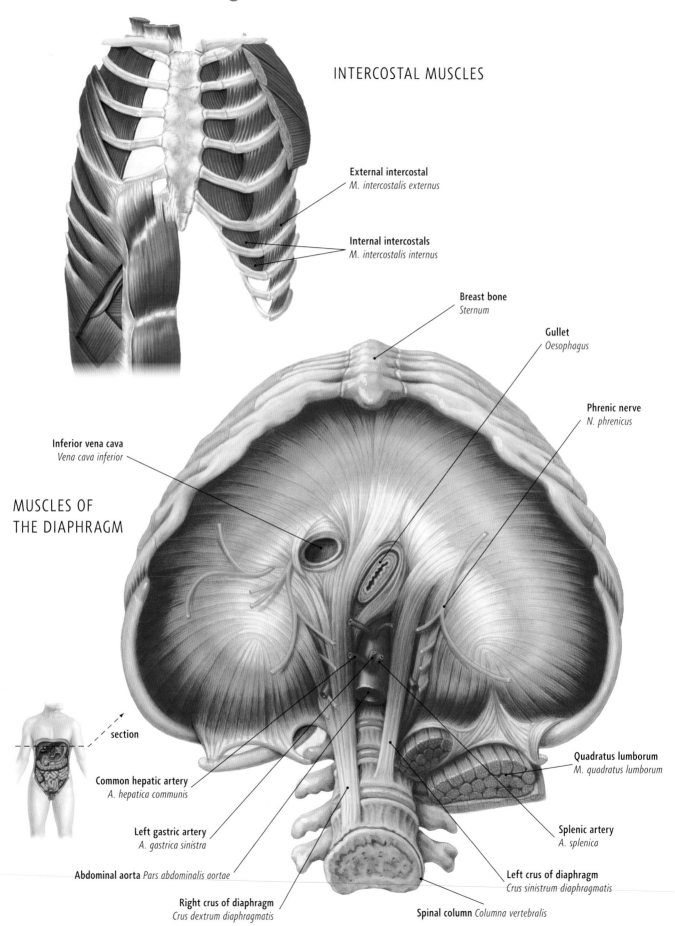

INTERCOSTAL MUSCLES

External intercostal
M. intercostalis externus

Internal intercostals
M. intercostalis internus

Breast bone
Sternum

Gullet
Oesophagus

Phrenic nerve
N. phrenicus

Inferior vena cava
Vena cava inferior

MUSCLES OF THE DIAPHRAGM

section

Quadratus lumborum
M. quadratus lumborum

Common hepatic artery
A. hepatica communis

Splenic artery
A. splenica

Left gastric artery
A. gastrica sinistra

Abdominal aorta *Pars abdominalis aortae*

Left crus of diaphragm
Crus sinistrum diaphragmatis

Right crus of diaphragm
Crus dextrum diaphragmatis

Spinal column *Columna vertebralis*

PELVIC FLOOR MUSCLES

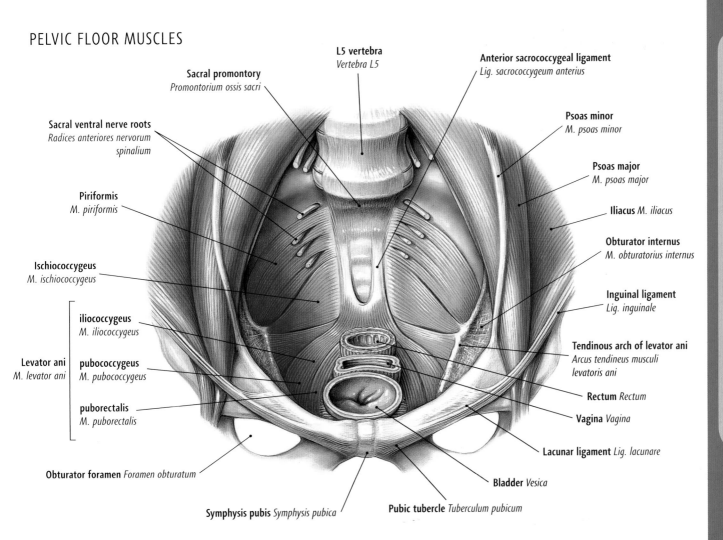

L5 vertebra
Vertebra L5

Sacral promontory
Promontorium ossis sacri

Anterior sacrococcygeal ligament
Lig. sacrococcygeum anterius

Sacral ventral nerve roots
Radices anteriores nervorum spinalium

Psoas minor
M. psoas minor

Psoas major
M. psoas major

Iliacus *M. iliacus*

Piriformis
M. piriformis

Obturator internus
M. obturatorius internus

Ischiococcygeus
M. ischiococcygeus

Inguinal ligament
Lig. inguinale

iliococcygeus
M. iliococcygeus

Tendinous arch of levator ani
Arcus tendineus musculi levatoris ani

Levator ani
M. levator ani

pubococcygeus
M. pubococcygeus

Rectum *Rectum*

puborectalis
M. puborectalis

Vagina *Vagina*

Lacunar ligament *Lig. lacunare*

Obturator foramen *Foramen obturatum*

Bladder *Vesica*

Symphysis pubis *Symphysis pubica*

Pubic tubercle *Tuberculum pubicum*

MUSCLES OF THE GROIN

Iliopsoas
M. iliopsoas

Pectineus
M. pectineus

Adductor longus
M. adductor longus

Adductor magnus
M. adductor magnus

[~] = no direct Latin equivalent

Muscles of the Arm

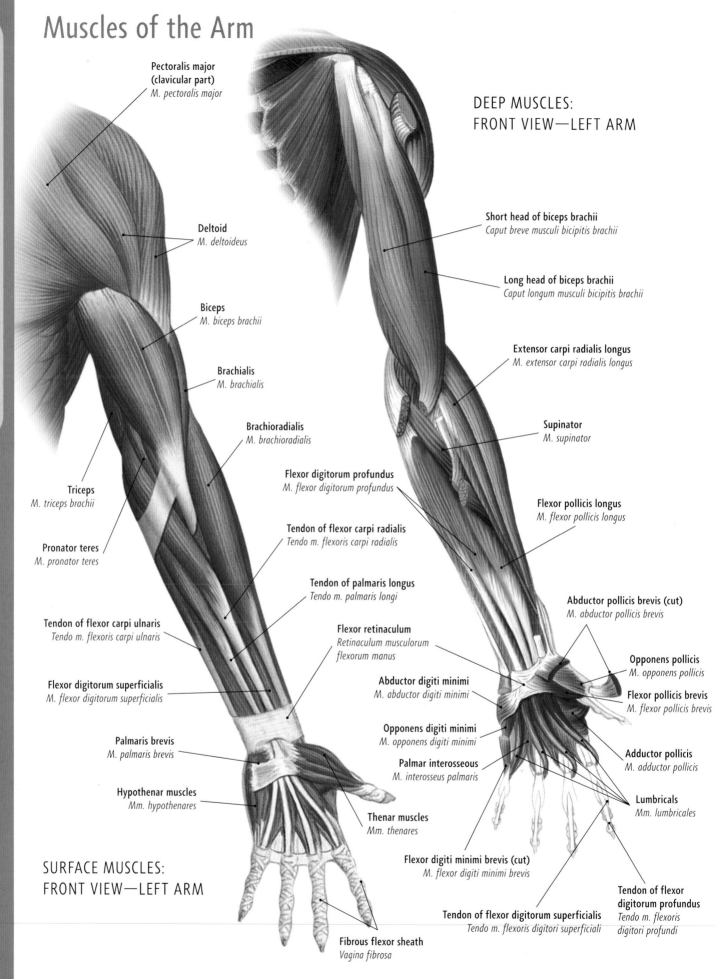

**Pectoralis major
(clavicular part)**
M. pectoralis major

Deltoid
M. deltoideus

Biceps
M. biceps brachii

Brachialis
M. brachialis

Brachioradialis
M. brachioradialis

Triceps
M. triceps brachii

Pronator teres
M. pronator teres

Tendon of flexor carpi ulnaris
Tendo m. flexoris carpi ulnaris

Flexor digitorum superficialis
M. flexor digitorum superficialis

Palmaris brevis
M. palmaris brevis

Hypothenar muscles
Mm. hypothenares

**SURFACE MUSCLES:
FRONT VIEW—LEFT ARM**

**DEEP MUSCLES:
FRONT VIEW—LEFT ARM**

Short head of biceps brachii
Caput breve musculi bicipitis brachii

Long head of biceps brachii
Caput longum musculi bicipitis brachii

Extensor carpi radialis longus
M. extensor carpi radialis longus

Supinator
M. supinator

Flexor digitorum profundus
M. flexor digitorum profundus

Flexor pollicis longus
M. flexor pollicis longus

Tendon of flexor carpi radialis
Tendo m. flexoris carpi radialis

Tendon of palmaris longus
Tendo m. palmaris longi

Flexor retinaculum
*Retinaculum musculorum
flexorum manus*

Abductor pollicis brevis (cut)
M. abductor pollicis brevis

Abductor digiti minimi
M. abductor digiti minimi

Opponens pollicis
M. opponens pollicis

Flexor pollicis brevis
M. flexor pollicis brevis

Opponens digiti minimi
M. opponens digiti minimi

Palmar interosseous
M. interosseus palmaris

Adductor pollicis
M. adductor pollicis

Thenar muscles
Mm. thenares

Lumbricals
Mm. lumbricales

Flexor digiti minimi brevis (cut)
M. flexor digiti minimi brevis

Tendon of flexor digitorum superficialis
Tendo m. flexoris digitori superficiali

**Tendon of flexor
digitorum profundus**
*Tendo m. flexoris
digitori profundi*

Fibrous flexor sheath
Vagina fibrosa

Spine of scapula *Spina scapulae*

Supraspinatus
M. supraspinatus

Spine of scapula
Spina scapulae

Bone *Os*

Deltoid
M. deltoideus

Infraspinatus *M. infraspinatus*

Teres major *M. teres major*

Long head of triceps brachii
Caput longum musculi tricipitis brachii

Long head of triceps brachii
Caput longum musculi tricipitis brachii

Lateral head of triceps brachii
Caput laterale musculi tricipitis brachii

Lateral head of triceps brachii
Caput laterale musculi tricipitis brachii

Supinator
M. supinator

Tendon of triceps brachii
Tendo m. tricipitis brachii

Abductor pollicis longus
M. abductor pollicis longus

Brachioradialis
M. brachioradialis

Anconeus
M. anconeus

Extensor pollicis brevis
M. extensor pollicis brevis

Olecranon
Olecranon

Extensor pollicis longus
M. extensor pollicis longus

Extensor digiti minimi
M. extensor digiti minimi

Tendon of extensor indicis
Tendo m. extensoris indicis

Extensor digitorum
M. extensor digitorum

Flexor carpi ulnaris
M. flexor carpi ulnaris

Abductor pollicis longus
M. abductor pollicis longus

Extensor retinaculum
*Retinaculum musculorum
extensorum manus*

Extensor pollicis brevis
M. extensor pollicis brevis

SURFACE MUSCLES: REAR VIEW—RIGHT ARM

Tendons of extensors of the digits
Tendines m. extensorum digitorum

[~] = no direct Latin equivalent

Muscles of the Arm

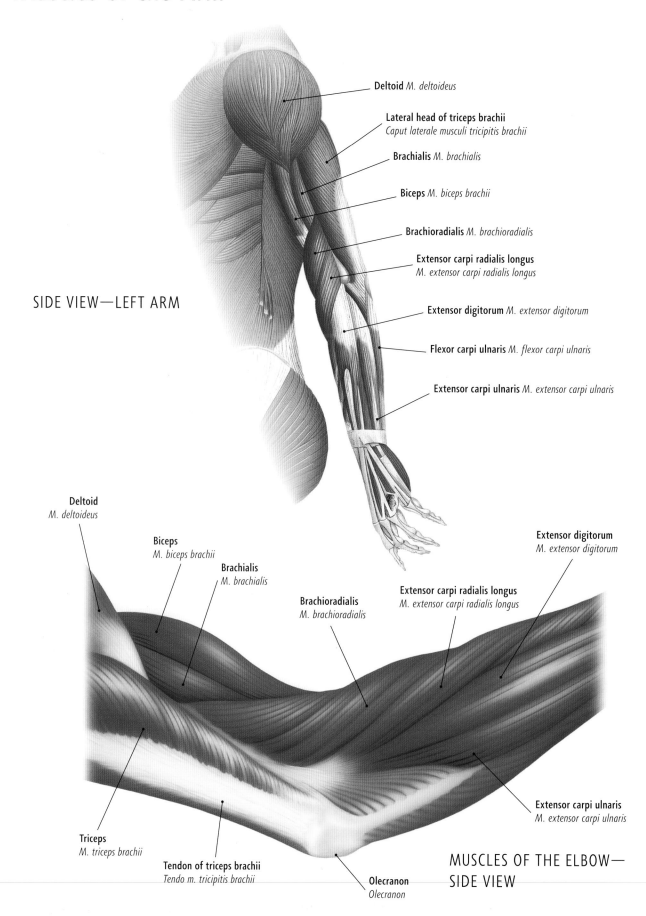

Deltoid *M. deltoideus*

Lateral head of triceps brachii
Caput laterale musculi tricipitis brachii

Brachialis *M. brachialis*

Biceps *M. biceps brachii*

Brachioradialis *M. brachioradialis*

Extensor carpi radialis longus
M. extensor carpi radialis longus

Extensor digitorum *M. extensor digitorum*

Flexor carpi ulnaris *M. flexor carpi ulnaris*

Extensor carpi ulnaris *M. extensor carpi ulnaris*

SIDE VIEW—LEFT ARM

Deltoid
M. deltoideus

Biceps
M. biceps brachii

Brachialis
M. brachialis

Brachioradialis
M. brachioradialis

Extensor digitorum
M. extensor digitorum

Extensor carpi radialis longus
M. extensor carpi radialis longus

Extensor carpi ulnaris
M. extensor carpi ulnaris

Triceps
M. triceps brachii

Tendon of triceps brachii
Tendo m. tricipitis brachii

Olecranon
Olecranon

MUSCLES OF THE ELBOW—
SIDE VIEW

116

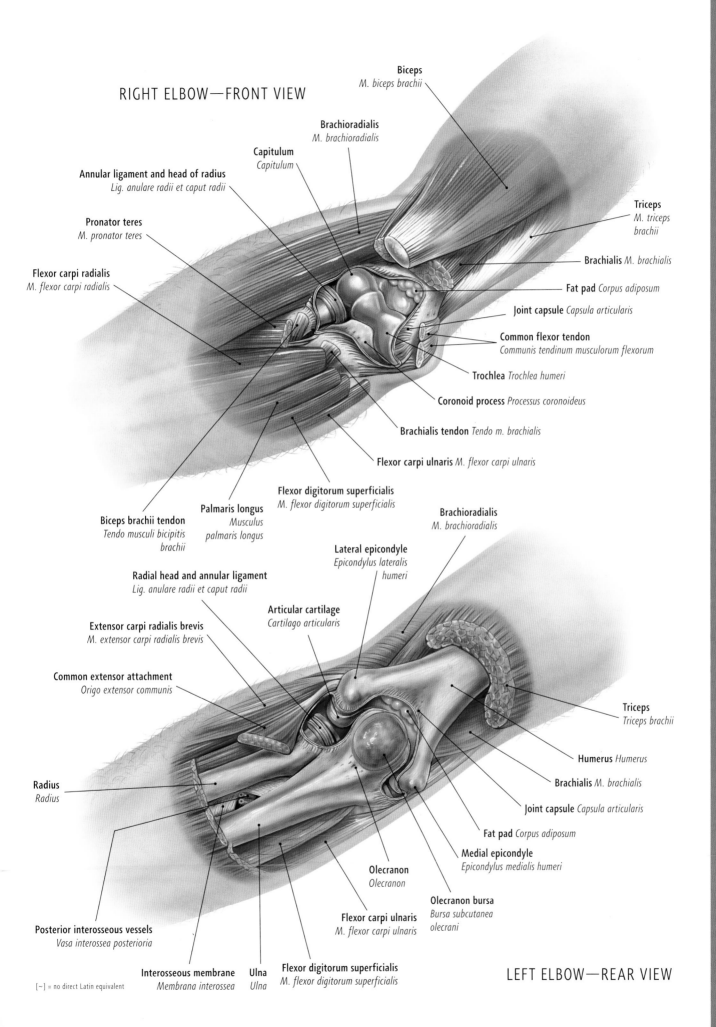

RIGHT ELBOW—FRONT VIEW

Biceps
M. biceps brachii

Brachioradialis
M. brachioradialis

Capitulum
Capitulum

Annular ligament and head of radius
Lig. anulare radii et caput radii

Pronator teres
M. pronator teres

Flexor carpi radialis
M. flexor carpi radialis

Triceps
M. triceps brachii

Brachialis *M. brachialis*

Fat pad *Corpus adiposum*

Joint capsule *Capsula articularis*

Common flexor tendon
Communis tendinum musculorum flexorum

Trochlea *Trochlea humeri*

Coronoid process *Processus coronoideus*

Brachialis tendon *Tendo m. brachialis*

Flexor carpi ulnaris *M. flexor carpi ulnaris*

Flexor digitorum superficialis
M. flexor digitorum superficialis

Biceps brachii tendon
Tendo musculi bicipitis brachii

Palmaris longus
Musculus palmaris longus

Radial head and annular ligament
Lig. anulare radii et caput radii

Extensor carpi radialis brevis
M. extensor carpi radialis brevis

Common extensor attachment
Origo extensor communis

Articular cartilage
Cartilago articularis

Lateral epicondyle
Epicondylus lateralis humeri

Brachioradialis
M. brachioradialis

Triceps
Triceps brachii

Humerus *Humerus*

Brachialis *M. brachialis*

Joint capsule *Capsula articularis*

Fat pad *Corpus adiposum*

Medial epicondyle
Epicondylus medialis humeri

Olecranon
Olecranon

Olecranon bursa
Bursa subcutanea olecrani

Radius
Radius

Posterior interosseous vessels
Vasa interossea posterioria

Interosseous membrane
Membrana interossea

Ulna
Ulna

Flexor digitorum superficialis
M. flexor digitorum superficialis

Flexor carpi ulnaris
M. flexor carpi ulnaris

[~] = no direct Latin equivalent

LEFT ELBOW—REAR VIEW

Muscles of the Arm and Hand

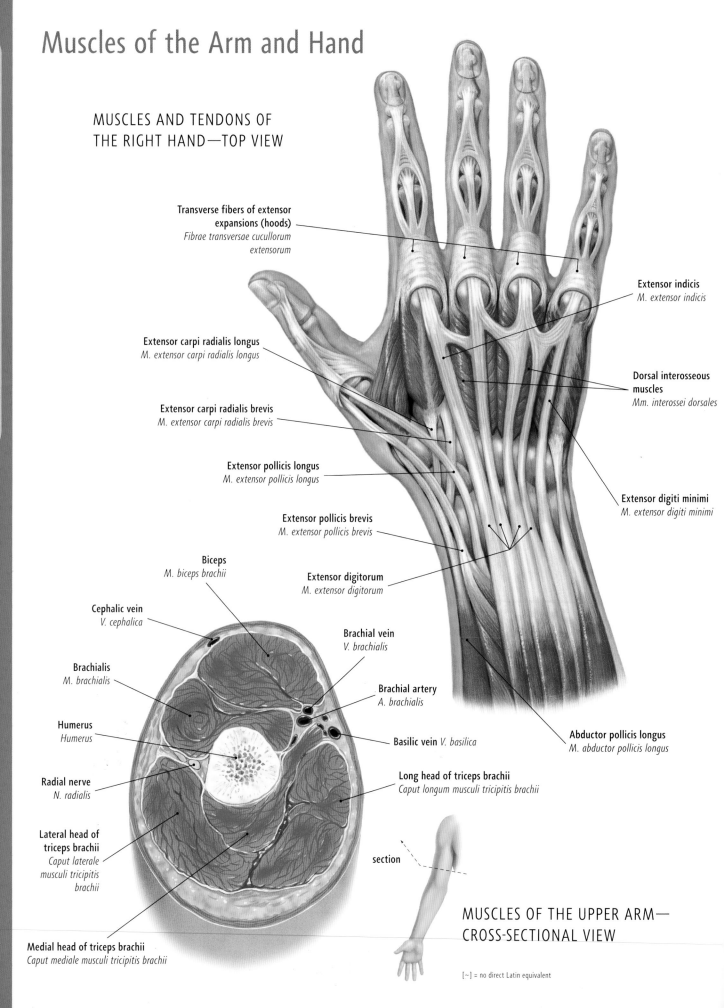

MUSCLES AND TENDONS OF THE RIGHT HAND—TOP VIEW

Transverse fibers of extensor expansions (hoods)
Fibrae transversae cucullorum extensorum

Extensor indicis
M. extensor indicis

Extensor carpi radialis longus
M. extensor carpi radialis longus

Dorsal interosseous muscles
Mm. interossei dorsales

Extensor carpi radialis brevis
M. extensor carpi radialis brevis

Extensor pollicis longus
M. extensor pollicis longus

Extensor digiti minimi
M. extensor digiti minimi

Extensor pollicis brevis
M. extensor pollicis brevis

Extensor digitorum
M. extensor digitorum

Biceps
M. biceps brachii

Cephalic vein
V. cephalica

Brachial vein
V. brachialis

Brachialis
M. brachialis

Brachial artery
A. brachialis

Humerus
Humerus

Basilic vein *V. basilica*

Radial nerve
N. radialis

Long head of triceps brachii
Caput longum musculi tricipitis brachii

Abductor pollicis longus
M. abductor pollicis longus

Lateral head of triceps brachii
Caput laterale musculi tricipitis brachii

section

Medial head of triceps brachii
Caput mediale musculi tricipitis brachii

MUSCLES OF THE UPPER ARM— CROSS-SECTIONAL VIEW

[~] = no direct Latin equivalent

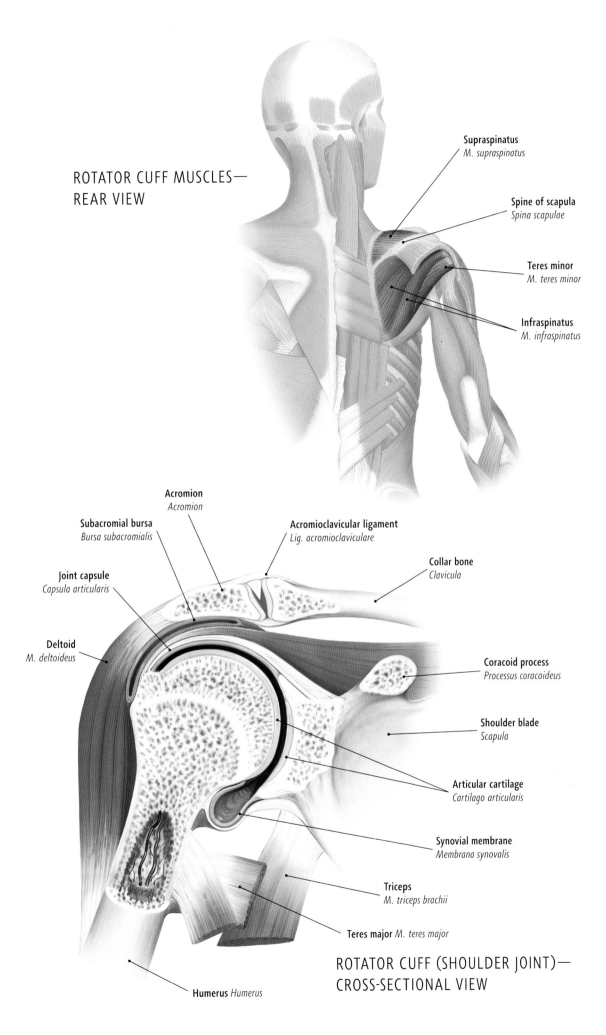

ROTATOR CUFF MUSCLES—
REAR VIEW

Supraspinatus
M. supraspinatus

Spine of scapula
Spina scapulae

Teres minor
M. teres minor

Infraspinatus
M. infraspinatus

Acromion
Acromion

Subacromial bursa
Bursa subacromialis

Acromioclavicular ligament
Lig. acromioclaviculare

Collar bone
Clavicula

Joint capsule
Capsula articularis

Deltoid
M. deltoideus

Coracoid process
Processus coracoideus

Shoulder blade
Scapula

Articular cartilage
Cartilago articularis

Synovial membrane
Membrana synovialis

Triceps
M. triceps brachii

Teres major *M. teres major*

Humerus *Humerus*

ROTATOR CUFF (SHOULDER JOINT)—
CROSS-SECTIONAL VIEW

Muscles of the Leg

Inguinal ligament
Lig. inguinale

Iliopsoas
M. iliopsoas

Pectineus
M. pectineus

Adductor longus
M. adductor longus

Gracilis
M. gracilis

Pectineus
M. pectineus

Adductor brevis
M. adductor brevis

Vastus intermedius
M. vastus intermedius

Vastus lateralis
M. vastus lateralis

Rectus femoris (cut)
M. rectus femoris

Vastus medialis
M. vastus medialis

Quadriceps
M. quadriceps femoris

Adductor longus (cut)
M. adductor longus

Adductor magnus
M. adductor magnus

Iliotibial tract
Tractus iliotibialis

Fibularis (peroneus) longus
M. fibularis (peroneus) longus

Extensor digitorum longus
M. extensor digitorum longus

Tibialis anterior
M. tibialis anterior

Gastrocnemius
M. gastrocnemius

Calf muscles
M. triceps surae

Soleus
M. soleus

Tibialis anterior
M. tibialis anterior

Superior extensor retinaculum
Retinaculum musculorum extensorum superius pedis

Inferior extensor retinaculum
Retinaculum musculorum extensorum inferius pedis

Extensor hallucis longus
M. extensor hallucis longus

Tendon of extensor digitorum longus
Tendo m. extensor digitorum longus

DEEP MUSCLES: FRONT VIEW—RIGHT LEG

SURFACE MUSCLES: FRONT VIEW—RIGHT LEG

Gluteus medius
M. gluteus medius

Gluteus maximus
M. gluteus maximus

Iliotibial tract
Tractus iliotibialis

Biceps femoris
M. biceps femoris

Hamstrings
*Musculi
mpartimenti
ris posterius*

Semimembranosus
M. semimembranosus

Semitendinosus
M. semitendinosus

Piriformis
M. piriformis

Sacrotuberous
ligament
Lig. sacrotuberale

Quadratus femoris
M. quadratus femoris

Tendon of
semitendinosus (cut)
*Tendo m.
semitendinosus*

Gracilis *M. gracilis*

Hamstring part of adductor magnus
*Pars medialis musculi adductorius
magnus*

Adductor magnus
M. adductor magnus

Semimembranosus
M. semimembranosus

Tendon of semitendinosus (cut)
Tendo m. semitendinosi

Oblique popliteal ligament
Lig. popliteum obliquum

Plantaris
M. plantaris

Gracilis
M. gracilis

Lateral head of gastrocnemius
Caput laterale musculi gastrocnemius

Medial head of gastrocnemius
Caput mediale musculi gastrocnemii

Gluteus minimus
M. gluteus minimus

Gemellus superior
M. gemellus superior

Gemellus inferior
M. gemellus inferior

Tendon of long head of biceps
femoris (cut)
*Tendo caput longum m. bicipitis
femoris*

Adductor magnus
M. adductor magnus

Adductor part of
adductor magnus
*Pars addcutorius musculi
adductorius magnus*

Vastus lateralis
M. vastus lateralis

Short head of biceps femoris
Caput breve musculi bicipitis femoris

Tendon of long head of
biceps femoris (cut)
*Tendo capitis longi m.
bicipitis femoris*

Popliteus *M. popliteus*

Soleus (cut)
M. soleus

Fibularis (peroneus) longus
M. fibularis (peroneus) longus

Tibialis posterior
M. tibialis posterior

Flexor digitorum longus
M. flexor digitorum longus

Flexor hallucis longus
M. flexor hallucis longus

DEEP MUSCLES:
REAR VIEW—RIGHT LEG

SURFACE MUSCLES:
REAR VIEW—LEFT LEG

Achilles tendon
Tendo calcaneus

[~] = no direct Latin equivalent

Muscles of the Leg and Foot

Sartorius
M. sartorius

Gluteus maximus
M. gluteus maximus

Quadriceps femoris (vastus lateralis)
M. quadriceps femoris (m. vastus lateralis)

Iliotibial tract
Tractus iliotibialis

SIDE VIEW—LEFT LEG

Lateral head of gastrocnemius
Caput laterale musculi gastrocnemius

Tibialis anterior
M. tibialis anterior

Fibularis (peroneus) longus
M. fibularis (peroneus) longus

Soleus *M. soleus*

MUSCLES OF THE THIGH—
CROSS-SECTIONAL VIEW

Superior extensor retinaculum
Retinaculum musculorum extensorum superius pedis

Extensor digitorum longus
M. extensor digitorum longus

Inferior extensor retinaculum
Retinaculum musculorum extensorum inferius pedis

Achilles tendon
Tendo calcaneus

Hamstrings
Musculi compartimenti femoris posterius

Superior peroneal retinaculum
Retinaculum musculorum peroneorum superius

Biceps femoris (long head)
M. biceps femoris (caput longum)

Semitendinosus
M. semitendinosus

Semimembranosus
M. semimembranosus

Biceps femoris
(short head)
*M. biceps femoris
(caput breve)*

Adductor magnus *M. adductor magnus*

Deep femoral vein *V. profunda femoris*

Obturator nerve *N. obturatorius*

Adductor longus *M. adductor longus*

Deep femoral
artery
*A. profunda
femoris*

Gracilis *M. gracilis*

Great saphenous vein
V. saphena magna

Saphenous nerve
N. saphenus

section

Sartorius
M. sartorius

Femoral artery and vein
Arteria femoralis et v. femoralis

Vastus lateralis
M. vastus lateralis

Vastus intermedius
M. vastus intermedius

Rectus femoris
M. rectus femoris

Vastus medialis
M. vastus medialis

Quadriceps
M. quadriceps femoris

MUSCLES OF THE FOOT—REAR VIEW

Tibialis posterior *M. tibialis posterior*

Flexor digitorum longus *M. flexor digitorum longus*

Shin bone *Tibia*

Flexor digitorum longus tendon *M. flexor digitorum longus*

Tibialis posterior tendon *Tendo m. tibialis posterioris*

Posterior tibial artery *Arteria tibialis posterior*

Tibial nerve *N. tibialis*

Flexor retinaculum *Retinaculum musculorum flexorum pedis*

First metatarsal *Os metatarsi I*

Flexor hallucis longus *M. flexor hallucis longus*

Fibula *Fibula*

Fibularis (peroneus) longus tendon *Tendo m. fibularis longi*

Flexor hallucis longus tendon *Tendo m. flexoris hallucis longi*

Achilles tendon *Tendo calcaneus*

Calcaneal tuberosity *Tuber calcanei*

Fibularis (peroneus) longus tendon *Tendo m. fibularis longi*

Fibularis (peroneus) brevis *M. fibularis (peroneus) brevis*

Achilles tendon *Tendo calcaneus*

Superior peroneal retinaculum *naculum musculorum peroneorum superius*

Heel bone *Calcaneus*

Inferior peroneal retinaculum *etinaculum musculorum peroneorum inferius*

Fibularis (peroneus) longus tendon *Tendo m. fibularis longi*

ensor digitorum brevis *M. extensor digitorum brevis*

Tuberosity of fifth metatarsal *Tuberositas ossis metatarsi quinti [V]*

Fibularis (peroneus) tertius *M. fibularis (peroneus) tertius*

Tibialis anterior *M. tibialis anterior*

Extensor hallucis longus *M. extensor hallucis longus*

Extensor digitorum longus *M. extensor digitorum longus*

Superior extensor retinaculum *Retinaculum musculorum extensorum superius pedis*

Tendon sheaths *Vaginae tendines*

MUSCLES OF THE FOOT—SIDE VIEW

Inferior extensor retinaculum *Retinaculum musculorum extensorum inferius pedis*

Tendon sheath *Vagina tendinis*

Extensor hallucis longus tendon *Tendo m. extensor hallucis longus*

Extensor digitorum longus tendons *Tendo m. extensor digitorum longus*

Extensor digitorum brevis tendons *Tendo m. extensor digitorum brevis*

Metatarsophalangeal joint *Articulatio metatarsophalangea*

Muscles of the Foot

FIRST LAYER MUSCLES OF THE FOOT—VIEW FROM BELOW

Abductor digiti minimi
Abductor digiti minimi

Flexor digitorum brevis
M. flexor digitorum brevis

Abductor hallucis
Abductor hallucis

Quadratus plantae
M. quadratus plantae

Lumbricals
Mm. lumbricales

SECOND LAYER MUSCLES OF THE FOOT—
VIEW FROM BELOW

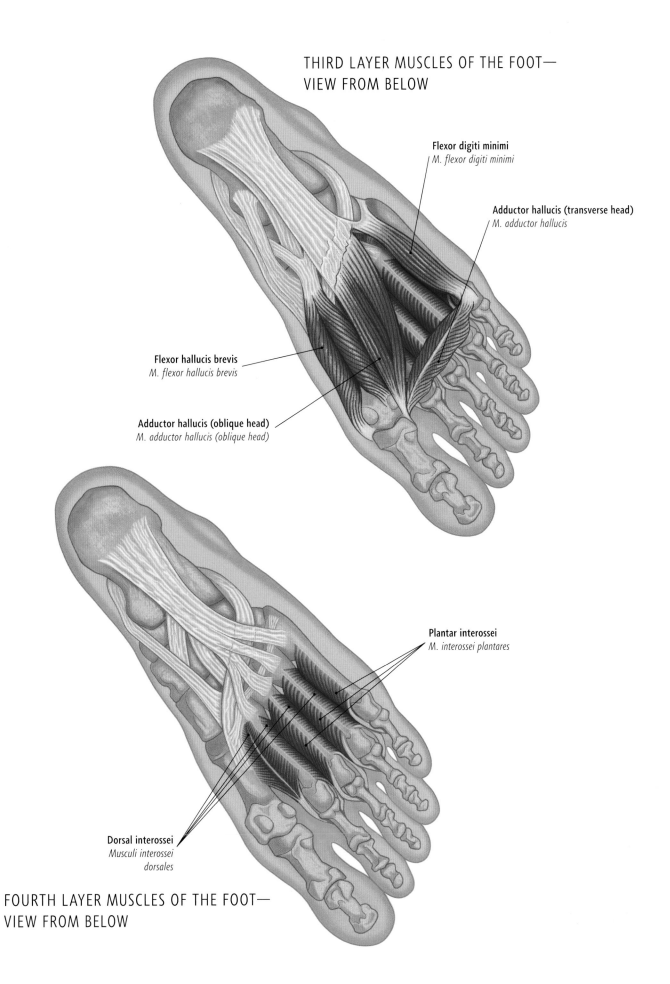

THIRD LAYER MUSCLES OF THE FOOT—
VIEW FROM BELOW

Flexor digiti minimi
M. flexor digiti minimi

Adductor hallucis (transverse head)
M. adductor hallucis

Flexor hallucis brevis
M. flexor hallucis brevis

Adductor hallucis (oblique head)
M. adductor hallucis (oblique head)

Plantar interossei
M. interossei plantares

Dorsal interossei
Musculi interossei dorsales

FOURTH LAYER MUSCLES OF THE FOOT—
VIEW FROM BELOW

The Nervous System

The Nervous System

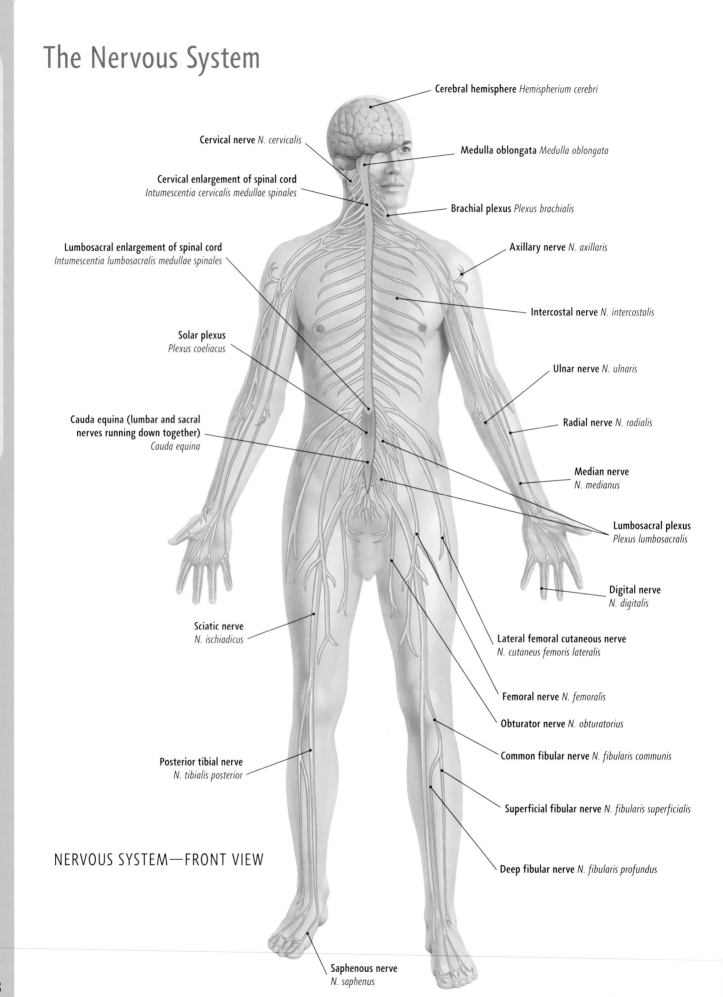

Cerebral hemisphere *Hemispherium cerebri*

Cervical nerve *N. cervicalis*

Medulla oblongata *Medulla oblongata*

Cervical enlargement of spinal cord
Intumescentia cervicalis medullae spinales

Brachial plexus *Plexus brachialis*

Lumbosacral enlargement of spinal cord
Intumescentia lumbosacralis medullae spinales

Axillary nerve *N. axillaris*

Intercostal nerve *N. intercostalis*

Solar plexus
Plexus coeliacus

Ulnar nerve *N. ulnaris*

Radial nerve *N. radialis*

Cauda equina (lumbar and sacral nerves running down together)
Cauda equina

Median nerve
N. medianus

Lumbosacral plexus
Plexus lumbosacralis

Digital nerve
N. digitalis

Sciatic nerve
N. ischiadicus

Lateral femoral cutaneous nerve
N. cutaneus femoris lateralis

Femoral nerve *N. femoralis*

Obturator nerve *N. obturatorius*

Posterior tibial nerve
N. tibialis posterior

Common fibular nerve *N. fibularis communis*

Superficial fibular nerve *N. fibularis superficialis*

Deep fibular nerve *N. fibularis profundus*

NERVOUS SYSTEM—FRONT VIEW

Saphenous nerve
N. saphenus

Synaptic knob (bouton)
Bulbus terminalis axonis

Axon terminal
Telodendron

Cell body *Neurosoma*

Golgi apparatus
Apparatus golgiensis

Nuclear membrane
Membrana nuclearis

Nucleolus
Nucleolus

Mitochondrion
Mitochondrion

Dendrite *Dendritum*

Myelin sheath
Stratum myelini

Axon *Axon*

NEURON

Neurons are specialized cells that conduct nerve impulses. Each neuron has three main parts: a cell body, several branching dendrites that carry impulses to the cell body, and an axon that conveys impulses away from the cell body.

Cerebrum
Cerebrum

Pons *Pons*

Cerebellum
Cerebellum

Spinal cord
Medulla spinalis

Conus medullaris
Conus medullaris

Cauda equina
Cauda equina

CENTRAL NERVOUS SYSTEM— CROSS-SECTIONAL VIEW

The central nervous system (CNS) comprises the brain and spinal cord. Nerves connect the CNS to peripheral regions such as the muscles, skin, and internal organs. Most nerve cells of the autonomic nervous system (which controls involuntary body functions) are found peripherally, but some are located in the CNS.

[~] = no direct Latin equivalent

The Brain

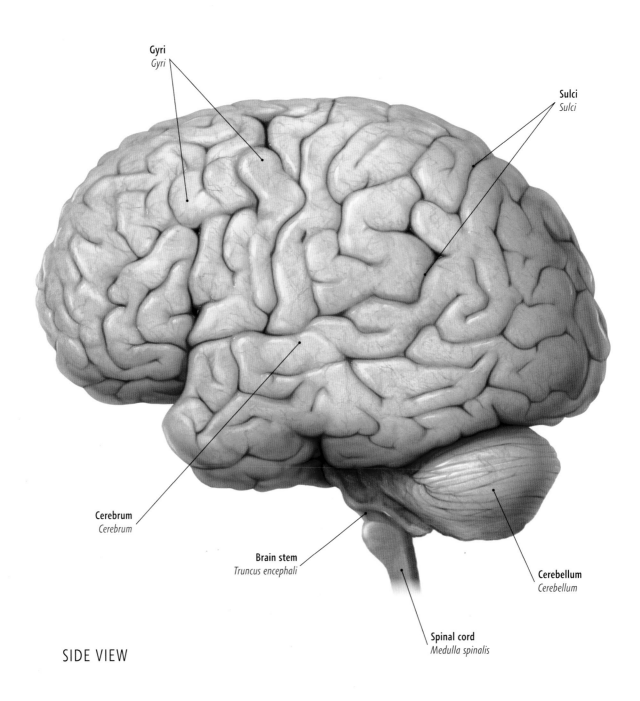

Gyri
Gyri

Sulci
Sulci

Cerebrum
Cerebrum

Brain stem
Truncus encephali

Cerebellum
Cerebellum

Spinal cord
Medulla spinalis

SIDE VIEW

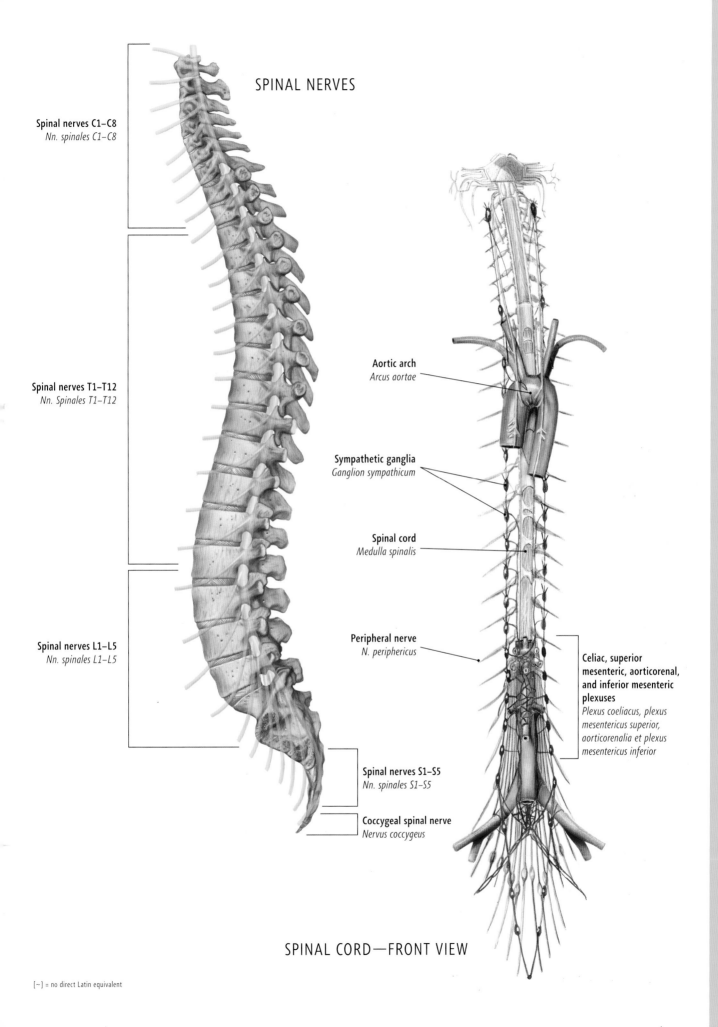

SPINAL NERVES

Spinal nerves C1–C8
Nn. spinales C1–C8

Spinal nerves T1–T12
Nn. Spinales T1–T12

Spinal nerves L1–L5
Nn. spinales L1–L5

Aortic arch
Arcus aortae

Sympathetic ganglia
Ganglion sympathicum

Spinal cord
Medulla spinalis

Peripheral nerve
N. periphericus

**Celiac, superior
mesenteric, aorticorenal,
and inferior mesenteric
plexuses**
*Plexus coeliacus, plexus
mesentericus superior,
aorticorenalia et plexus
mesentericus inferior*

Spinal nerves S1–S5
Nn. spinales S1–S5

Coccygeal spinal nerve
Nervus coccygeus

SPINAL CORD—FRONT VIEW

[~] = no direct Latin equivalent

Dermatomes

Spinal nerves are numbered and correspond closely to the spinal vertebrae. Each pair of nerves supplies a specific dermatome (skin area) of the body. However, there is usually some overlap between adjacent dermatomes. The skin of the face is supplied by branches of the trigeminal nerve (cranial nerves V1, V2, and V3).

NERVE TO SKIN LINK

DERMATOMES—SIDE VIEW

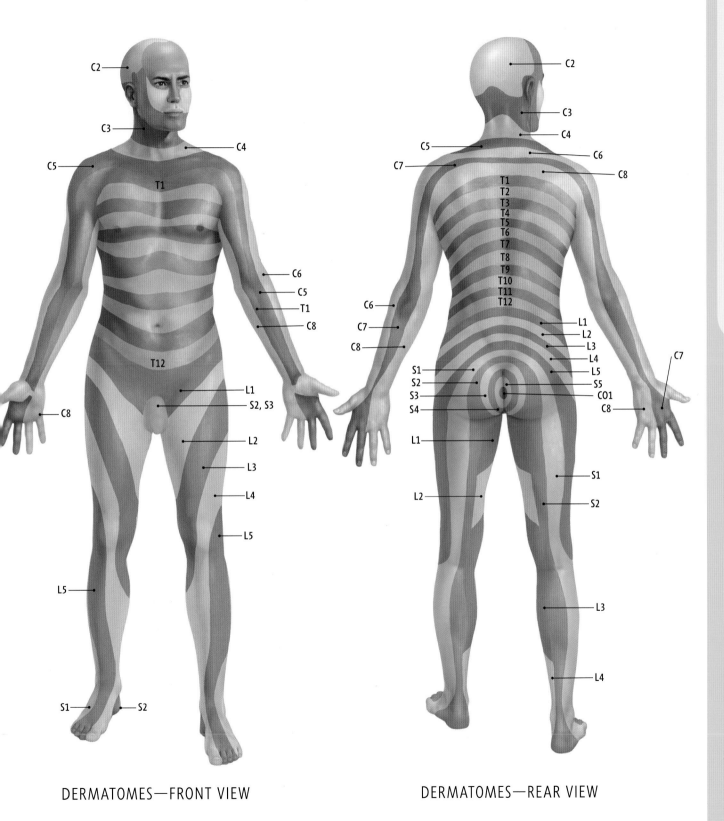

DERMATOMES—FRONT VIEW

DERMATOMES—REAR VIEW

Nerves of the Head, Arms, and Legs

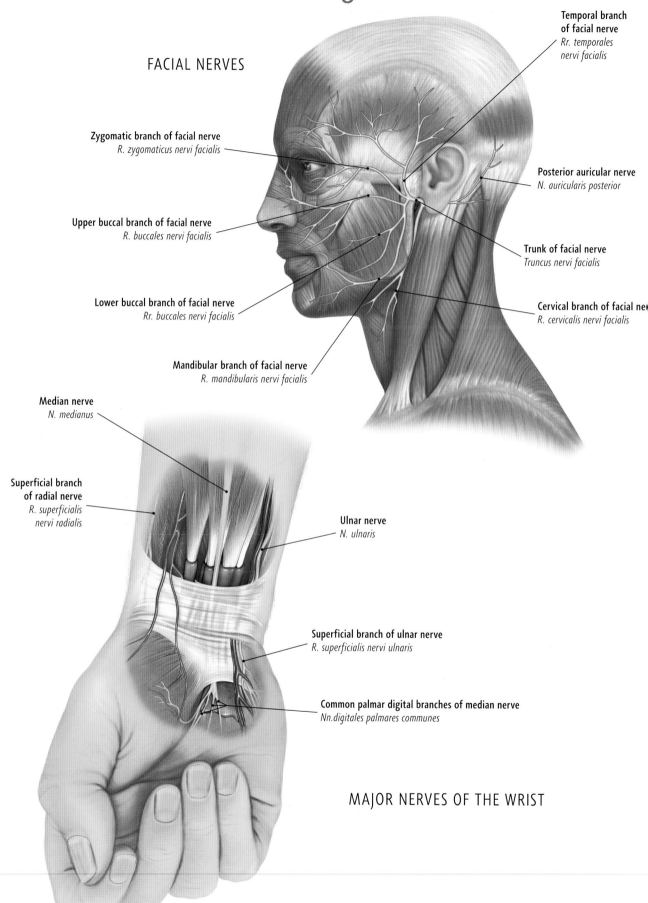

FACIAL NERVES

Temporal branch of facial nerve
Rr. temporales nervi facialis

Zygomatic branch of facial nerve
R. zygomaticus nervi facialis

Posterior auricular nerve
N. auricularis posterior

Upper buccal branch of facial nerve
R. buccales nervi facialis

Trunk of facial nerve
Truncus nervi facialis

Lower buccal branch of facial nerve
Rr. buccales nervi facialis

Cervical branch of facial nerve
R. cervicalis nervi facialis

Mandibular branch of facial nerve
R. mandibularis nervi facialis

Median nerve
N. medianus

Superficial branch of radial nerve
R. superficialis nervi radialis

Ulnar nerve
N. ulnaris

Superficial branch of ulnar nerve
R. superficialis nervi ulnaris

Common palmar digital branches of median nerve
Nn. digitales palmares communes

MAJOR NERVES OF THE WRIST

NERVES OF THE ARM:
FRONT VIEW—LEFT ARM

Axillary nerve
N. axillaris

Musculocutaneous nerve
N. musculocutaneus

Radial nerve
N. radialis

Ulnar nerve
N. ulnaris

Median nerve
N. medianus

Common palmar digital nerves
Nn. digitales palmares communes

Lateral femoral cutaneous nerve
N. cutaneus femoris lateralis

Femoral nerve
N. femoralis

Sciatic nerve
N. ischiadicus

Obturator nerve
N. obturatorius

Common fibular nerve
N. fibularis communis

Superficial fibular nerve
N. fibularis superficialis

Posterior tibial nerve
N. tibialis posterior

Deep fibular nerve
N. fibularis profundus

NERVES OF THE LEG:
FRONT VIEW—RIGHT LEG

Autonomic Nervous System

AUTONOMIC NERVOUS SYSTEM: SYMPATHETIC DIVISION

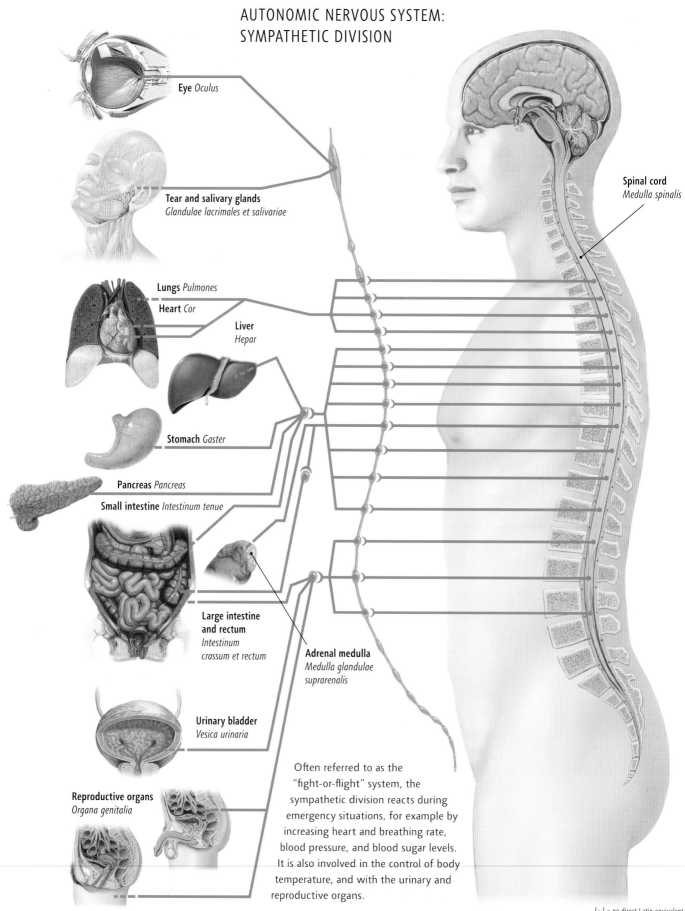

Eye *Oculus*

Tear and salivary glands
Glandulae lacrimales et salivariae

Spinal cord
Medulla spinalis

Lungs *Pulmones*

Heart *Cor*

Liver
Hepar

Stomach *Gaster*

Pancreas *Pancreas*

Small intestine *Intestinum tenue*

Large intestine
and rectum
*Intestinum
crassum et rectum*

Adrenal medulla
*Medulla glandulae
suprarenalis*

Urinary bladder
Vesica urinaria

Reproductive organs
Organa genitalia

Often referred to as the
"fight-or-flight" system, the
sympathetic division reacts during
emergency situations, for example by
increasing heart and breathing rate,
blood pressure, and blood sugar levels.
It is also involved in the control of body
temperature, and with the urinary and
reproductive organs.

[~] = no direct Latin equivalent

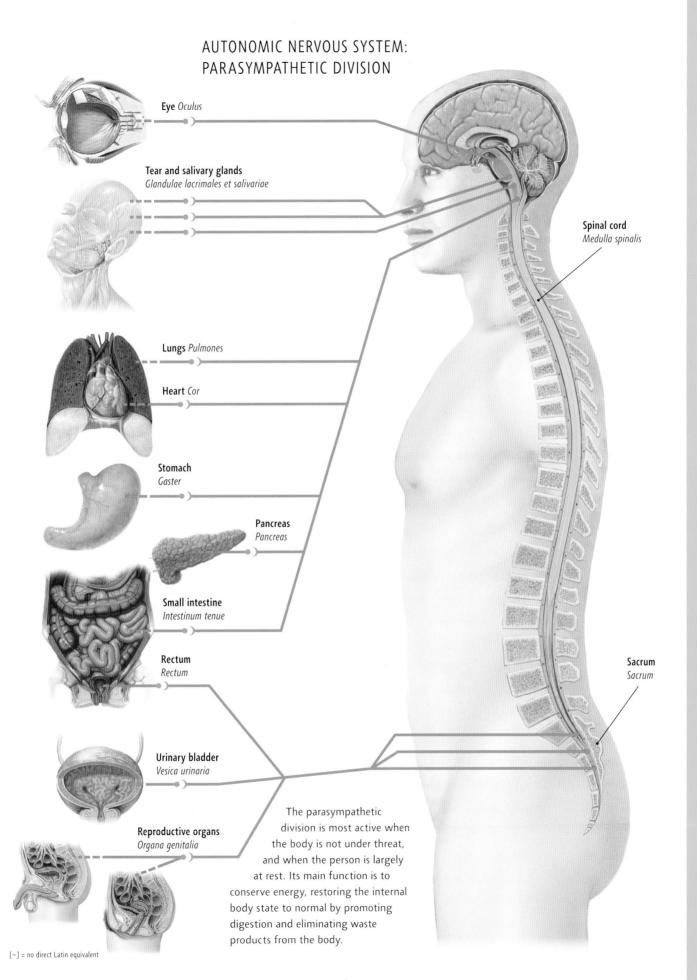

AUTONOMIC NERVOUS SYSTEM: PARASYMPATHETIC DIVISION

Eye *Oculus*

Tear and salivary glands *Glandulae lacrimales et salivariae*

Lungs *Pulmones*

Heart *Cor*

Stomach *Gaster*

Pancreas *Pancreas*

Small intestine *Intestinum tenue*

Rectum *Rectum*

Urinary bladder *Vesica urinaria*

Reproductive organs *Organa genitalia*

Spinal cord *Medulla spinalis*

Sacrum *Sacrum*

The parasympathetic division is most active when the body is not under threat, and when the person is largely at rest. Its main function is to conserve energy, restoring the internal body state to normal by promoting digestion and eliminating waste products from the body.

[~] = no direct Latin equivalent

Special Sense Organs

The Eye

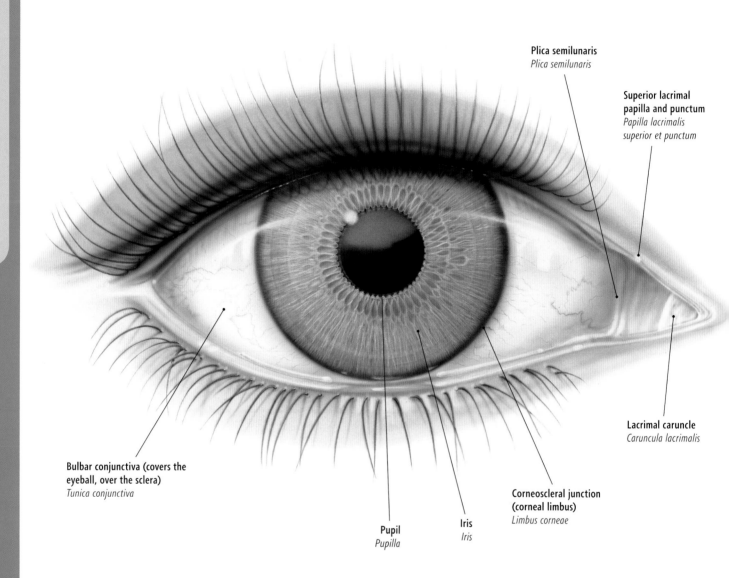

Plica semilunaris
Plica semilunaris

Superior lacrimal papilla and punctum
Papilla lacrimalis superior et punctum

Lacrimal caruncle
Caruncula lacrimalis

Bulbar conjunctiva (covers the eyeball, over the sclera)
Tunica conjunctiva

Pupil
Pupilla

Iris
Iris

Corneoscleral junction (corneal limbus)
Limbus corneae

FRONT VIEW

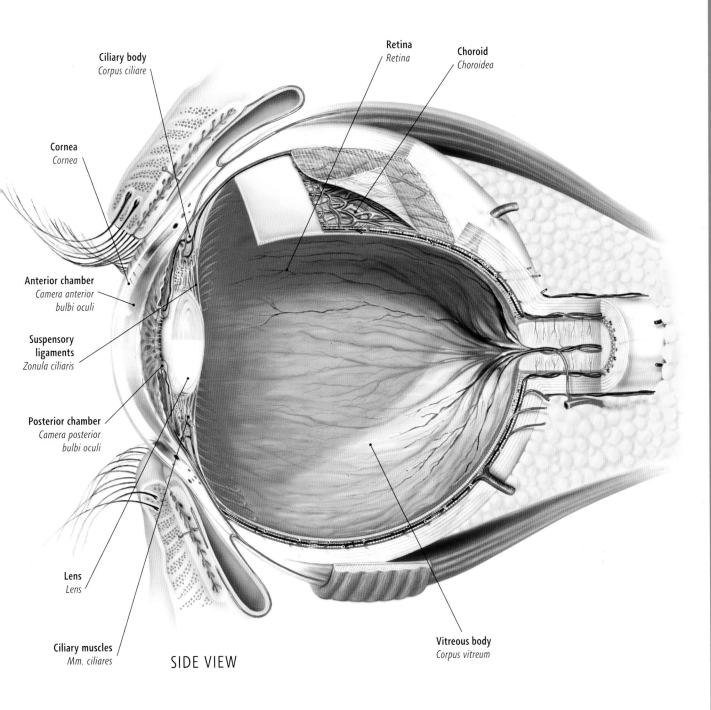

Ciliary body
Corpus ciliare

Retina
Retina

Choroid
Choroidea

Cornea
Cornea

Anterior chamber
*Camera anterior
bulbi oculi*

Suspensory
ligaments
Zonula ciliaris

Posterior chamber
*Camera posterior
bulbi oculi*

Lens
Lens

Ciliary muscles
Mm. ciliares

SIDE VIEW

Vitreous body
Corpus vitreum

Sight

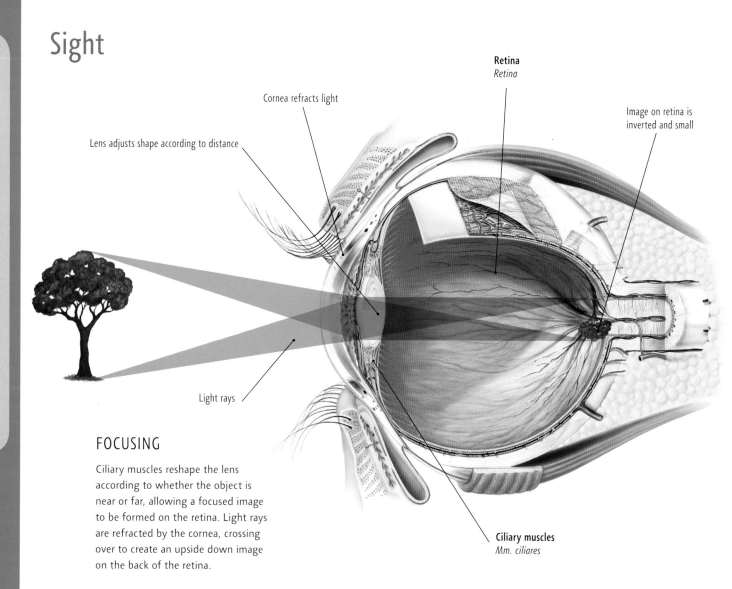

Retina
Retina

Cornea refracts light

Image on retina is inverted and small

Lens adjusts shape according to distance

Light rays

FOCUSING

Ciliary muscles reshape the lens according to whether the object is near or far, allowing a focused image to be formed on the retina. Light rays are refracted by the cornea, crossing over to create an upside down image on the back of the retina.

Ciliary muscles
Mm. ciliares

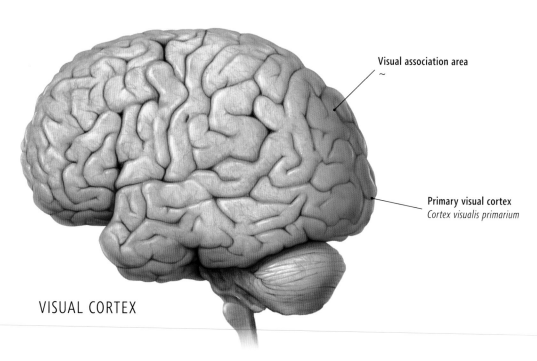

Visual association area
~

Primary visual cortex
Cortex visualis primarium

VISUAL CORTEX

[~] = no direct Latin equivalent

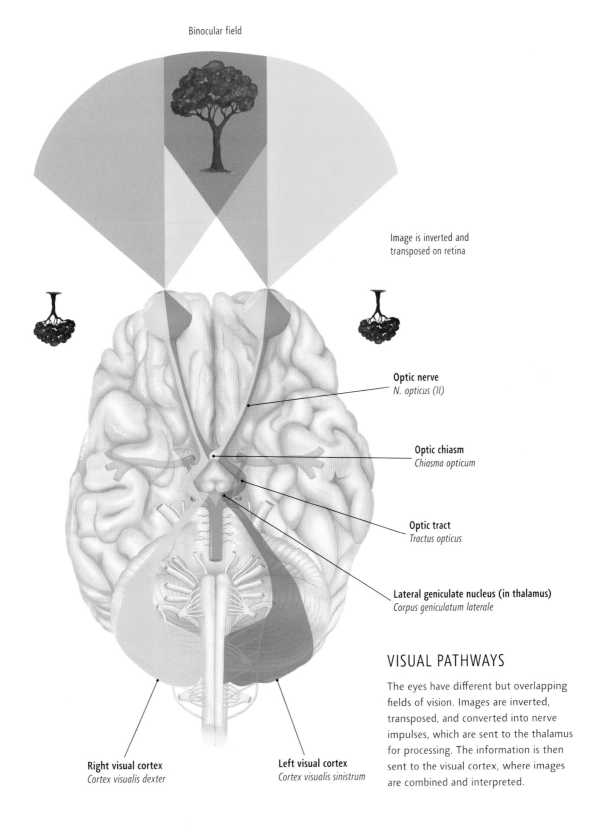

Binocular field

Image is inverted and transposed on retina

Optic nerve
N. opticus (II)

Optic chiasm
Chiasma opticum

Optic tract
Tractus opticus

Lateral geniculate nucleus (in thalamus)
Corpus geniculatum laterale

Right visual cortex
Cortex visualis dexter

Left visual cortex
Cortex visualis sinistrum

VISUAL PATHWAYS

The eyes have different but overlapping fields of vision. Images are inverted, transposed, and converted into nerve impulses, which are sent to the thalamus for processing. The information is then sent to the visual cortex, where images are combined and interpreted.

The Ear

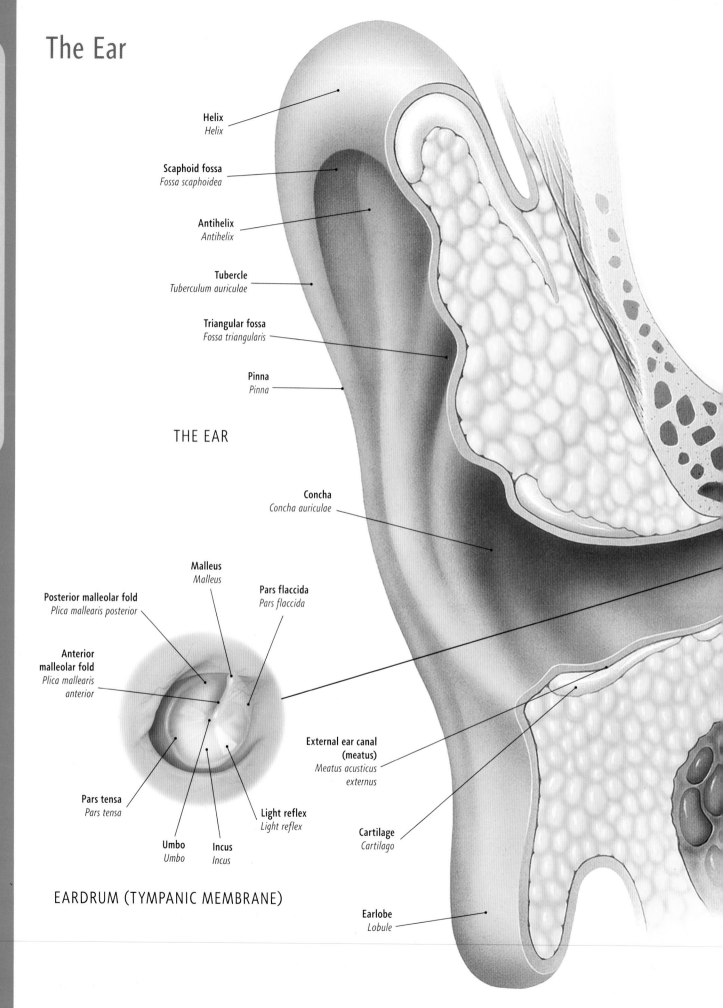

Helix
Helix

Scaphoid fossa
Fossa scaphoidea

Antihelix
Antihelix

Tubercle
Tuberculum auriculae

Triangular fossa
Fossa triangularis

Pinna
Pinna

THE EAR

Concha
Concha auriculae

Malleus
Malleus

Posterior malleolar fold
Plica mallearis posterior

Pars flaccida
Pars flaccida

Anterior
malleolar fold
*Plica mallearis
anterior*

External ear canal
(meatus)
*Meatus acusticus
externus*

Pars tensa
Pars tensa

Light reflex
Light reflex

Umbo
Umbo

Incus
Incus

Cartilage
Cartilago

EARDRUM (TYMPANIC MEMBRANE)

Earlobe
Lobule

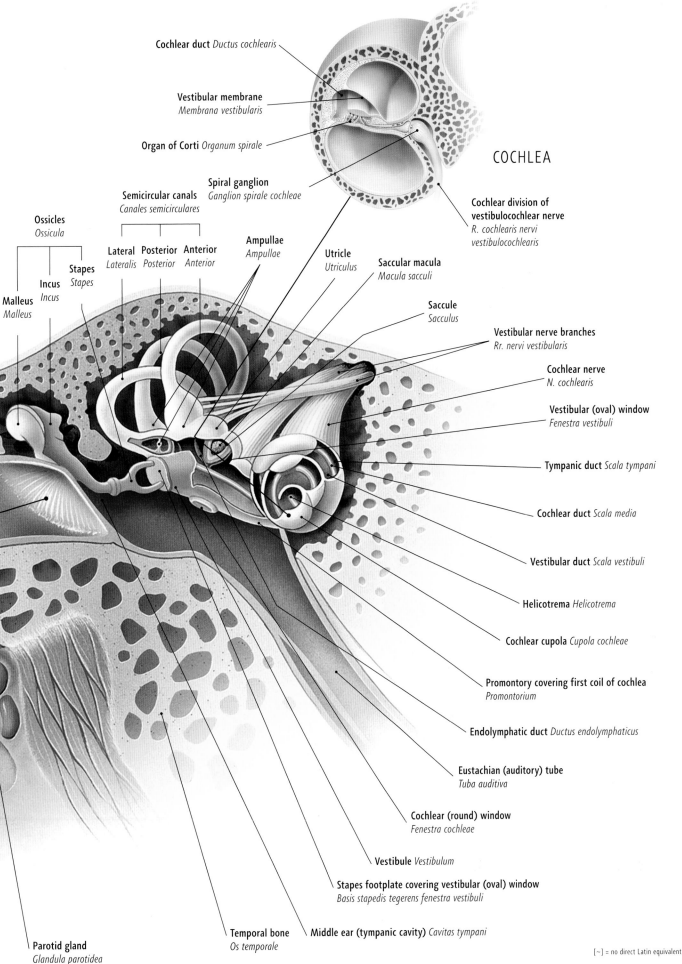

Cochlear duct *Ductus cochlearis*

Vestibular membrane
Membrana vestibularis

Organ of Corti *Organum spirale*

Spiral ganglion
Ganglion spirale cochleae

Semicircular canals
Canales semicirculares

COCHLEA

Cochlear division of
vestibulocochlear nerve
*R. cochlearis nervi
vestibulocochlearis*

Ossicles
Ossicula

Stapes
Stapes

Incus
Incus

Malleus
Malleus

Lateral
Lateralis

Posterior
Posterior

Anterior
Anterior

Ampullae
Ampullae

Utricle
Utriculus

Saccular macula
Macula sacculi

Saccule
Sacculus

Vestibular nerve branches
Rr. nervi vestibularis

Cochlear nerve
N. cochlearis

Vestibular (oval) window
Fenestra vestibuli

Tympanic duct *Scala tympani*

Cochlear duct *Scala media*

Vestibular duct *Scala vestibuli*

Helicotrema *Helicotrema*

Cochlear cupola *Cupola cochleae*

Promontory covering first coil of cochlea
Promontorium

Endolymphatic duct *Ductus endolymphaticus*

Eustachian (auditory) tube
Tuba auditiva

Cochlear (round) window
Fenestra cochleae

Vestibule *Vestibulum*

Stapes footplate covering vestibular (oval) window
Basis stapedis tegerens fenestra vestibuli

Parotid gland
Glandula parotidea

Temporal bone
Os temporale

Middle ear (tympanic cavity) *Cavitas tympani*

THE EAR

[~] = no direct Latin equivalent

Hearing and Balance

HEARING: AUDITORY CENTERS

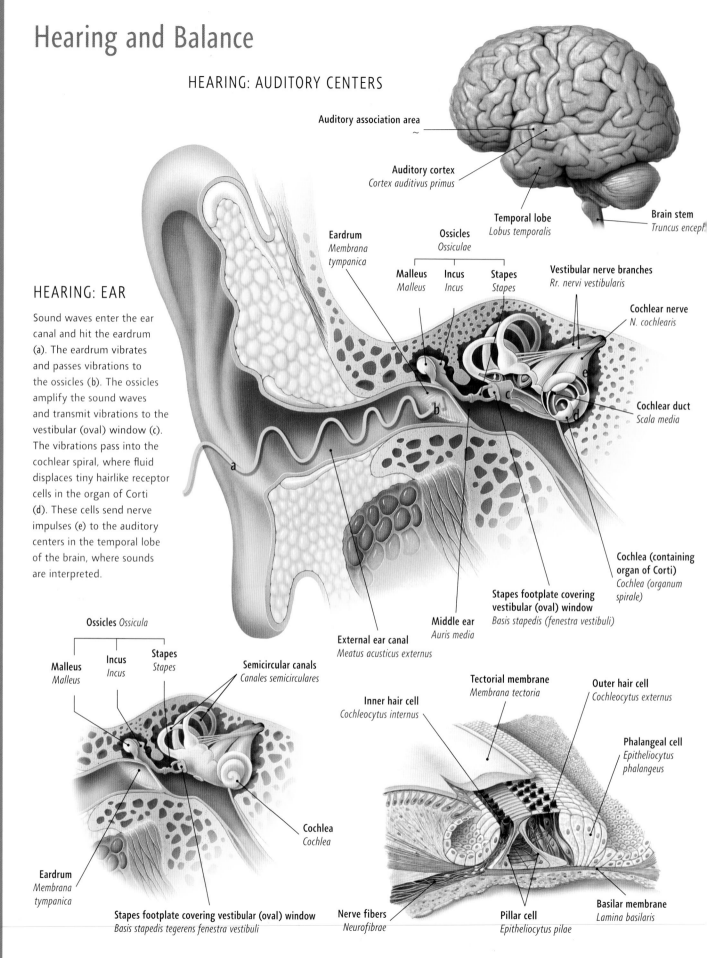

Auditory association area
~

Auditory cortex
Cortex auditivus primus

Temporal lobe
Lobus temporalis

Brain stem
Truncus encepl.

HEARING: EAR

Sound waves enter the ear canal and hit the eardrum (a). The eardrum vibrates and passes vibrations to the ossicles (b). The ossicles amplify the sound waves and transmit vibrations to the vestibular (oval) window (c). The vibrations pass into the cochlear spiral, where fluid displaces tiny hairlike receptor cells in the organ of Corti (d). These cells send nerve impulses (e) to the auditory centers in the temporal lobe of the brain, where sounds are interpreted.

Eardrum
Membrana tympanica

Ossicles
Ossiculae

Malleus
Malleus

Incus
Incus

Stapes
Stapes

Vestibular nerve branches
Rr. nervi vestibularis

Cochlear nerve
N. cochlearis

Cochlear duct
Scala media

Cochlea (containing organ of Corti)
Cochlea (organum spirale)

Stapes footplate covering vestibular (oval) window
Basis stapedis (fenestra vestibuli)

Middle ear
Auris media

External ear canal
Meatus acusticus externus

Ossicles *Ossicula*

Malleus
Malleus

Incus
Incus

Stapes
Stapes

Semicircular canals
Canales semicirculares

Cochlea
Cochlea

Eardrum
Membrana tympanica

Stapes footplate covering vestibular (oval) window
Basis stapedis tegerens fenestra vestibuli

Tectorial membrane
Membrana tectoria

Inner hair cell
Cochleocytus internus

Outer hair cell
Cochleocytus externus

Phalangeal cell
Epitheliocytus phalangeus

Nerve fibers
Neurofibrae

Pillar cell
Epitheliocytus pilae

Basilar membrane
Lamina basilaris

HEARING: AUDITORY OSSICLES

HEARING: ORGAN OF CORTI

[~] = no direct Latin equivalent

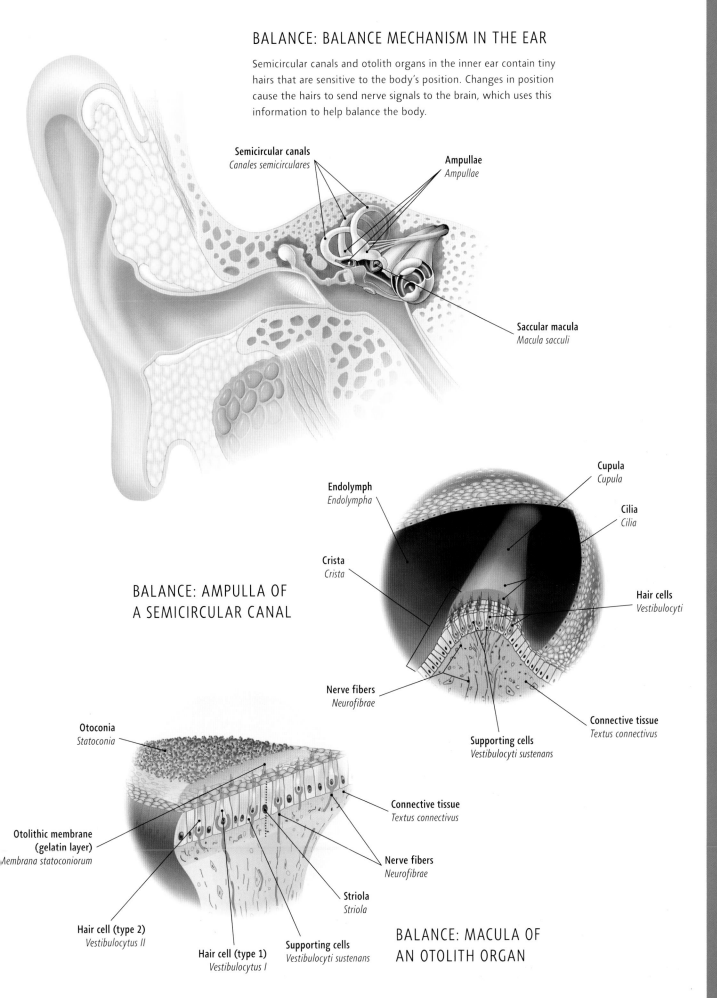

BALANCE: BALANCE MECHANISM IN THE EAR

Semicircular canals and otolith organs in the inner ear contain tiny hairs that are sensitive to the body's position. Changes in position cause the hairs to send nerve signals to the brain, which uses this information to help balance the body.

Semicircular canals
Canales semicirculares

Ampullae
Ampullae

Saccular macula
Macula sacculi

BALANCE: AMPULLA OF A SEMICIRCULAR CANAL

Endolymph
Endolympha

Crista
Crista

Cupula
Cupula

Cilia
Cilia

Hair cells
Vestibulocyti

Nerve fibers
Neurofibrae

Supporting cells
Vestibulocyti sustenans

Connective tissue
Textus connectivus

Otoconia
Statoconia

Otolithic membrane
(gelatin layer)
Membrana statoconiorum

Connective tissue
Textus connectivus

Nerve fibers
Neurofibrae

Hair cell (type 2)
Vestibulocytus II

Hair cell (type 1)
Vestibulocytus I

Supporting cells
Vestibulocyti sustenans

Striola
Striola

BALANCE: MACULA OF AN OTOLITH ORGAN

159

Taste

TASTE PATHWAYS

Taste buds on the tongue and in the throat send nerve impulses via the medulla and thalamus to taste-receiving areas in the parietal lobe, where the taste is identified. The olfactory organs provide additional information vital for interpreting different tastes.

Parietal lobe
Lobus parietalis

Thalamus
Thalamus

Medulla
Medulla

Tongue
Lingua

Epiglottis
Epiglottis

Olfactory organs
Organa olfactoria

Taste buds
Caliculi gustatorii

Filiform papilla
Papilla filiformis

Vallate papilla
Papilla vallata

Taste bud
Caliculus gustatorius

Trench
Sulcus

Serous gland (Ebner's gland)
Glandula serosa

Muscular layer
Tunica muscularis

Fungiform papilla
Papilla fungiformis

TONGUE—CROSS-SECTIONAL VIEW

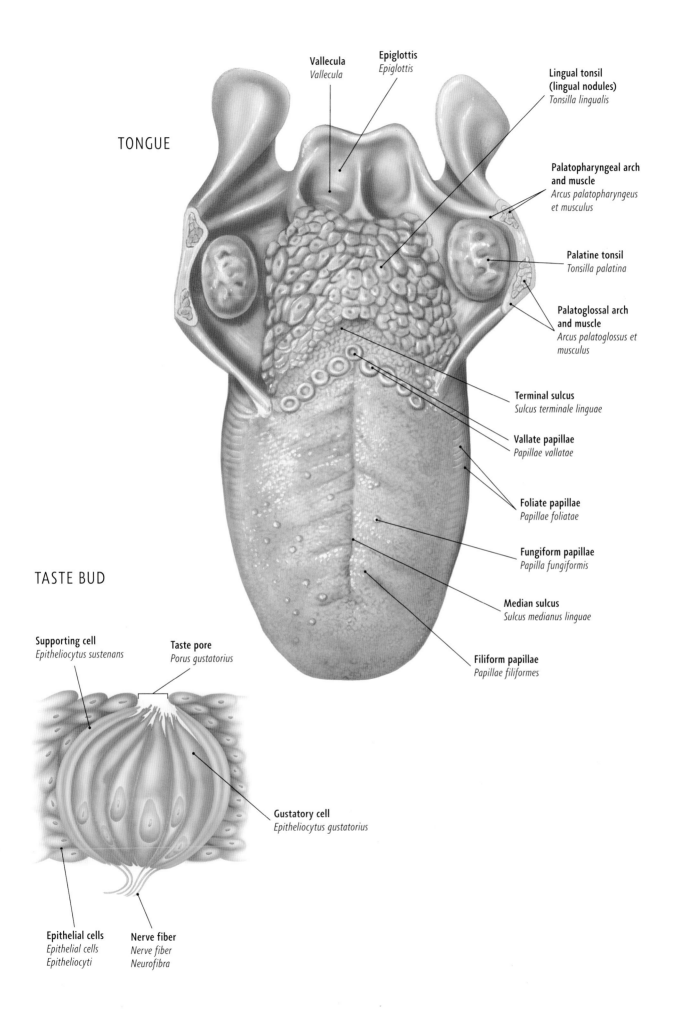

TONGUE

Vallecula
Vallecula

Epiglottis
Epiglottis

**Lingual tonsil
(lingual nodules)**
Tonsilla lingualis

**Palatopharyngeal arch
and muscle**
*Arcus palatopharyngeus
et musculus*

Palatine tonsil
Tonsilla palatina

**Palatoglossal arch
and muscle**
*Arcus palatoglossus et
musculus*

Terminal sulcus
Sulcus terminale linguae

Vallate papillae
Papillae vallatae

Foliate papillae
Papillae foliatae

Fungiform papillae
Papilla fungiformis

Median sulcus
Sulcus medianus linguae

Filiform papillae
Papillae filiformes

TASTE BUD

Supporting cell
Epitheliocytus sustenans

Taste pore
Porus gustatorius

Gustatory cell
Epitheliocytus gustatorius

Epithelial cells
*Epithelial cells
Epitheliocyti*

Nerve fiber
*Nerve fiber
Neurofibra*

Smell

OLFACTORY PATHWAY

Odor molecules enter the nostrils and pass into the nasal cavity, where they dissolve in olfactory mucosa in the nasal lining. Receptors send nerve signals
via the olfactory bulb to the olfactory center in the brain, where smells are identified.

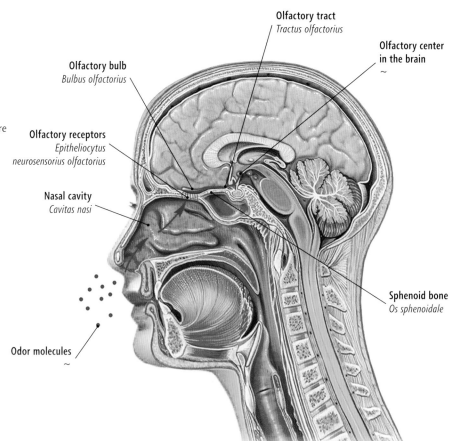

Olfactory tract
Tractus olfactorius

Olfactory center in the brain
~

Olfactory bulb
Bulbus olfactorius

Olfactory receptors
Epitheliocytus neurosensorius olfactorius

Nasal cavity
Cavitas nasi

Sphenoid bone
Os sphenoidale

Odor molecules
~

Anterior nucleus of thalamus
Nucleus anterior thalami

Cingulate gyrus
Gyrus cinguli

Olfactory bulb
Bulbus olfactorius

Thalamus
Thalamus

Amygdaloid body
Corpus amygdaloideum

Hippocampus
Hippocampus

SMELL AND THE LIMBIC SYSTEM

The olfactory bulb is directly connected to the hippocampus and amygdala in the limbic system, which is important for memory and emotion. This is why smells are evocative of past places and feelings, and can trigger responses like pleasure and fear.

[~] = no direct Latin equivalent

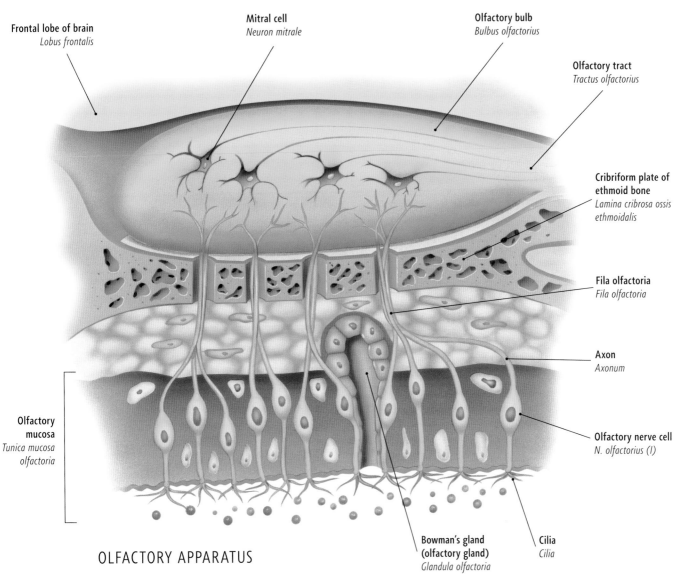

Frontal lobe of brain
Lobus frontalis

Mitral cell
Neuron mitrale

Olfactory bulb
Bulbus olfactorius

Olfactory tract
Tractus olfactorius

Cribriform plate of ethmoid bone
Lamina cribrosa ossis ethmoidalis

Fila olfactoria
Fila olfactoria

Axon
Axonum

Olfactory nerve cell
N. olfactorius (I)

Olfactory mucosa
Tunica mucosa olfactoria

Bowman's gland (olfactory gland)
Glandula olfactoria

Cilia
Cilia

OLFACTORY APPARATUS

The mucous membrane (olfactory epithelium) of the olfactory receptors contains millions of nerve cells bearing cilia. Odor molecules stimulate the nerve cells to send impulses along the nerve fibers through holes in the cribriform plate of the ethmoid bone to the olfactory bulb.

Pain

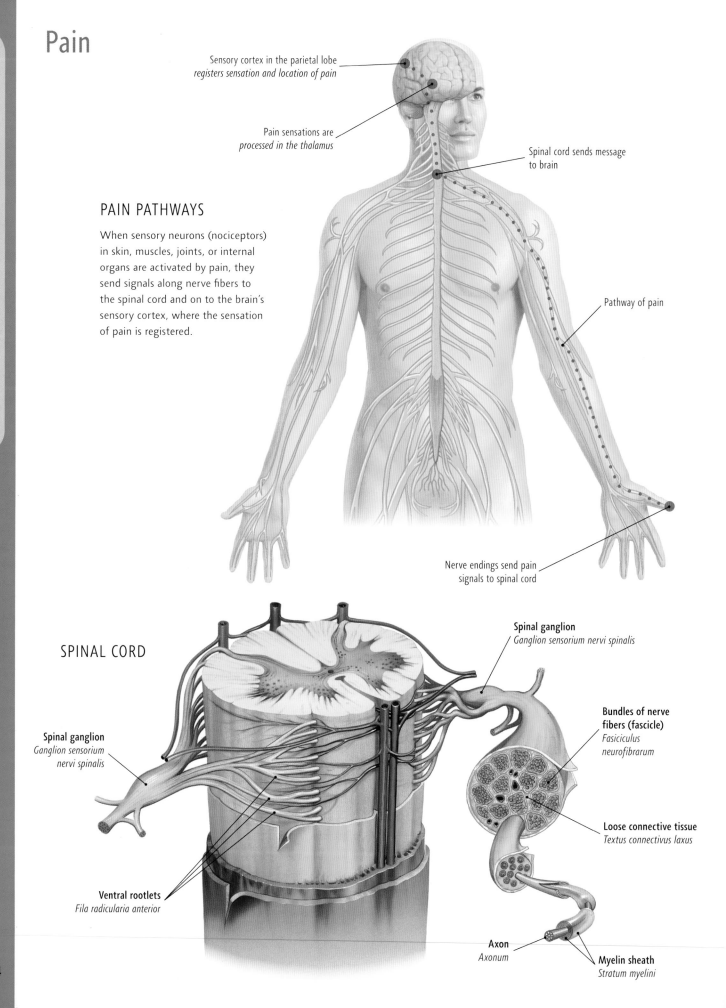

Sensory cortex in the parietal lobe
registers sensation and location of pain

Pain sensations are
processed in the thalamus

Spinal cord sends message
to brain

PAIN PATHWAYS

When sensory neurons (nociceptors)
in skin, muscles, joints, or internal
organs are activated by pain, they
send signals along nerve fibers to
the spinal cord and on to the brain's
sensory cortex, where the sensation
of pain is registered.

Pathway of pain

Nerve endings send pain
signals to spinal cord

SPINAL CORD

Spinal ganglion
Ganglion sensorium nervi spinalis

Bundles of nerve
fibers (fascicle)
*Fasciculus
neurofibrarum*

Spinal ganglion
*Ganglion sensorium
nervi spinalis*

Loose connective tissue
Textus connectivus laxus

Ventral rootlets
Fila radicularia anterior

Axon
Axonum

Myelin sheath
Stratum myelini

REFERRED PAIN

The pain from internal organs may be felt on the surface of the skin as well as internally. This is because the skin and internal organs may share the same pain pathways.

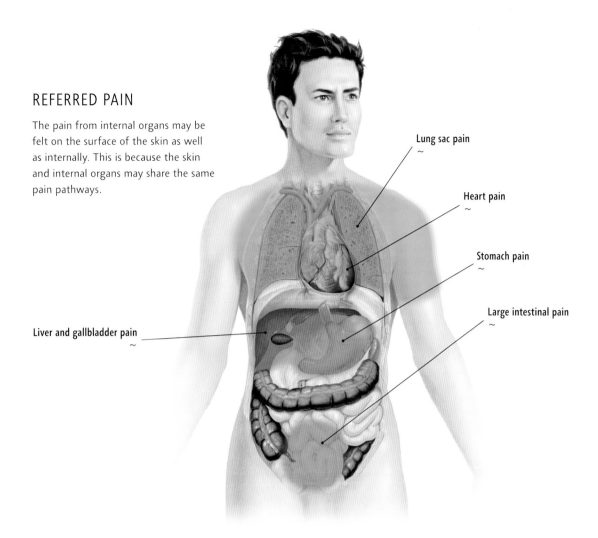

Lung sac pain
~

Heart pain
~

Stomach pain
~

Large intestinal pain
~

Liver and gallbladder pain
~

Sensory cortex
~

Thalamus
Thalamus

Limbic system
Lobus limbicus

Reticular activating
system in brain stem
~

PROCESSING PAIN

Different areas of the brain control pain perception. Pain signals are relayed to the brain via the thalamus. The sensation and location of pain is registered in the sensory cortex, and emotional responses are governed by the limbic system.

[~] = no direct Latin equivalent

The Lymphatic System

The Lymphatic System

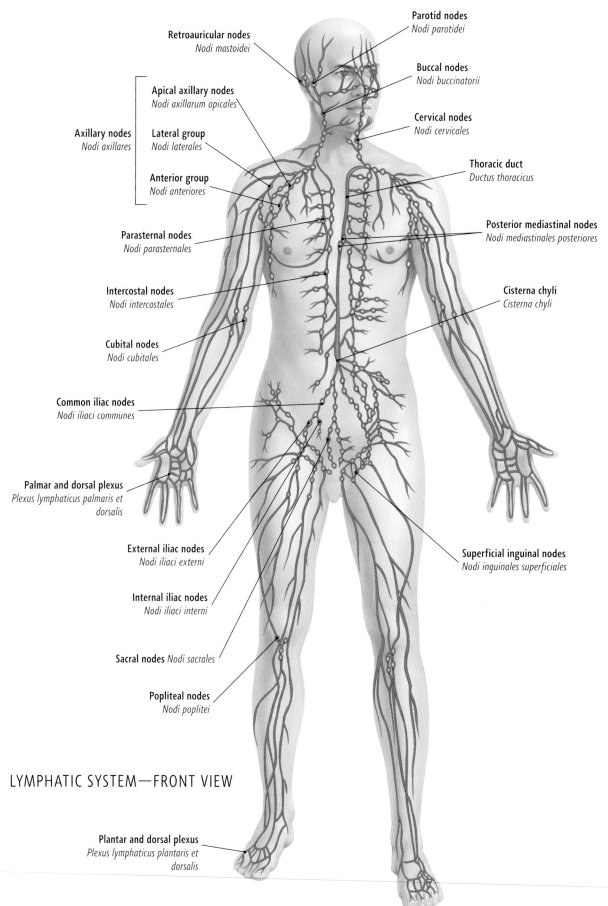

Parotid nodes
Nodi parotidei

Retroauricular nodes
Nodi mastoidei

Buccal nodes
Nodi buccinatorii

Apical axillary nodes
Nodi axillarum apicales

Cervical nodes
Nodi cervicales

Axillary nodes
Nodi axillares

Lateral group
Nodi laterales

Thoracic duct
Ductus thoracicus

Anterior group
Nodi anteriores

Posterior mediastinal nodes
Nodi mediastinales posteriores

Parasternal nodes
Nodi parasternales

Intercostal nodes
Nodi intercostales

Cisterna chyli
Cisterna chyli

Cubital nodes
Nodi cubitales

Common iliac nodes
Nodi iliaci communes

Palmar and dorsal plexus
Plexus lymphaticus palmaris et dorsalis

External iliac nodes
Nodi iliaci externi

Superficial inguinal nodes
Nodi inguinales superficiales

Internal iliac nodes
Nodi iliaci interni

Sacral nodes *Nodi sacrales*

Popliteal nodes
Nodi poplitei

LYMPHATIC SYSTEM—FRONT VIEW

Plantar and dorsal plexus
Plexus lymphaticus plantaris et dorsalis

[~] = no direct Latin equivalent

The Circulatory System

The Circulatory System

Superficial temporal vein *V. temporalis superficialis*

Posterior auricular vein *V. auricularis posterior*

External jugular vein *V. jugularis externa*

Internal jugular vein *V. jugularis interna*

Brachiocephalic vein *V. brachiocephalica*

Subclavian vein *V. subclavia*

Superior vena cava *Vena cava superior*

Axillary vein *V. axillaris*

Cephalic vein *V. cephalica*

Brachial vein *V. brachialis*

Basilic vein *V. basilica*

Azygos vein *V. azygos*

Median cubital vein
V. mediana cubiti

Renal vein *V. renalis*

Inferior vena cava *Vena cava inferior*

Radial vein *V. radialis*

Ulnar vein *V. ulnaris*

Common iliac vein
V. iliaca communis

Palmar venous arch
Arcus venosus palmaris

Digital veins *Vv. digitales*

Superficial temporal artery *Arteria temporalis superficialis*

Posterior auricular artery *Arteria auricularis posterior*

Facial artery *Arteria facialis*

Common carotid artery *Arteria carotis communis*

Subclavian artery *Arteria subclavia*

Axillary artery *Arteria axillaris*

Aortic arch *Arcus aortae*

Intercostal arteries *Intercostal arteries*

Brachial artery *Arteria brachialis*

Descending aorta *Pars descendens aortae*

Renal artery *A. renalis*

Superior ulnar collateral artery
A. collateralis ulnaris superior

Common iliac artery *Arteria iliaca communis*

Ulnar artery *A. ulnaris*

Radial artery *A. radialis*

Deep palmar arterial arch
Arcus palmaris profundus

Digital arteries
Aa. digitales

Internal iliac artery
Arteria iliaca interna

External iliac artery
Arteria iliaca externa

External iliac vein *V. iliaca externa*

Internal iliac vein *V. iliaca interna*

Femoral vein *V. femoralis*

Great saphenous vein *V. saphena magna*

Popliteal vein *V. poplitea*

Small saphenous vein *V. saphena parva*

Fibular vein *V. fibularis*

Anterior tibial vein
V. tibialis anterior

Deep femoral artery *Arteria profunda femoris*

Femoral artery *Arteria femoralis*

Popliteal artery *A. poplitea*

Fibular artery *A. fibularis*

Anterior tibial artery *Arteria tibialis anterior*

Posterior tibial artery *Arteria tibialis posterior*

CIRCULATORY SYSTEM—FRONT VIEW

Dorsal venous arch *Arcus venosus dorsalis pedis*

Plantar venous arch *Arcus venosus plantaris*

Digital veins
Vv. digitales

Dorsalis pedis artery *Arteria dorsalis pedis*

Dorsal arch *Arcus arterialis dorsalis pedis*

Plantar arch *Arcus plantaris profundus*

Digital arteries *Aa. digitales*

BLOOD COMPOSITION

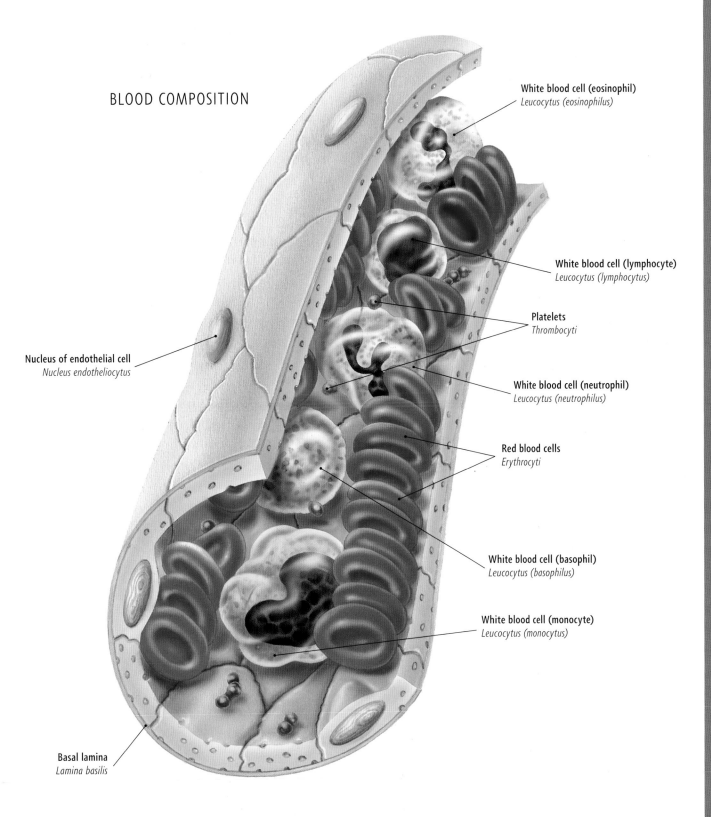

White blood cell (eosinophil)
Leucocytus (eosinophilus)

White blood cell (lymphocyte)
Leucocytus (lymphocytus)

Platelets
Thrombocyti

White blood cell (neutrophil)
Leucocytus (neutrophilus)

Red blood cells
Erythrocyti

White blood cell (basophil)
Leucocytus (basophilus)

White blood cell (monocyte)
Leucocytus (monocytus)

Nucleus of endothelial cell
Nucleus endotheliocytus

Basal lamina
Lamina basilis

Blood Vessels

Artery wall
Paries arteriae

ARTERY

Intima
Tunica intima

Tunica media
Tunica media cum myocytis levibus

Tunica media
Tunica media cum myocytis levibus

Intima
Tunica intima

Adventitia
Tunica adventitia

Valves (closed)
Valvae

Vasa vasorum
Vasa vasorum

VEIN

Arterioles
Arteriolae

Artery
Arteria

Capillaries
Vasa capillares

Venules
Venulae

CAPILLARY BED

Vein
Vena

[~] = no direct Latin equivalent

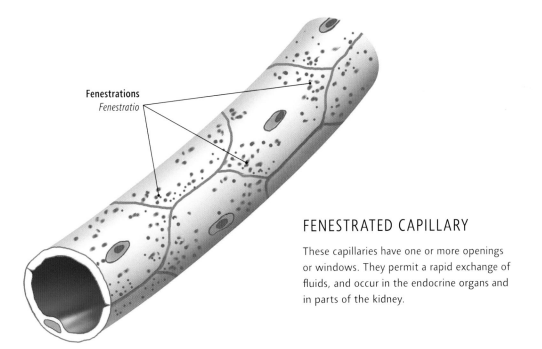

Fenestrations
Fenestratio

FENESTRATED CAPILLARY

These capillaries have one or more openings or windows. They permit a rapid exchange of fluids, and occur in the endocrine organs and in parts of the kidney.

CONTINUOUS CAPILLARY

These capillaries do not have openings in their walls. Continuous capillaries are located in most regions of the body.

Major Arteries and Veins of the Body

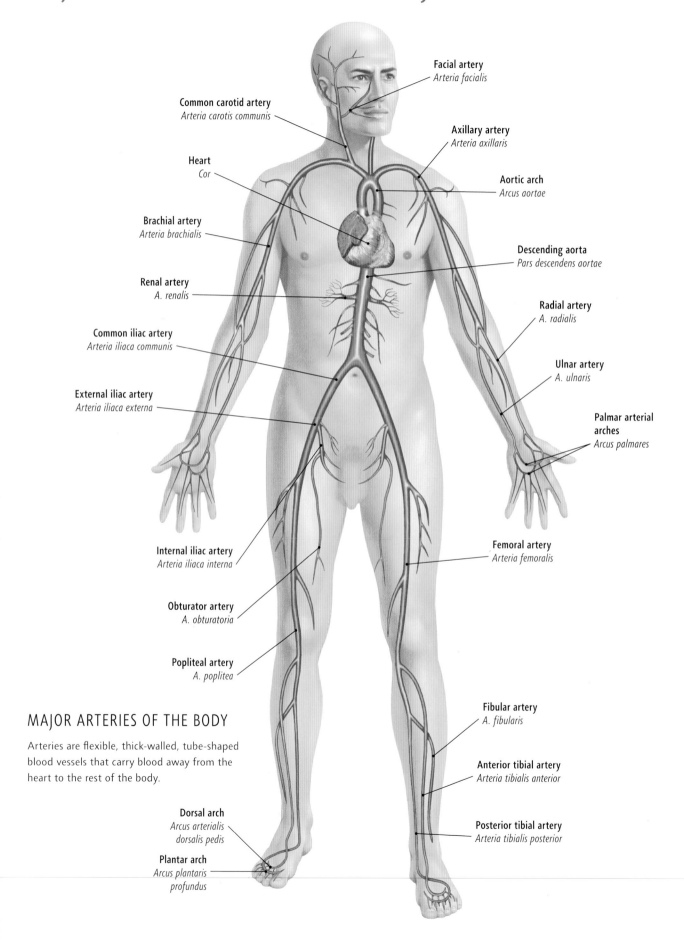

Facial artery
Arteria facialis

Common carotid artery
Arteria carotis communis

Axillary artery
Arteria axillaris

Heart
Cor

Aortic arch
Arcus aortae

Brachial artery
Arteria brachialis

Descending aorta
Pars descendens aortae

Renal artery
A. renalis

Radial artery
A. radialis

Common iliac artery
Arteria iliaca communis

Ulnar artery
A. ulnaris

External iliac artery
Arteria iliaca externa

Palmar arterial arches
Arcus palmares

Internal iliac artery
Arteria iliaca interna

Femoral artery
Arteria femoralis

Obturator artery
A. obturatoria

Popliteal artery
A. poplitea

Fibular artery
A. fibularis

MAJOR ARTERIES OF THE BODY

Arteries are flexible, thick-walled, tube-shaped blood vessels that carry blood away from the heart to the rest of the body.

Anterior tibial artery
Arteria tibialis anterior

Dorsal arch
Arcus arterialis dorsalis pedis

Posterior tibial artery
Arteria tibialis posterior

Plantar arch
Arcus plantaris profundus

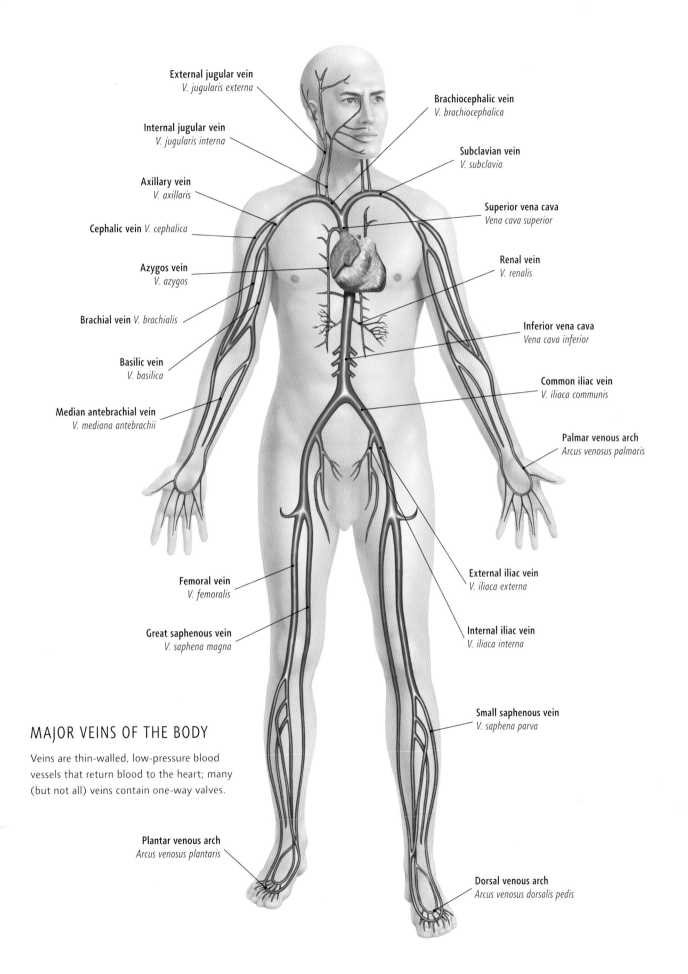

External jugular vein
V. jugularis externa

Internal jugular vein
V. jugularis interna

Axillary vein
V. axillaris

Cephalic vein *V. cephalica*

Azygos vein
V. azygos

Brachial vein *V. brachialis*

Basilic vein
V. basilica

Median antebrachial vein
V. mediana antebrachii

Brachiocephalic vein
V. brachiocephalica

Subclavian vein
V. subclavia

Superior vena cava
Vena cava superior

Renal vein
V. renalis

Inferior vena cava
Vena cava inferior

Common iliac vein
V. iliaca communis

Palmar venous arch
Arcus venosus palmaris

Femoral vein
V. femoralis

Great saphenous vein
V. saphena magna

External iliac vein
V. iliaca externa

Internal iliac vein
V. iliaca interna

Small saphenous vein
V. saphena parva

MAJOR VEINS OF THE BODY

Veins are thin-walled, low-pressure blood
vessels that return blood to the heart; many
(but not all) veins contain one-way valves.

Plantar venous arch
Arcus venosus plantaris

Dorsal venous arch
Arcus venosus dorsalis pedis

181

Arteries of the Brain

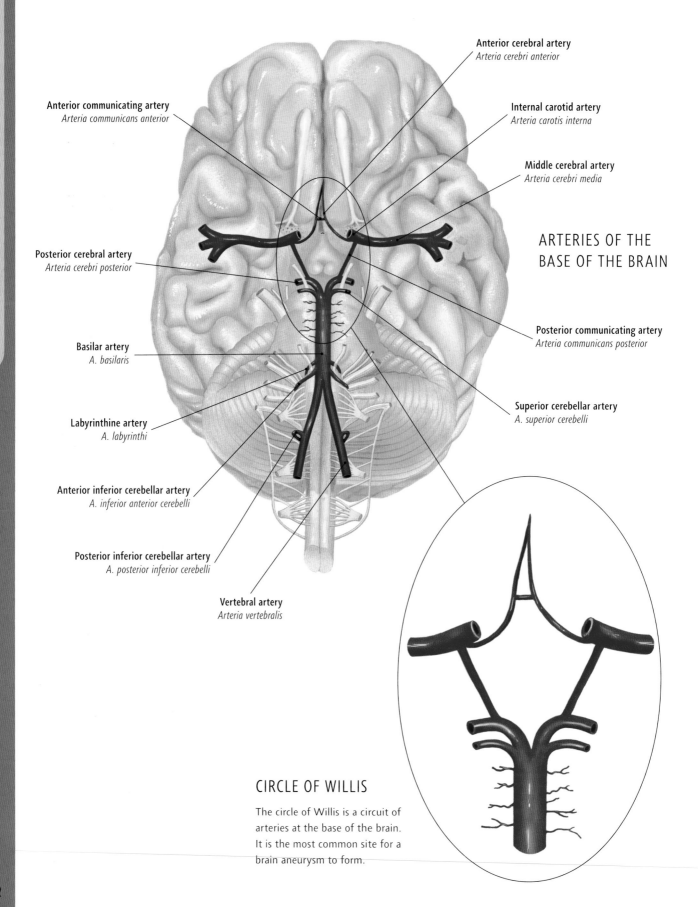

Anterior cerebral artery
Arteria cerebri anterior

Anterior communicating artery
Arteria communicans anterior

Internal carotid artery
Arteria carotis interna

Middle cerebral artery
Arteria cerebri media

Posterior cerebral artery
Arteria cerebri posterior

ARTERIES OF THE
BASE OF THE BRAIN

Posterior communicating artery
Arteria communicans posterior

Basilar artery
A. basilaris

Superior cerebellar artery
A. superior cerebelli

Labyrinthine artery
A. labyrinthi

Anterior inferior cerebellar artery
A. inferior anterior cerebelli

Posterior inferior cerebellar artery
A. posterior inferior cerebelli

Vertebral artery
Arteria vertebralis

CIRCLE OF WILLIS

The circle of Willis is a circuit of
arteries at the base of the brain.
It is the most common site for a
brain aneurysm to form.

HEPATIC ARTERY

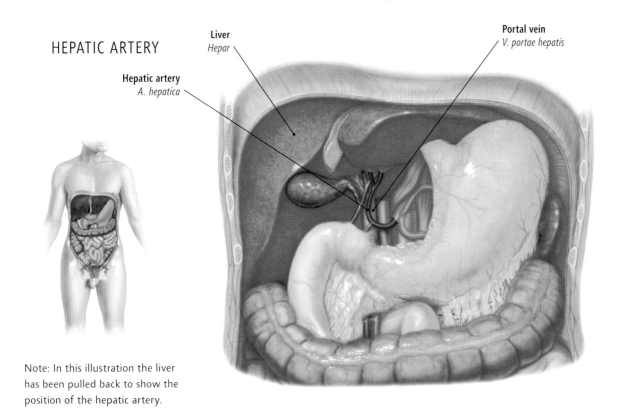

Liver
Hepar

Portal vein
V. portae hepatis

Hepatic artery
A. hepatica

Note: In this illustration the liver has been pulled back to show the position of the hepatic artery.

RENAL ARTERY

Renal artery
A. renalis

Kidney
Ren

Adrenal gland
Glandula suprarenalis

Blood Vessels of the Arms and Legs

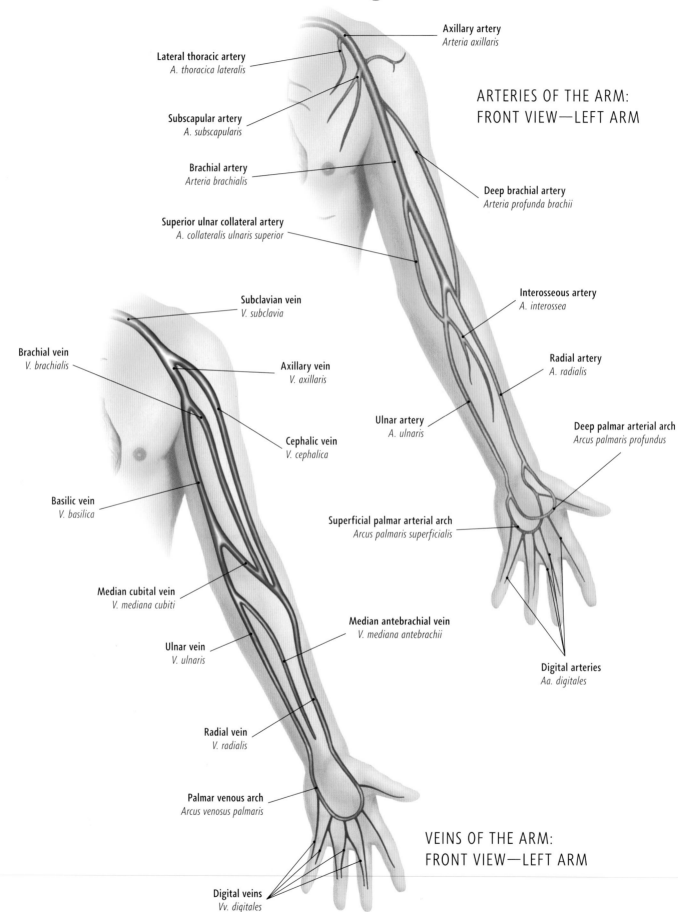

**ARTERIES OF THE ARM:
FRONT VIEW—LEFT ARM**

Axillary artery
Arteria axillaris

Lateral thoracic artery
A. thoracica lateralis

Subscapular artery
A. subscapularis

Brachial artery
Arteria brachialis

Deep brachial artery
Arteria profunda brachii

Superior ulnar collateral artery
A. collateralis ulnaris superior

Interosseous artery
A. interossea

Radial artery
A. radialis

Subclavian vein
V. subclavia

Brachial vein
V. brachialis

Axillary vein
V. axillaris

Cephalic vein
V. cephalica

Ulnar artery
A. ulnaris

Deep palmar arterial arch
Arcus palmaris profundus

Basilic vein
V. basilica

Superficial palmar arterial arch
Arcus palmaris superficialis

Median cubital vein
V. mediana cubiti

Median antebrachial vein
V. mediana antebrachii

Ulnar vein
V. ulnaris

Digital arteries
Aa. digitales

Radial vein
V. radialis

Palmar venous arch
Arcus venosus palmaris

**VEINS OF THE ARM:
FRONT VIEW—LEFT ARM**

Digital veins
Vv. digitales

194

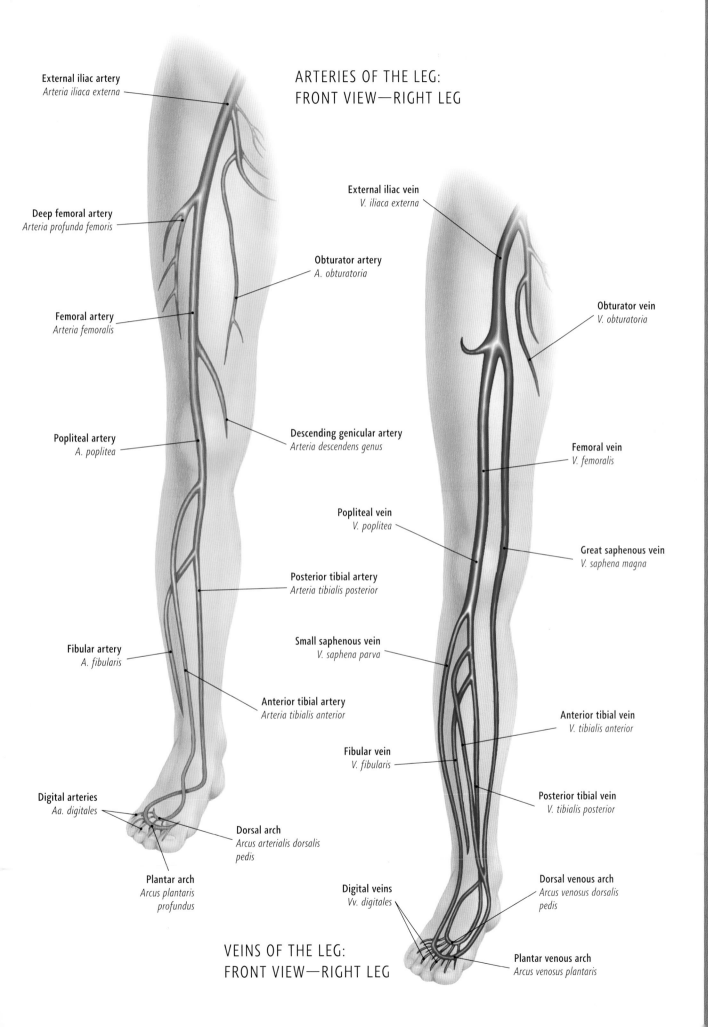

ARTERIES OF THE LEG:
FRONT VIEW—RIGHT LEG

External iliac artery
Arteria iliaca externa

Deep femoral artery
Arteria profunda femoris

Femoral artery
Arteria femoralis

Popliteal artery
A. poplitea

Fibular artery
A. fibularis

Digital arteries
Aa. digitales

Plantar arch
Arcus plantaris profundus

External iliac vein
V. iliaca externa

Obturator artery
A. obturatoria

Obturator vein
V. obturatoria

Descending genicular artery
Arteria descendens genus

Femoral vein
V. femoralis

Popliteal vein
V. poplitea

Great saphenous vein
V. saphena magna

Posterior tibial artery
Arteria tibialis posterior

Small saphenous vein
V. saphena parva

Anterior tibial artery
Arteria tibialis anterior

Anterior tibial vein
V. tibialis anterior

Fibular vein
V. fibularis

Posterior tibial vein
V. tibialis posterior

Dorsal arch
Arcus arterialis dorsalis pedis

Digital veins
Vv. digitales

Dorsal venous arch
Arcus venosus dorsalis pedis

Plantar venous arch
Arcus venosus plantaris

VEINS OF THE LEG:
FRONT VIEW—RIGHT LEG

195

The Respiratory System

The Respiratory System

RESPIRATORY SYSTEM—FRONT VIEW

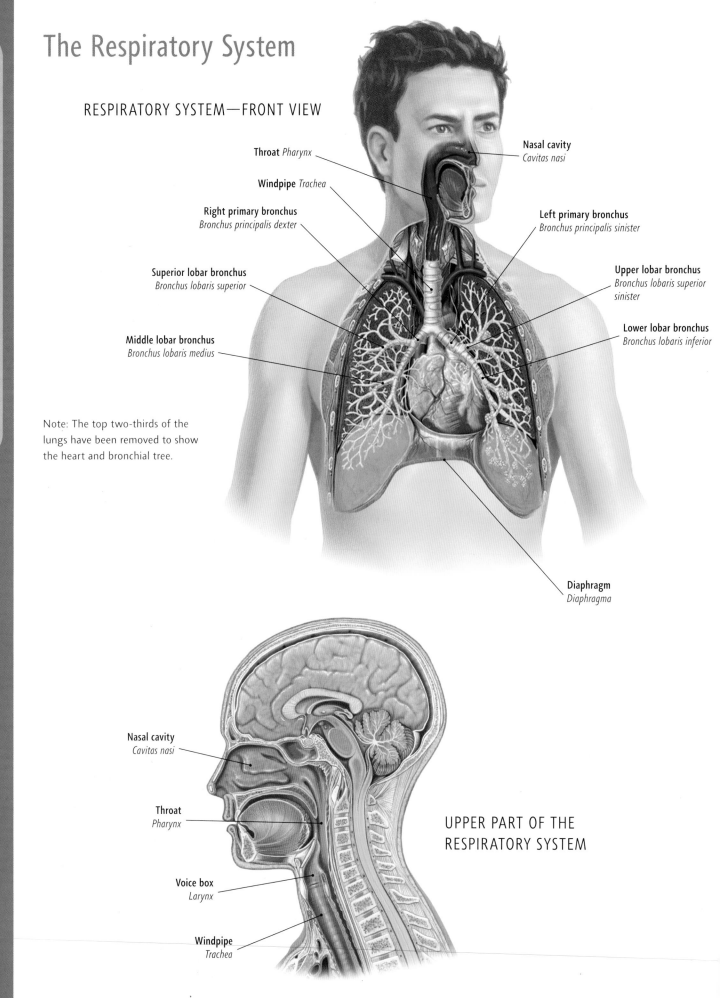

Throat *Pharynx*

Windpipe *Trachea*

Right primary bronchus
Bronchus principalis dexter

Superior lobar bronchus
Bronchus lobaris superior

Middle lobar bronchus
Bronchus lobaris medius

Nasal cavity
Cavitas nasi

Left primary bronchus
Bronchus principalis sinister

Upper lobar bronchus
Bronchus lobaris superior sinister

Lower lobar bronchus
Bronchus lobaris inferior

Note: The top two-thirds of the lungs have been removed to show the heart and bronchial tree.

Diaphragm
Diaphragma

Nasal cavity
Cavitas nasi

Throat
Pharynx

Voice box
Larynx

Windpipe
Trachea

UPPER PART OF THE
RESPIRATORY SYSTEM

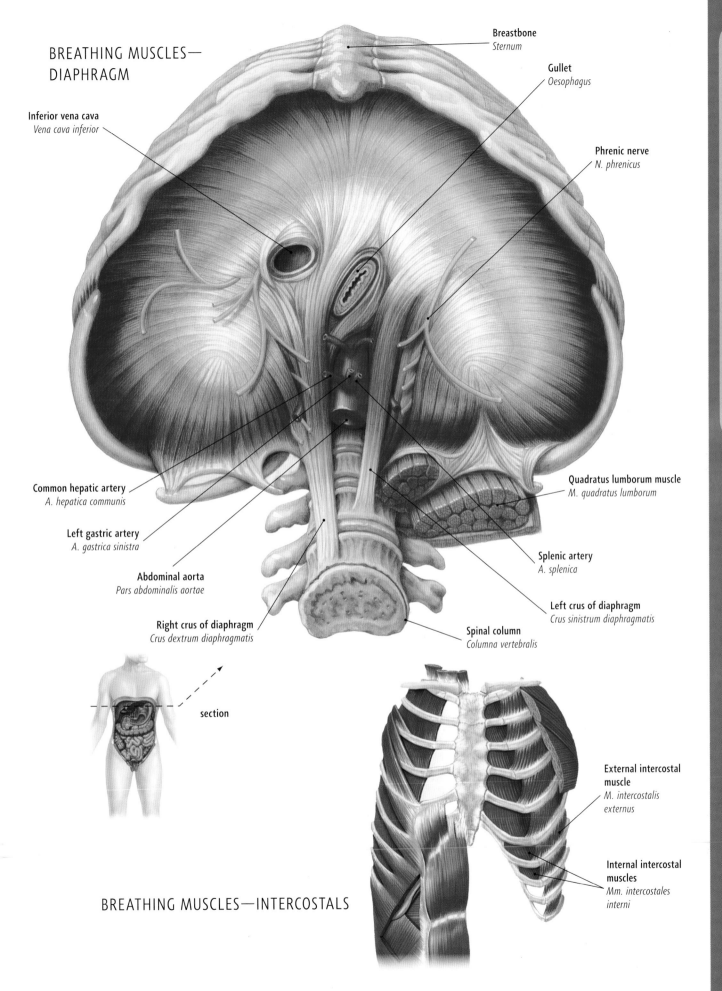

BREATHING MUSCLES— DIAPHRAGM

Breastbone
Sternum

Gullet
Oesophagus

Inferior vena cava
Vena cava inferior

Phrenic nerve
N. phrenicus

Common hepatic artery
A. hepatica communis

Left gastric artery
A. gastrica sinistra

Abdominal aorta
Pars abdominalis aortae

Right crus of diaphragm
Crus dextrum diaphragmatis

Quadratus lumborum muscle
M. quadratus lumborum

Splenic artery
A. splenica

Left crus of diaphragm
Crus sinistrum diaphragmatis

Spinal column
Columna vertebralis

section

External intercostal muscle
M. intercostalis externus

Internal intercostal muscles
Mm. intercostales interni

BREATHING MUSCLES—INTERCOSTALS

Nose and Throat

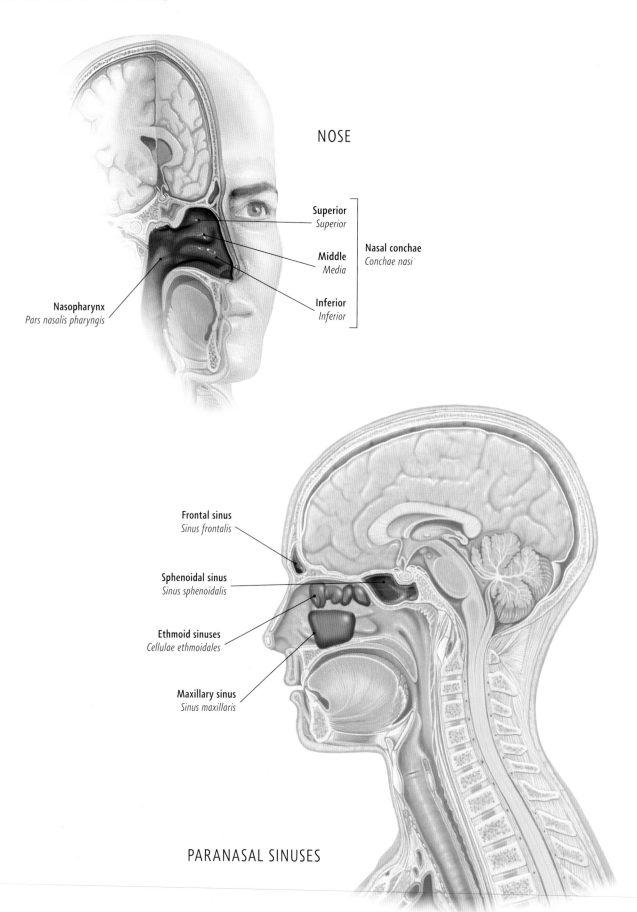

NOSE

Superior
Superior

Middle
Media

Nasal conchae
Conchae nasi

Inferior
Inferior

Nasopharynx
Pars nasalis pharyngis

Frontal sinus
Sinus frontalis

Sphenoidal sinus
Sinus sphenoidalis

Ethmoid sinuses
Cellulae ethmoidales

Maxillary sinus
Sinus maxillaris

PARANASAL SINUSES

THROAT—REAR VIEW

Superior constrictor
M. constrictor pharyngis superior

Stylohyoid *M. stylohyoideus*

Stylopharyngeus
M. stylopharyngeus

Pharyngeal muscles

Middle constrictor
M. constrictor pharyngis medias

Inferior constrictor
M. constrictor pharyngis superior

Soft palate
Palatum molle

Cutaway view

Dorsum of tongue
Dorsum linguae

Epiglottis *Epiglottis*

Laryngopharynx
(leading to esophagus)
Pars laryngea pharyngis

Gullet
Oesophagus

Pharyngeal tonsil
Tonsilla pharyngea

Nasopharynx
Pars nasalis pharyngis

Soft palate
Palatum molle

Oropharynx
Pars oralis pharyngis

Epiglottis
Epiglottis

Laryngopharynx
Pars laryngea pharyngis

Oral cavity
Cavitas oris

Tongue
Lingua

THROAT—CROSS-SECTIONAL VIEW

201

Larynx

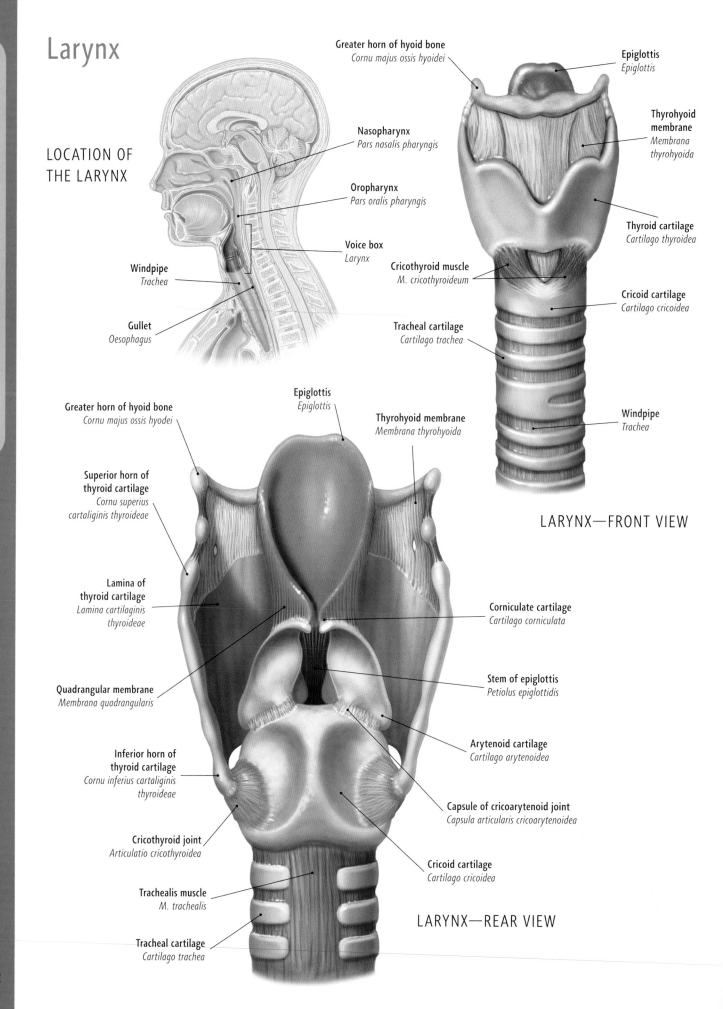

LOCATION OF THE LARYNX

Greater horn of hyoid bone
Cornu majus ossis hyoidei

Nasopharynx
Pars nasalis pharyngis

Oropharynx
Pars oralis pharyngis

Voice box
Larynx

Windpipe
Trachea

Gullet
Oesophagus

Epiglottis
Epiglottis

Thyrohyoid membrane
Membrana thyrohyoida

Thyroid cartilage
Cartilago thyroidea

Cricothyroid muscle
M. cricothyroideum

Cricoid cartilage
Cartilago cricoidea

Tracheal cartilage
Cartilago trachea

Windpipe
Trachea

LARYNX—FRONT VIEW

Greater horn of hyoid bone
Cornu majus ossis hyodei

Superior horn of thyroid cartilage
Cornu superius cartaliginis thyroideae

Lamina of thyroid cartilage
Lamina cartilaginis thyroideae

Quadrangular membrane
Membrana quadrangularis

Inferior horn of thyroid cartilage
Cornu inferius cartaliginis thyroideae

Cricothyroid joint
Articulatio cricothyroidea

Trachealis muscle
M. trachealis

Tracheal cartilage
Cartilago trachea

Epiglottis
Epiglottis

Thyrohyoid membrane
Membrana thyrohyoida

Corniculate cartilage
Cartilago corniculata

Stem of epiglottis
Petiolus epiglottidis

Arytenoid cartilage
Cartilago arytenoidea

Capsule of cricoarytenoid joint
Capsula articularis cricoarytenoidea

Cricoid cartilage
Cartilago cricoidea

LARYNX—REAR VIEW

EPIGLOTTIS: SWALLOWING

The epiglottis is a flap of elastic cartilage in the larynx. During swallowing it folds down over the glottis to prevent food and drink passing into the airway.

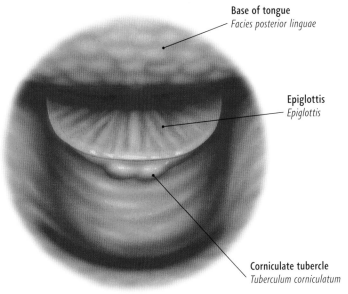

Base of tongue
Facies posterior linguae

Epiglottis
Epiglottis

Corniculate tubercle
Tuberculum corniculatum

facies inferior linguae

Epiglottis
Epiglottis

Root of tongue
Radix linguae

EPIGLOTTIS: SPEAKING

During speaking, the epiglottis remains upright so that exhaled air can flow through the larynx and vibrate the vocal folds (vocal cords), producing sound. The tension and length of the cords determines the pitch of the sound.

Vocal cords
Plicae vocales

Vocal process of arytenoid cartilage
Processus vocalis cartilaginis arytenoideae

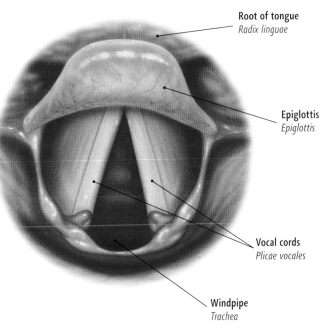

Root of tongue
Radix linguae

Epiglottis
Epiglottis

EPIGLOTTIS: BREATHING

During breathing, the epiglottis remains upright, and the vocal folds (vocal cords) are moved apart by muscles in the larynx, allowing air to flow downward into the trachea.

Vocal cords
Plicae vocales

Windpipe
Trachea

Trachea and Bronchi

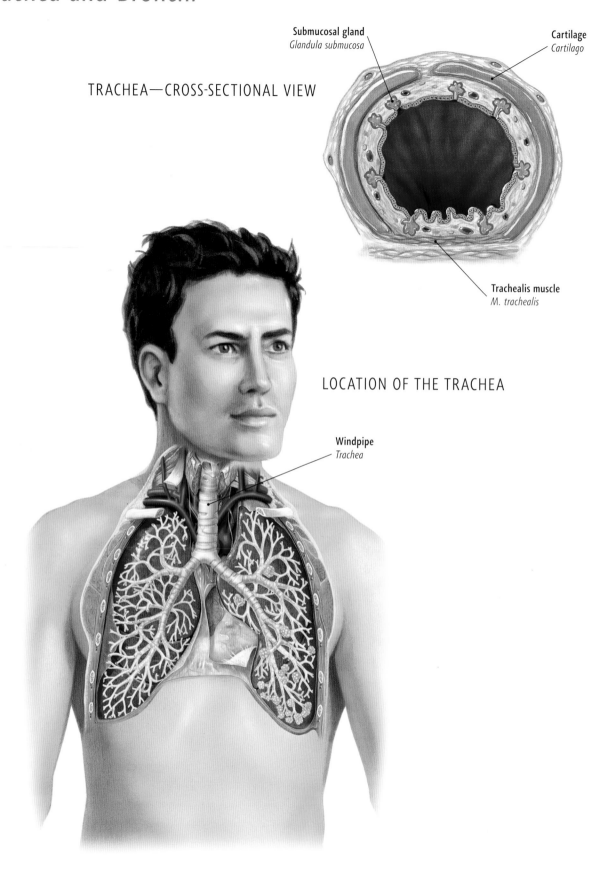

TRACHEA—CROSS-SECTIONAL VIEW

Submucosal gland
Glandula submucosa

Cartilage
Cartilago

Trachealis muscle
M. trachealis

LOCATION OF THE TRACHEA

Windpipe
Trachea

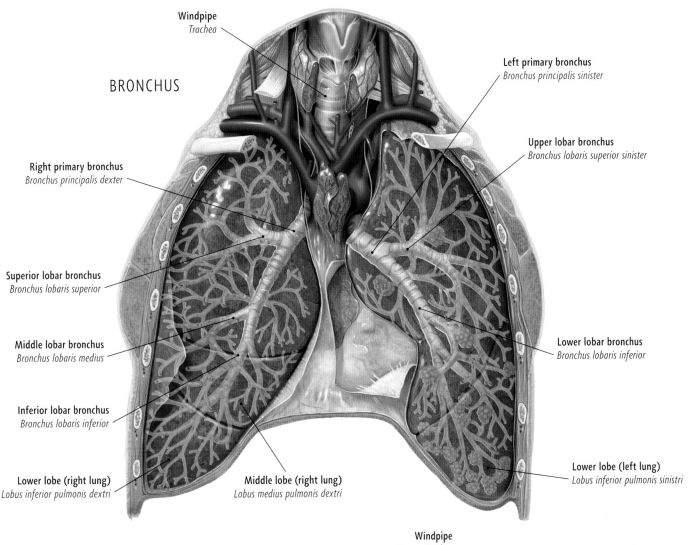

BRONCHUS

Windpipe
Trachea

Left primary bronchus
Bronchus principalis sinister

Upper lobar bronchus
Bronchus lobaris superior sinister

Right primary bronchus
Bronchus principalis dexter

Superior lobar bronchus
Bronchus lobaris superior

Middle lobar bronchus
Bronchus lobaris medius

Inferior lobar bronchus
Bronchus lobaris inferior

Lower lobar bronchus
Bronchus lobaris inferior

Lower lobe (right lung)
Lobus inferior pulmonis dextri

Middle lobe (right lung)
Lobus medius pulmonis dextri

Lower lobe (left lung)
Lobus inferior pulmonis sinistri

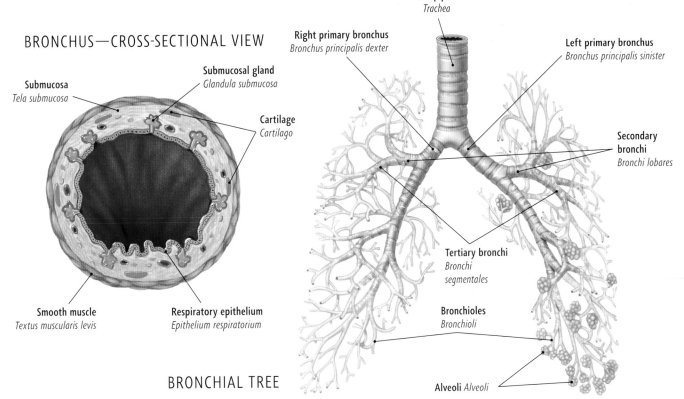

BRONCHUS—CROSS-SECTIONAL VIEW

Submucosa
Tela submucosa

Submucosal gland
Glandula submucosa

Cartilage
Cartilago

Smooth muscle
Textus muscularis levis

Respiratory epithelium
Epithelium respiratorium

Windpipe
Trachea

Right primary bronchus
Bronchus principalis dexter

Left primary bronchus
Bronchus principalis sinister

Secondary bronchi
Bronchi lobares

Tertiary bronchi
Bronchi segmentales

Bronchioles
Bronchioli

Alveoli *Alveoli*

BRONCHIAL TREE

205

Lungs

LUNGS—FRONT VIEW

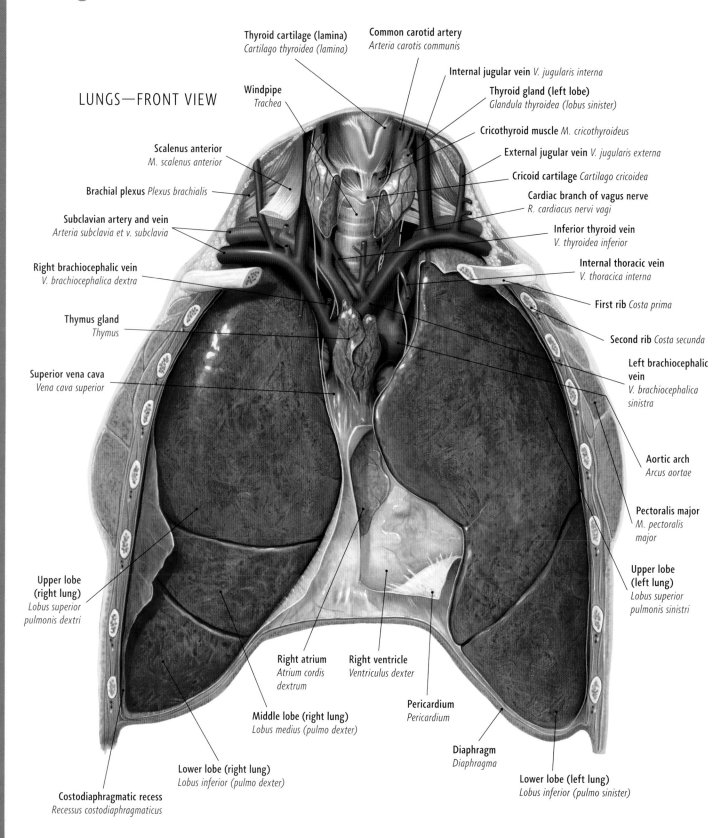

Thyroid cartilage (lamina)
Cartilago thyroidea (lamina)

Common carotid artery
Arteria carotis communis

Internal jugular vein *V. jugularis interna*

Thyroid gland (left lobe)
Glandula thyroidea (lobus sinister)

Cricothyroid muscle *M. cricothyroideus*

External jugular vein *V. jugularis externa*

Cricoid cartilage *Cartilago cricoidea*

Cardiac branch of vagus nerve
R. cardiacus nervi vagi

Inferior thyroid vein
V. thyroidea inferior

Internal thoracic vein
V. thoracica interna

First rib *Costa prima*

Second rib *Costa secunda*

Left brachiocephalic
vein
*V. brachiocephalica
sinistra*

Aortic arch
Arcus aortae

Pectoralis major
*M. pectoralis
major*

Upper lobe
(left lung)
*Lobus superior
pulmonis sinistri*

Windpipe
Trachea

Scalenus anterior
M. scalenus anterior

Brachial plexus *Plexus brachialis*

Subclavian artery and vein
Arteria subclavia et v. subclavia

Right brachiocephalic vein
V. brachiocephalica dextra

Thymus gland
Thymus

Superior vena cava
Vena cava superior

Upper lobe
(right lung)
*Lobus superior
pulmonis dextri*

Costodiaphragmatic recess
Recessus costodiaphragmaticus

Lower lobe (right lung)
Lobus inferior (pulmo dexter)

Middle lobe (right lung)
Lobus medius (pulmo dexter)

Right atrium
*Atrium cordis
dextrum*

Right ventricle
Ventriculus dexter

Pericardium
Pericardium

Diaphragm
Diaphragma

Lower lobe (left lung)
Lobus inferior (pulmo sinister)

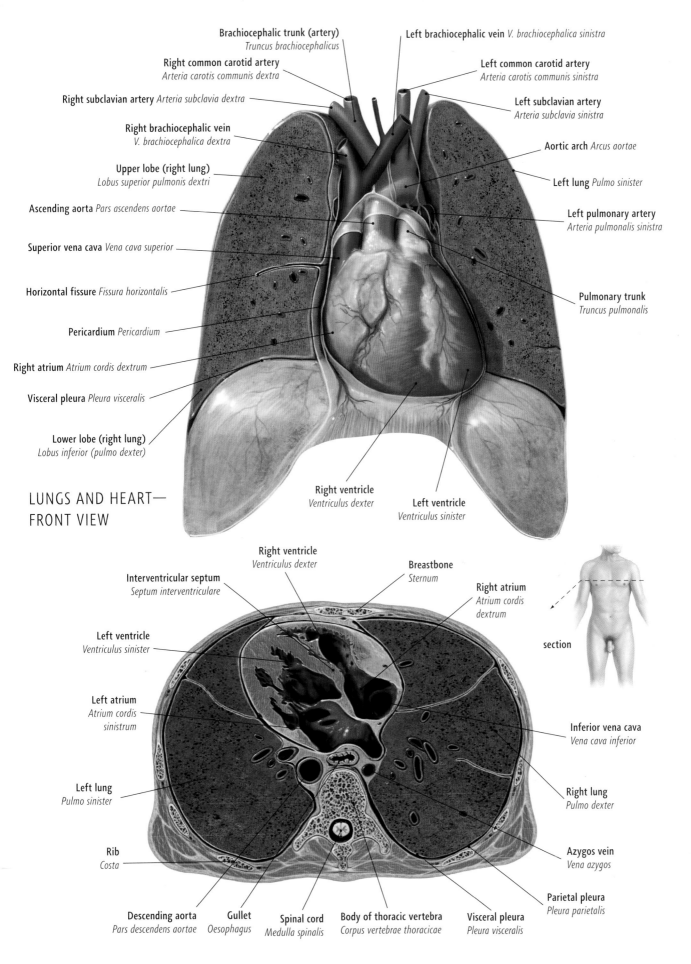

Brachiocephalic trunk (artery)
Truncus brachiocephalicus

Left brachiocephalic vein *V. brachiocephalica sinistra*

Right common carotid artery
Arteria carotis communis dextra

Left common carotid artery
Arteria carotis communis sinistra

Right subclavian artery *Arteria subclavia dextra*

Left subclavian artery
Arteria subclavia sinistra

Right brachiocephalic vein
V. brachiocephalica dextra

Aortic arch *Arcus aortae*

Upper lobe (right lung)
Lobus superior pulmonis dextri

Left lung *Pulmo sinister*

Ascending aorta *Pars ascendens aortae*

Left pulmonary artery
Arteria pulmonalis sinistra

Superior vena cava *Vena cava superior*

Horizontal fissure *Fissura horizontalis*

Pulmonary trunk
Truncus pulmonalis

Pericardium *Pericardium*

Right atrium *Atrium cordis dextrum*

Visceral pleura *Pleura visceralis*

Lower lobe (right lung)
Lobus inferior (pulmo dexter)

Right ventricle
Ventriculus dexter

Left ventricle
Ventriculus sinister

LUNGS AND HEART—FRONT VIEW

Right ventricle
Ventriculus dexter

Breastbone
Sternum

Interventricular septum
Septum interventriculare

Right atrium
Atrium cordis dextrum

Left ventricle
Ventriculus sinister

section

Left atrium
Atrium cordis sinistrum

Inferior vena cava
Vena cava inferior

Left lung
Pulmo sinister

Right lung
Pulmo dexter

Rib
Costa

Azygos vein
Vena azygos

Parietal pleura
Pleura parietalis

Descending aorta
Pars descendens aortae

Gullet
Oesophagus

Spinal cord
Medulla spinalis

Body of thoracic vertebra
Corpus vertebrae thoracicae

Visceral pleura
Pleura visceralis

LUNGS AND HEART—CROSS-SECTIONAL VIEW FROM ABOVE

Breathing

HOW WE BREATHE

Respiratory centers in the brain control the rate and depth of breathing, depending on oxygen and carbon dioxide levels in the blood. Contraction of the diaphragm and chest muscles draws air into the lungs via the nasal passage and trachea; the lungs transfer oxygen into the bloodstream.

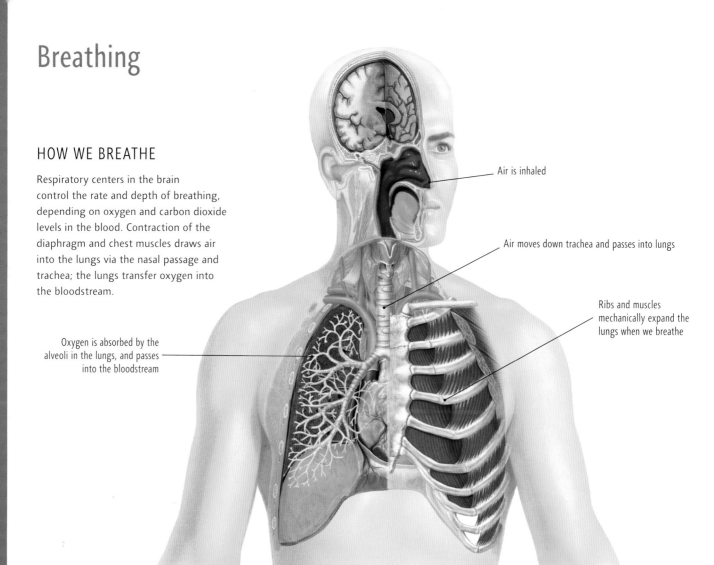

Air is inhaled

Air moves down trachea and passes into lungs

Ribs and muscles mechanically expand the lungs when we breathe

Oxygen is absorbed by the alveoli in the lungs, and passes into the bloodstream

RESPIRATORY CENTERS IN THE BRAIN

Pons *Pons*

Respiratory centers
~

Medulla
Medulla

[~] = no direct Latin equivalent

LUNGS AT REST

When we breathe in, the intercostal muscles move the ribs upward and outward, and the diaphragm pushes downward, drawing air into the expanded lungs. Breathing out depends mainly on the passive recoil of elastic tension built up in the lungs and chest during inspiration.

INSPIRATION
(BREATHING IN)

EXPIRATION
(BREATHING OUT)

Breathing

Bronchiole
Bronchiolus

Branch of pulmonary arter
R. arteriae pulmonalis

Branch of bronchial artery
R. arteriae brachialis

Capillary network around alveoli
Rete capillare circum alveoli

ALVEOLI

Branch of
pulmonary vein
*R. venae
pulmonalis*

Alveolar duct
Ductus alveolaris

Alveolar sac
Sacculus alveolaris

Alveolar pore
*Porus septalis
alveolaris*

Capillary
*Rete capillare
circa alveoli
pulmones*

Visceral pleura
Pleura visceralis

Alveolar macrophage
Macrophagocytus alveolaris

Parietal pleura
Pleura parietalis

Endothoracic fascia
Fascia endothoracica

[~] = no direct Latin equivalent

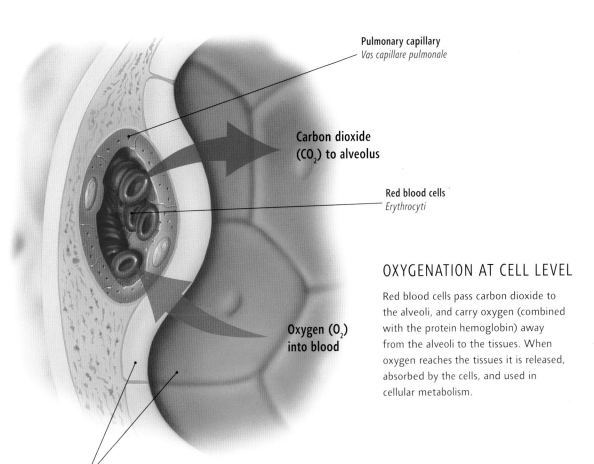

Pulmonary capillary
Vas capillare pulmonale

Carbon dioxide
(CO_2) to alveolus

Red blood cells
Erythrocyti

Oxygen (O_2)
into blood

Alveolar epithelium
Epithelium alveolare

OXYGENATION AT CELL LEVEL

Red blood cells pass carbon dioxide to the alveoli, and carry oxygen (combined with the protein hemoglobin) away from the alveoli to the tissues. When oxygen reaches the tissues it is released, absorbed by the cells, and used in cellular metabolism.

MOVING OXYGEN AROUND THE BODY

Blood travels continuously through two circulatory systems: the pulmonary (lung) and the systemic (body) circulations. The heart pumps oxygen-poor blood from the systemic circulation into the pulmonary circulation. This blood is oxygenated by the lungs and then pumped by the heart into the systemic circulation.

Note: Part of the lungs has been removed to reveal the pleura covering the diaphragm.

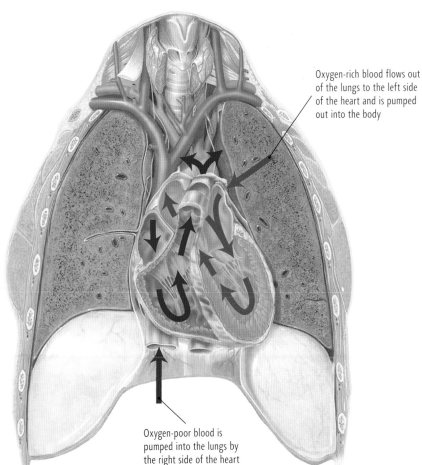

Oxygen-rich blood flows out of the lungs to the left side of the heart and is pumped out into the body

Oxygen-poor blood is pumped into the lungs by the right side of the heart

211

The Digestive System

The Digestive System

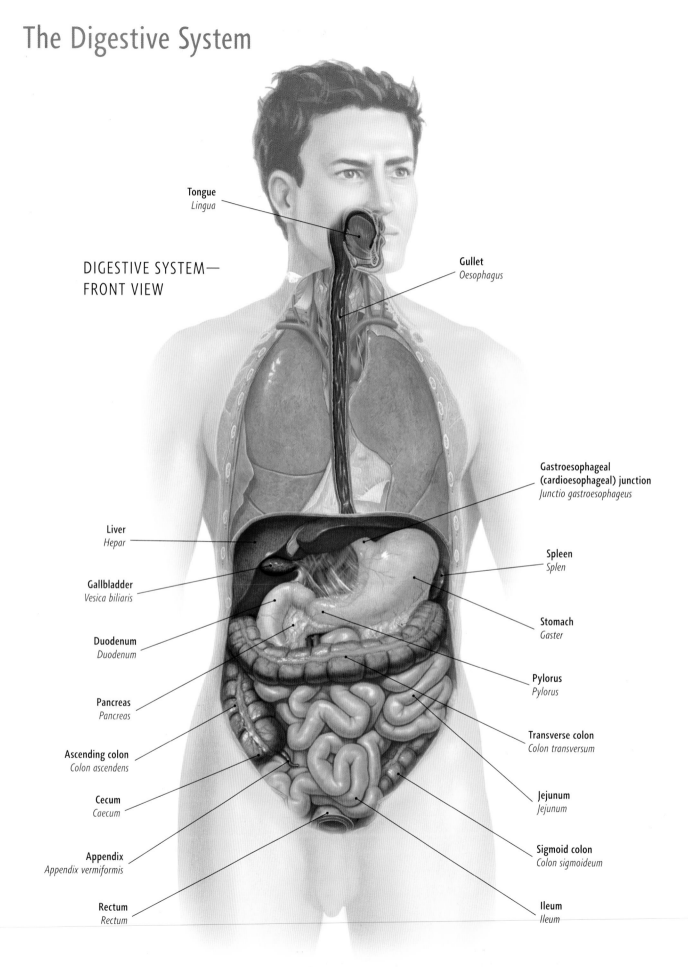

DIGESTIVE SYSTEM—
FRONT VIEW

Tongue
Lingua

Gullet
Oesophagus

**Gastroesophageal
(cardioesophageal) junction**
Junctio gastroesophageus

Liver
Hepar

Spleen
Splen

Gallbladder
Vesica biliaris

Stomach
Gaster

Duodenum
Duodenum

Pylorus
Pylorus

Pancreas
Pancreas

Transverse colon
Colon transversum

Ascending colon
Colon ascendens

Jejunum
Jejunum

Cecum
Caecum

Sigmoid colon
Colon sigmoideum

Appendix
Appendix vermiformis

Rectum
Rectum

Ileum
Ileum

[~] = no direct Latin equivalent

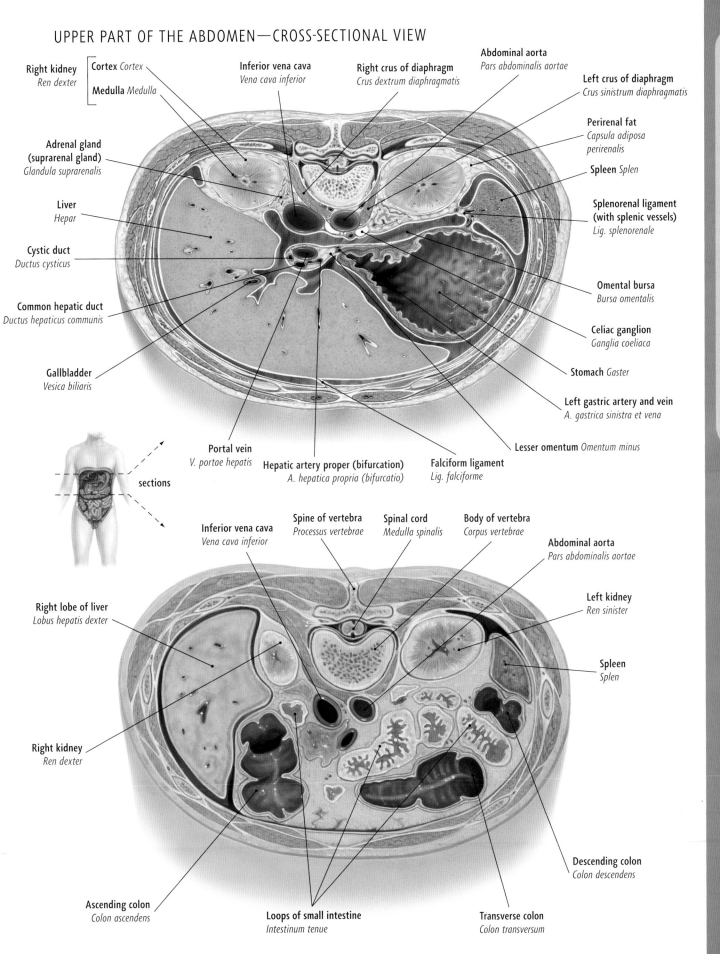

UPPER PART OF THE ABDOMEN—CROSS-SECTIONAL VIEW

Right kidney
Ren dexter

Cortex *Cortex*

Medulla *Medulla*

Inferior vena cava
Vena cava inferior

Right crus of diaphragm
Crus dextrum diaphragmatis

Abdominal aorta
Pars abdominalis aortae

Left crus of diaphragm
Crus sinistrum diaphragmatis

**Adrenal gland
(suprarenal gland)**
Glandula suprarenalis

Perirenal fat
*Capsula adiposa
perirenalis*

Spleen *Splen*

Liver
Hepar

**Splenorenal ligament
(with splenic vessels)**
Lig. splenorenale

Cystic duct
Ductus cysticus

Omental bursa
Bursa omentalis

Common hepatic duct
Ductus hepaticus communis

Celiac ganglion
Ganglia coeliaca

Stomach *Gaster*

Gallbladder
Vesica biliaris

Left gastric artery and vein
A. gastrica sinistra et vena

Lesser omentum *Omentum minus*

sections

Portal vein
V. portae hepatis

Hepatic artery proper (bifurcation)
A. hepatica propria (bifurcatio)

Falciform ligament
Lig. falciforme

Inferior vena cava
Vena cava inferior

Spine of vertebra
Processus vertebrae

Spinal cord
Medulla spinalis

Body of vertebra
Corpus vertebrae

Abdominal aorta
Pars abdominalis aortae

Right lobe of liver
Lobus hepatis dexter

Left kidney
Ren sinister

Spleen
Splen

Right kidney
Ren dexter

Ascending colon
Colon ascendens

Loops of small intestine
Intestinum tenue

Transverse colon
Colon transversum

Descending colon
Colon descendens

MIDDLE PART OF THE ABDOMEN—CROSS-SECTIONAL VIEW

The Digestive System

DIGESTIVE ORGANS AND GREATER OMENTUM

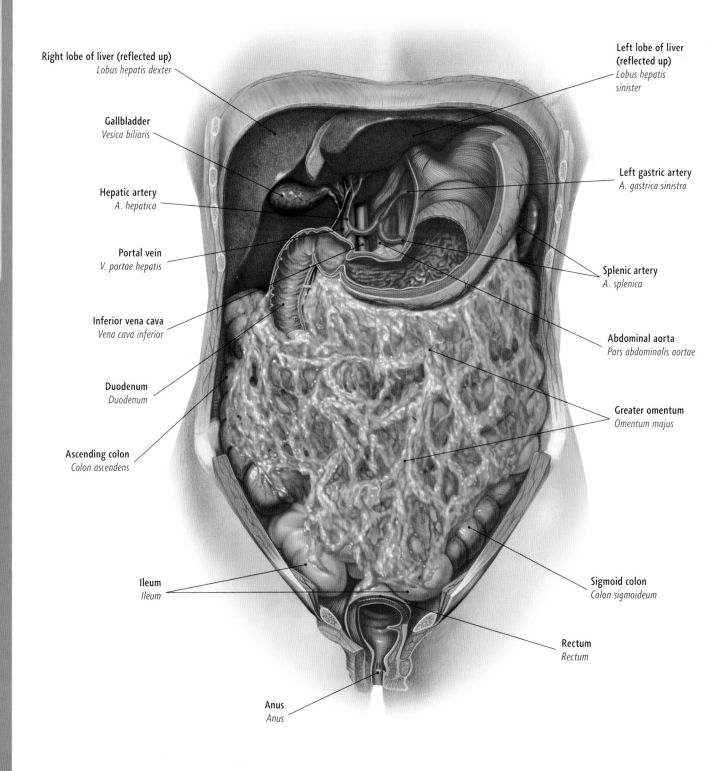

Right lobe of liver (reflected up)
Lobus hepatis dexter

Gallbladder
Vesica biliaris

Hepatic artery
A. hepatica

Portal vein
V. portae hepatis

Inferior vena cava
Vena cava inferior

Duodenum
Duodenum

Ascending colon
Colon ascendens

Ileum
Ileum

Anus
Anus

Left lobe of liver
(reflected up)
*Lobus hepatis
sinister*

Left gastric artery
A. gastrica sinistra

Splenic artery
A. splenica

Abdominal aorta
Pars abdominalis aortae

Greater omentum
Omentum majus

Sigmoid colon
Colon sigmoideum

Rectum
Rectum

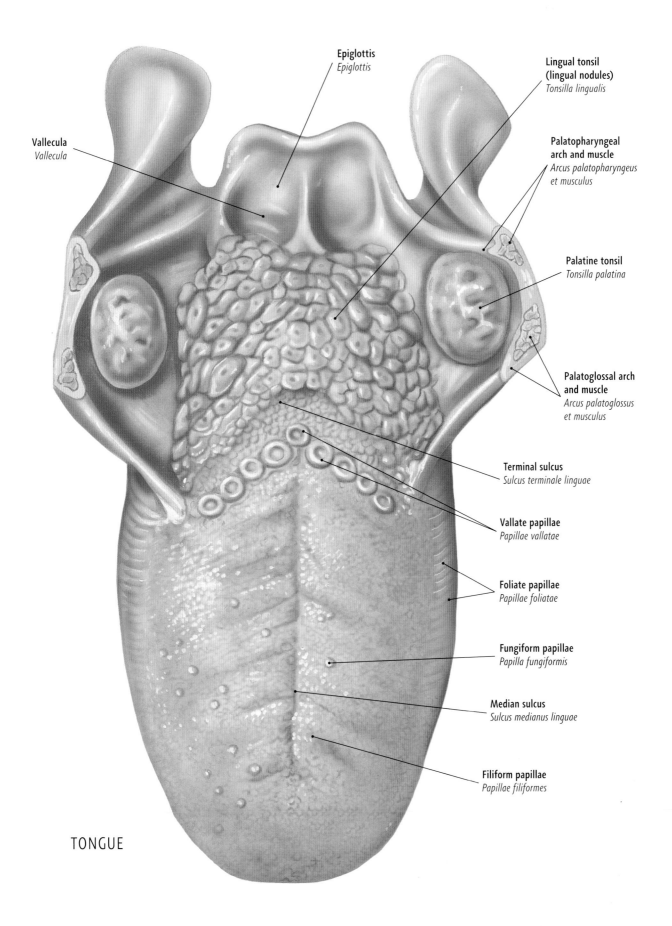

Epiglottis
Epiglottis

Lingual tonsil
(lingual nodules)
Tonsilla lingualis

Vallecula
Vallecula

Palatopharyngeal
arch and muscle
*Arcus palatopharyngeus
et musculus*

Palatine tonsil
Tonsilla palatina

Palatoglossal arch
and muscle
*Arcus palatoglossus
et musculus*

Terminal sulcus
Sulcus terminale linguae

Vallate papillae
Papillae vallatae

Foliate papillae
Papillae foliatae

Fungiform papillae
Papilla fungiformis

Median sulcus
Sulcus medianus linguae

Filiform papillae
Papillae filiformes

TONGUE

Teeth

Upper teeth

Central incisor *Dens incisivus centralis*

Lateral incisor *Dens incisivus lateralis*

Canine *Dens caninus*

First premolar *Dens premolaris primus*

Second premolar *Dens premolaris secundus*

First molar *Dens molaris primus*

Second molar *Dens molaris secundus*

Wisdom tooth *Dens molaris tertius*

Lower teeth

Wisdom tooth *Dens molaris tertius*

Second molar *Dens molaris secundus*

First molar *Dens molaris primus*

Second premolar *Dens premolaris secundus*

First premolar *Dens premolaris primus*

Canine *Dens caninus*

Lateral incisor *Dens incisivus lateralis*

Central incisor *Dens incisivus centralis*

TEETH

Upper teeth

| Central incisor *Dens incisivus centralis* | Lateral incisor *Dens incisivus lateralis* | Canine *Dens caninus* | First premolar *Dens premolaris primus* | Second premolar *Dens premolaris secundus* | First molar *Dens molaris primus* | Second molar *Dens molaris secundus* | Third molar (wisdom tooth) *Dens molaris tertius* |

Lower teeth

222

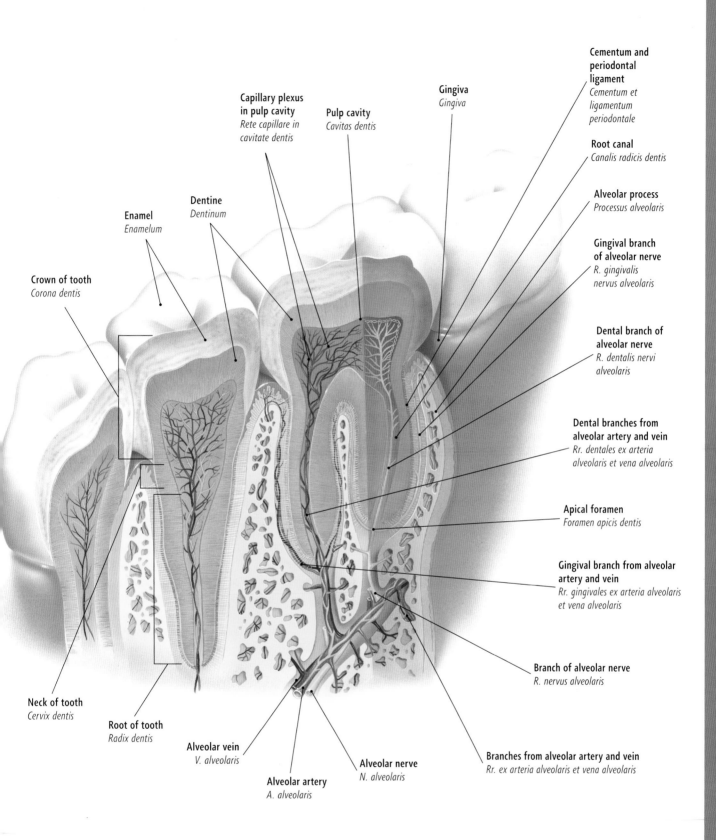

Capillary plexus
in pulp cavity
*Rete capillare in
cavitate dentis*

Pulp cavity
Cavitas dentis

Gingiva
Gingiva

Cementum and
periodontal
ligament
*Cementum et
ligamentum
periodontale*

Root canal
Canalis radicis dentis

Dentine
Dentinum

Alveolar process
Processus alveolaris

Enamel
Enamelum

Gingival branch
of alveolar nerve
*R. gingivalis
nervus alveolaris*

Crown of tooth
Corona dentis

Dental branch of
alveolar nerve
*R. dentalis nervi
alveolaris*

Dental branches from
alveolar artery and vein
*Rr. dentales ex arteria
alveolaris et vena alveolaris*

Apical foramen
Foramen apicis dentis

Gingival branch from alveolar
artery and vein
*Rr. gingivales ex arteria alveolaris
et vena alveolaris*

Branch of alveolar nerve
R. nervus alveolaris

Neck of tooth
Cervix dentis

Root of tooth
Radix dentis

Alveolar vein
V. alveolaris

Alveolar nerve
N. alveolaris

Branches from alveolar artery and vein
Rr. ex arteria alveolaris et vena alveolaris

Alveolar artery
A. alveolaris

STRUCTURE OF TEETH—CROSS-SECTIONAL VIEW

[~] = no direct Latin equivalent

Salivary Glands

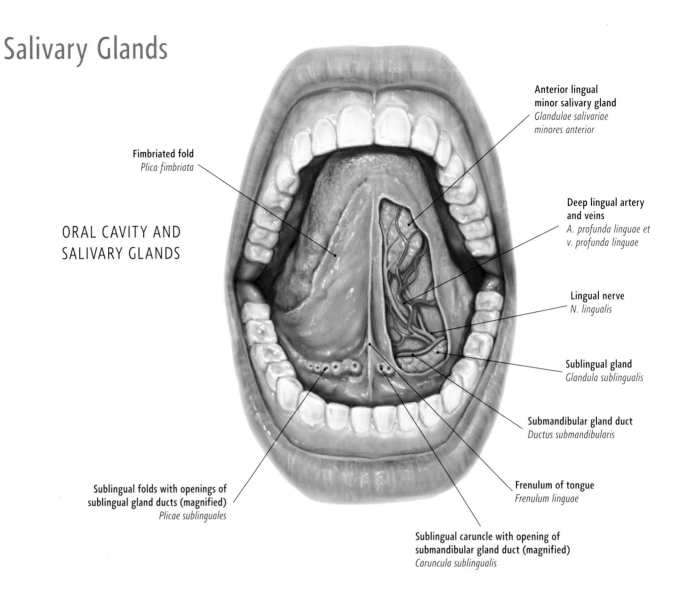

ORAL CAVITY AND
SALIVARY GLANDS

Fimbriated fold
Plica fimbriata

**Anterior lingual
minor salivary gland**
*Glandulae salivariae
minores anterior*

**Deep lingual artery
and veins**
*A. profunda linguae et
v. profunda linguae*

Lingual nerve
N. lingualis

Sublingual gland
Glandula sublingualis

Submandibular gland duct
Ductus submandibularis

Frenulum of tongue
Frenulum linguae

**Sublingual caruncle with opening of
submandibular gland duct (magnified)**
Caruncula sublingualis

**Sublingual folds with openings of
sublingual gland ducts (magnified)**
Plicae sublinguales

SALIVARY GLANDS

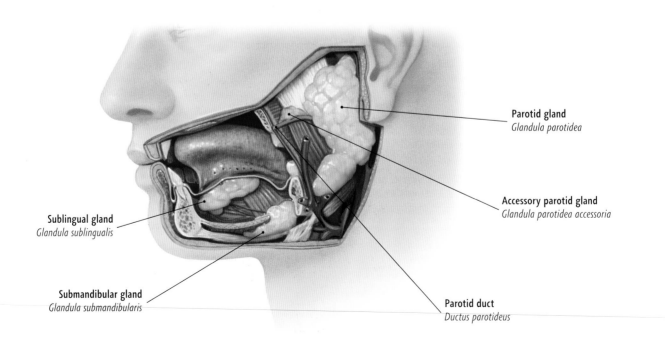

Parotid gland
Glandula parotidea

Accessory parotid gland
Glandula parotidea accessoria

Sublingual gland
Glandula sublingualis

Submandibular gland
Glandula submandibularis

Parotid duct
Ductus parotideus

PAROTID GLAND— MICROSTRUCTURE

The thin saliva produced by the parotid glands contains enzymes specially designed to break down starch.

Acinar cell
Acinocytus

Serous cell
Serocytus

Intercalated ducts
Ducti intercalati

Artery
Arteria

Septum
Septum

Interlobular duct
Ductus interlobularis

Vein
Vena

Striated duct
Ductus striatus

Interlobular duct
Ductus interlobularis

Septum of connective tissue
Septum texti connectivi

Serous cell (forming a serous crescent)
Serocytus

Mucous cell (forming a mucous acinus)
Mucocytus

SUBMANDIBULAR GLAND— MICROSTRUCTURE

The submandibular glands comprise a mixture of enzyme-producing serous cells and mucus-producing cells. Their saliva is predominantly water.

Serous crescent (serous demilune)
Semiluna serosa

Mucous tubule
Tubulus mucosae

Septum
Septum

Interlobular duct
Ductus interlobularis

Mucous tubules
Tubuli mucosae

SUBLINGUAL GLAND— MICROSTRUCTURE

The sublingual glands produce thicker, watery mucus, particularly in response to the presence of milk or cream, which helps to lubricate the mouth.

Acinar cell
Acinocytus

Mucous cell
Mucocytus

Intercalated duct (from acinar cells)
Ductus intercalatus

[~] = no direct Latin equivalent

225

Liver and Gallbladder

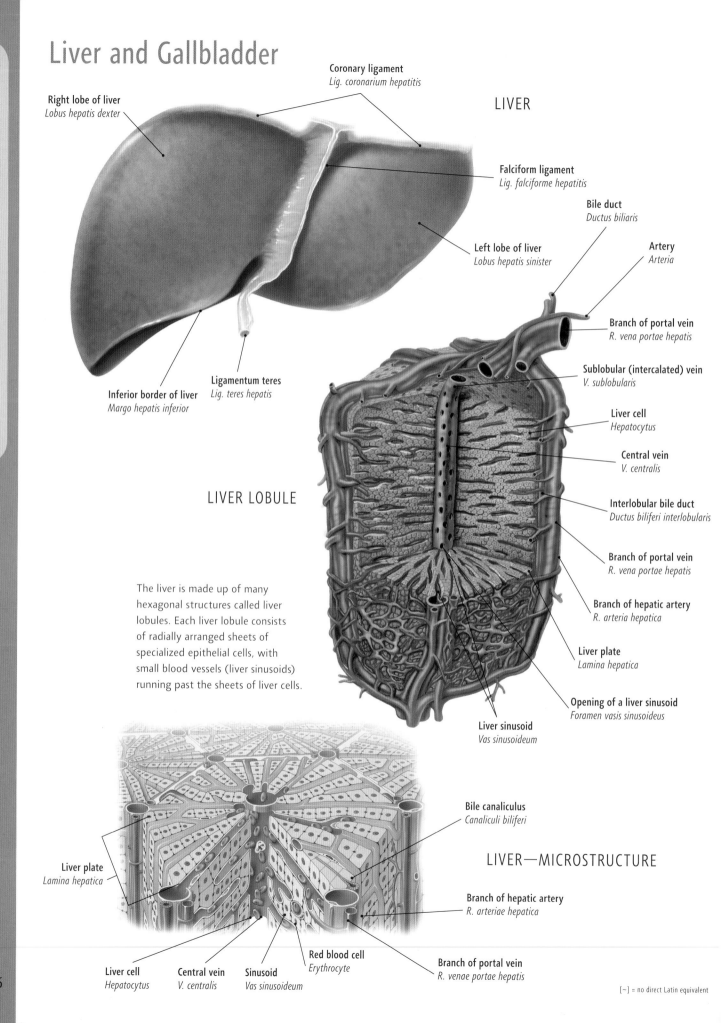

Coronary ligament
Lig. coronarium hepatitis

LIVER

Right lobe of liver
Lobus hepatis dexter

Falciform ligament
Lig. falciforme hepatitis

Bile duct
Ductus biliaris

Artery
Arteria

Left lobe of liver
Lobus hepatis sinister

Branch of portal vein
R. vena portae hepatis

Sublobular (intercalated) vein
V. sublobularis

Ligamentum teres
Lig. teres hepatis

Liver cell
Hepatocytus

Inferior border of liver
Margo hepatis inferior

Central vein
V. centralis

Interlobular bile duct
Ductus biliferi interlobularis

LIVER LOBULE

Branch of portal vein
R. vena portae hepatis

Branch of hepatic artery
R. arteria hepatica

The liver is made up of many
hexagonal structures called liver
lobules. Each liver lobule consists
of radially arranged sheets of
specialized epithelial cells, with
small blood vessels (liver sinusoids)
running past the sheets of liver cells.

Liver plate
Lamina hepatica

Opening of a liver sinusoid
Foramen vasis sinusoideus

Liver sinusoid
Vas sinusoideum

Bile canaliculus
Canaliculi biliferi

LIVER—MICROSTRUCTURE

Liver plate
Lamina hepatica

Branch of hepatic artery
R. arteriae hepatica

Liver cell
Hepatocytus

Central vein
V. centralis

Sinusoid
Vas sinusoideum

Red blood cell
Erythrocyte

Branch of portal vein
R. venae portae hepatis

[~] = no direct Latin equivalent

GALLBLADDER

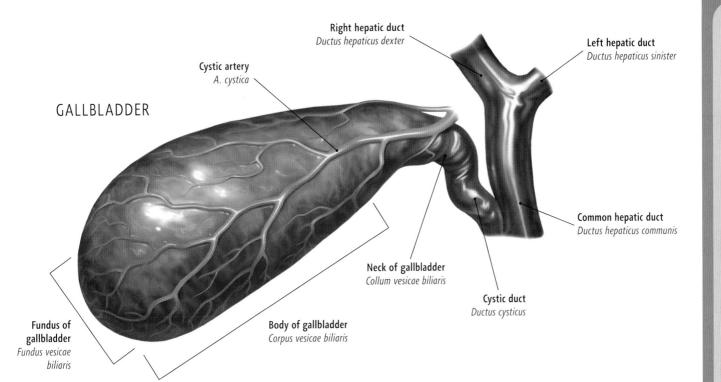

Right hepatic duct
Ductus hepaticus dexter

Left hepatic duct
Ductus hepaticus sinister

Cystic artery
A. cystica

Common hepatic duct
Ductus hepaticus communis

Neck of gallbladder
Collum vesicae biliaris

Cystic duct
Ductus cysticus

Fundus of gallbladder
Fundus vesicae biliaris

Body of gallbladder
Corpus vesicae biliaris

BILE DUCTS

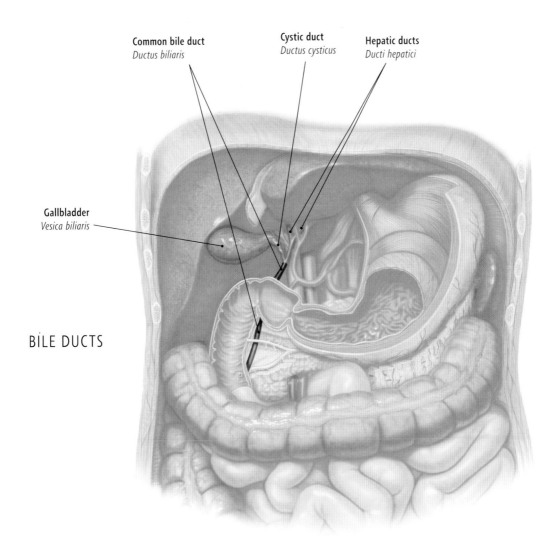

Common bile duct
Ductus biliaris

Cystic duct
Ductus cysticus

Hepatic ducts
Ducti hepatici

Gallbladder
Vesica biliaris

Stomach and Pancreas

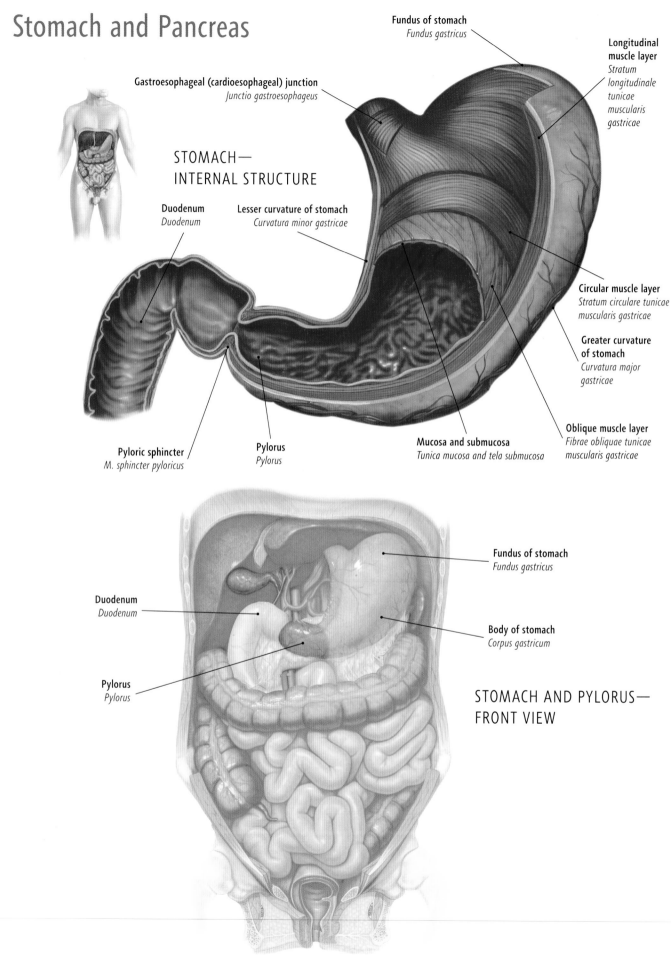

Fundus of stomach
Fundus gastricus

Longitudinal muscle layer
Stratum longitudinale tunicae muscularis gastricae

Gastroesophageal (cardioesophageal) junction
Junctio gastroesophageus

STOMACH— INTERNAL STRUCTURE

Duodenum
Duodenum

Lesser curvature of stomach
Curvatura minor gastricae

Circular muscle layer
Stratum circulare tunicae muscularis gastricae

Greater curvature of stomach
Curvatura major gastricae

Pyloric sphincter
M. sphincter pyloricus

Pylorus
Pylorus

Mucosa and submucosa
Tunica mucosa and tela submucosa

Oblique muscle layer
Fibrae obliquae tunicae muscularis gastricae

Duodenum
Duodenum

Fundus of stomach
Fundus gastricus

Body of stomach
Corpus gastricum

Pylorus
Pylorus

STOMACH AND PYLORUS— FRONT VIEW

228

[~] = no direct Latin equivalent

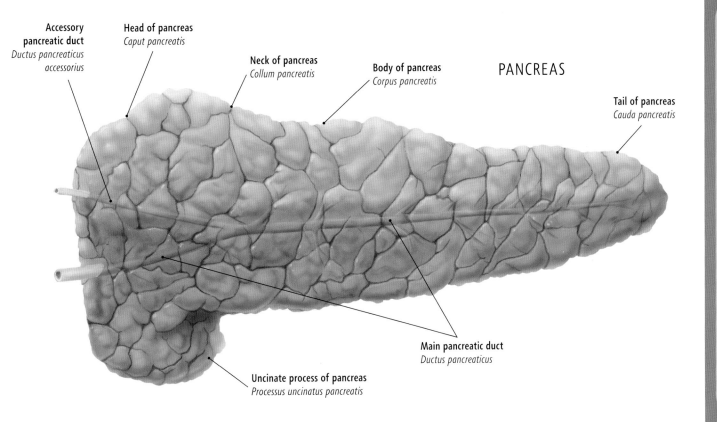

Accessory pancreatic duct
Ductus pancreaticus accessorius

Head of pancreas
Caput pancreatis

Neck of pancreas
Collum pancreatis

Body of pancreas
Corpus pancreatis

PANCREAS

Tail of pancreas
Cauda pancreatis

Main pancreatic duct
Ductus pancreaticus

Uncinate process of pancreas
Processus uncinatus pancreatis

PANCREAS: EXOCRINE CELLS

Most of the pancreas consists of acinar cells, which secrete digestive enzymes that aid in food processing. The enzymes flow from the cells into the small intestine along a network of attached ducts.

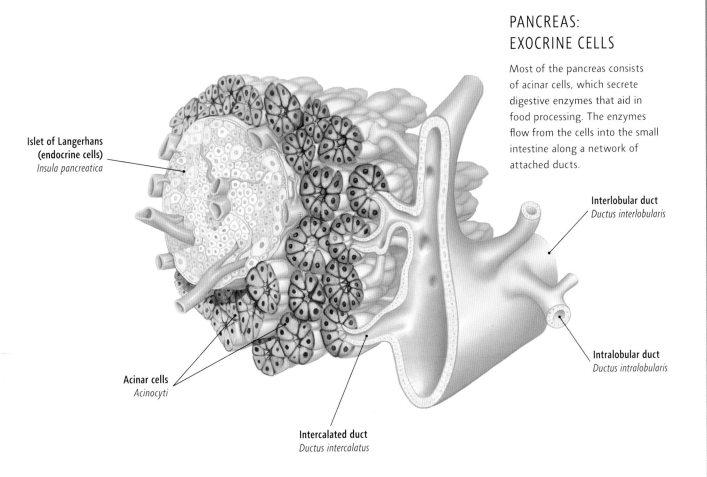

Islet of Langerhans (endocrine cells)
Insula pancreatica

Interlobular duct
Ductus interlobularis

Acinar cells
Acinocyti

Intralobular duct
Ductus intralobularis

Intercalated duct
Ductus intercalatus

Alimentary Canal and Peristalsis

ALIMENTARY CANAL

The alimentary canal is the body's "food processor." The first part breaks food down into fats, carbohydrates, and proteins, which are absorbed into the blood further along the canal. Water is absorbed along the final part, and anything left over is excreted.

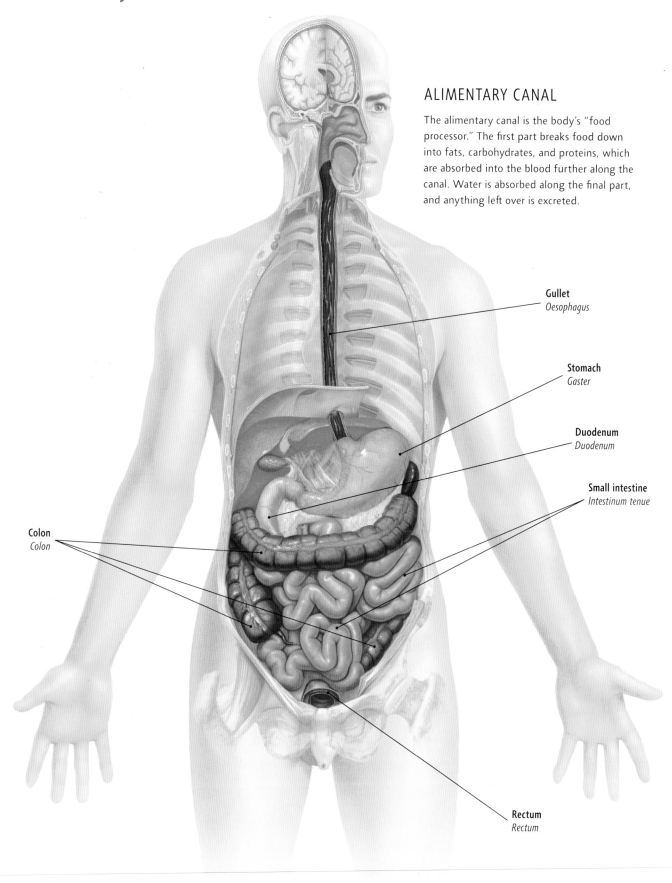

Gullet
Oesophagus

Stomach
Gaster

Duodenum
Duodenum

Small intestine
Intestinum tenue

Colon
Colon

Rectum
Rectum

Bolus of food
~

Tongue
Lingua

Throat
Pharynx

Windpipe
Trachea

Gullet
Oesophagus

Bolus of food
~

a

b

c

d

e

f

Colon
Colon

Rectum
Rectum

g

h

i

PERISTALSIS

Peristalsis consists of wavelike contractions in the muscular
walls of the esophagus, stomach, and intestines that propel
the contents along. After food is swallowed, it enters the
esophagus (a, b, c) and travels toward the stomach (d, e, f) before
moving to the small intestine and then the colon. Water and bile
salts are absorbed from the colon before peristaltic contractions
push the waste matter along to the rectum (g, h, i).

[~] = no direct Latin equivalent

Intestines

STOMACH AND INTESTINES

Gallbladder
Vesica biliaris

Stomach
Gaster

Transverse colon
Colon transversum

Duodenum
Duodenum

Jejunum
Jejunum

Small intestine
Intestinum tenue

Ileum
Ileum

Sigmoid colon
Colon sigmoideum

DUODENUM

Duodenum
Duodenum

Jejunum
Jejunum

JEJUNUM

Ileum
Ileum

ILEUM

COLON

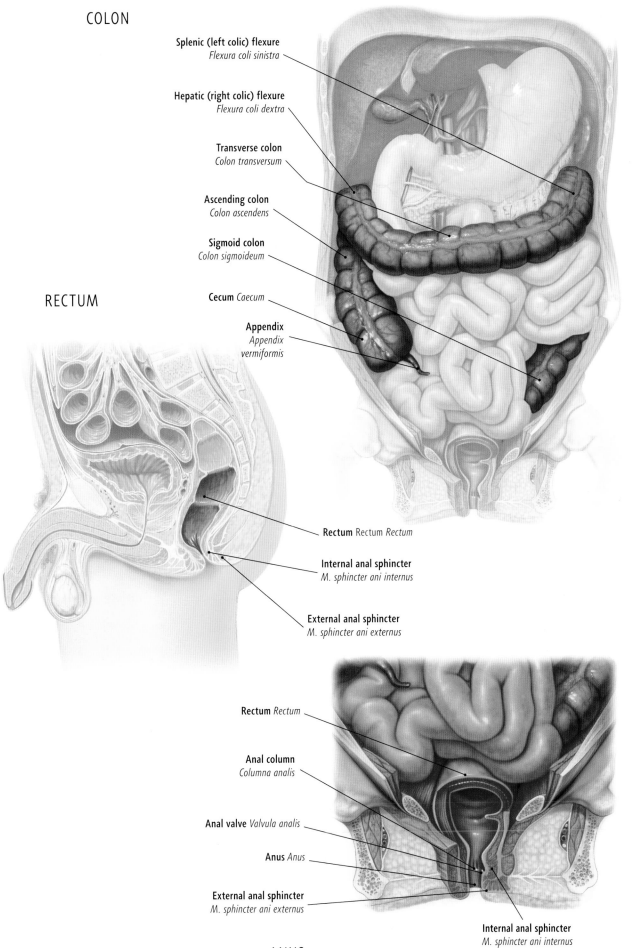

Splenic (left colic) flexure
Flexura coli sinistra

Hepatic (right colic) flexure
Flexura coli dextra

Transverse colon
Colon transversum

Ascending colon
Colon ascendens

Sigmoid colon
Colon sigmoideum

Cecum *Caecum*

Appendix
Appendix vermiformis

RECTUM

Rectum Rectum *Rectum*

Internal anal sphincter
M. sphincter ani internus

External anal sphincter
M. sphincter ani externus

Rectum *Rectum*

Anal column
Columna analis

Anal valve *Valvula analis*

Anus *Anus*

External anal sphincter
M. sphincter ani externus

Internal anal sphincter
M. sphincter ani internus

ANUS

Intestines

INTESTINAL JEJUNUM—CUT-AWAY VIEW

The jejunum is the part of the small intestine between the duodenum and the ileum. It digests and absorbs food, sending nutrients to the lymphatic vessels and liver.

Mesentery
Mesenterium

Nerve
Nervus

Mesentery
Mesenterium

**Inner circular layer
of muscularis externa**
*Lamina interna circularis
tunicae muscularis*

Outer longitudinal layer of muscularis externa
Lamina externa longitudinalis tunicae muscularis

Plicae circulares
Plicae circulares

**Nerves of
myenteric ple**
*Plexus nervosu
myentericus*

Serosa (mesothelium)
Tunica serosa (mesothelium)

Serosa (connective tissue)
Tunica serosa (textus connectivus)

Submucosa
Tela submucosa

Mucosa
Tunica mucosa

**Outer longitudinal layer
of smooth muscle cells**
*Lamina externa
longitudinalis tunicae
muscularis*

Muscularis mucosae
*Lamina muscularis
mucosae*

234

[~] = no direct Latin equivalent

INTESTINAL JEJUNUM PLICA—CROSS-SECTIONAL VIEW

The lining of the jejunum has many small folds (known as plicae circulares) that feature tiny fingerlike projections called villi. The plicae circulares and villi greatly increase the surface area available for the absorption of nutrients.

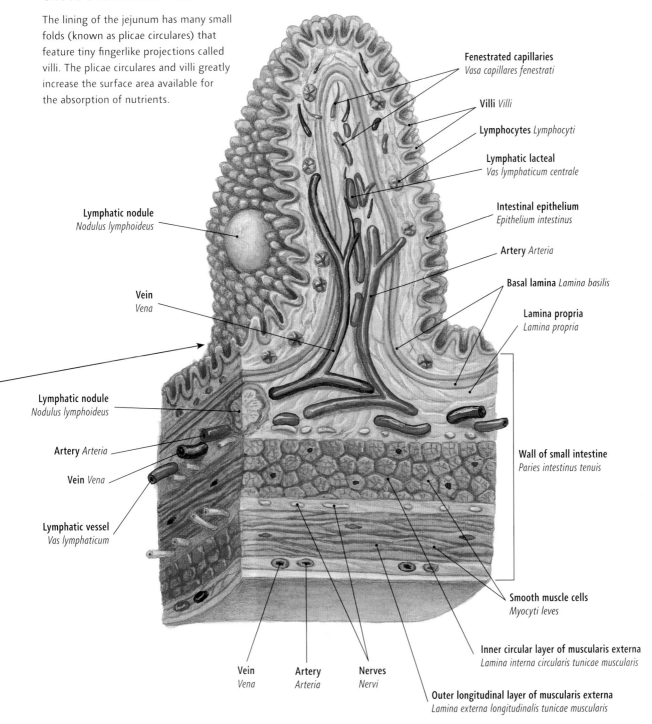

Fenestrated capillaries
Vasa capillares fenestrati

Villi *Villi*

Lymphocytes *Lymphocyti*

Lymphatic lacteal
Vas lymphaticum centrale

Intestinal epithelium
Epithelium intestinus

Artery *Arteria*

Basal lamina *Lamina basilis*

Lamina propria
Lamina propria

Wall of small intestine
Paries intestinus tenuis

Lymphatic nodule
Nodulus lymphoideus

Vein
Vena

Lymphatic nodule
Nodulus lymphoideus

Artery *Arteria*

Vein *Vena*

Lymphatic vessel
Vas lymphaticum

Smooth muscle cells
Myocyti leves

Inner circular layer of muscularis externa
Lamina interna circularis tunicae muscularis

Outer longitudinal layer of muscularis externa
Lamina externa longitudinalis tunicae muscularis

Vein
Vena

Artery
Arteria

Nerves
Nervi

The Urinary System

The Urinary System

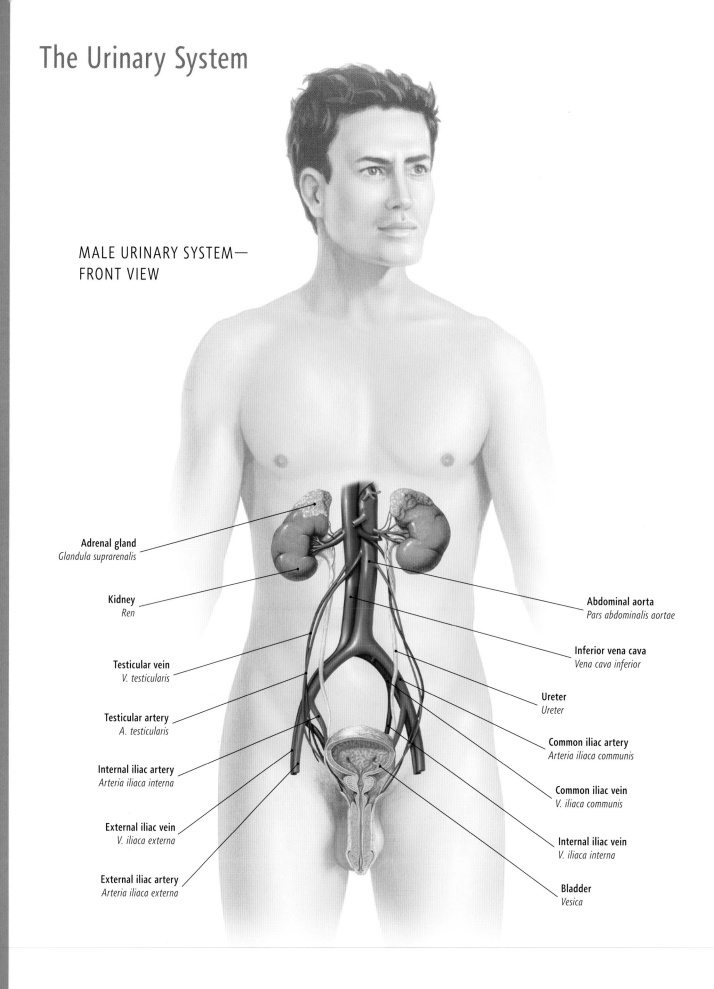

MALE URINARY SYSTEM—
FRONT VIEW

Adrenal gland
Glandula suprarenalis

Kidney
Ren

Testicular vein
V. testicularis

Testicular artery
A. testicularis

Internal iliac artery
Arteria iliaca interna

External iliac vein
V. iliaca externa

External iliac artery
Arteria iliaca externa

Abdominal aorta
Pars abdominalis aortae

Inferior vena cava
Vena cava inferior

Ureter
Ureter

Common iliac artery
Arteria iliaca communis

Common iliac vein
V. iliaca communis

Internal iliac vein
V. iliaca interna

Bladder
Vesica

FEMALE URINARY SYSTEM—
FRONT VIEW

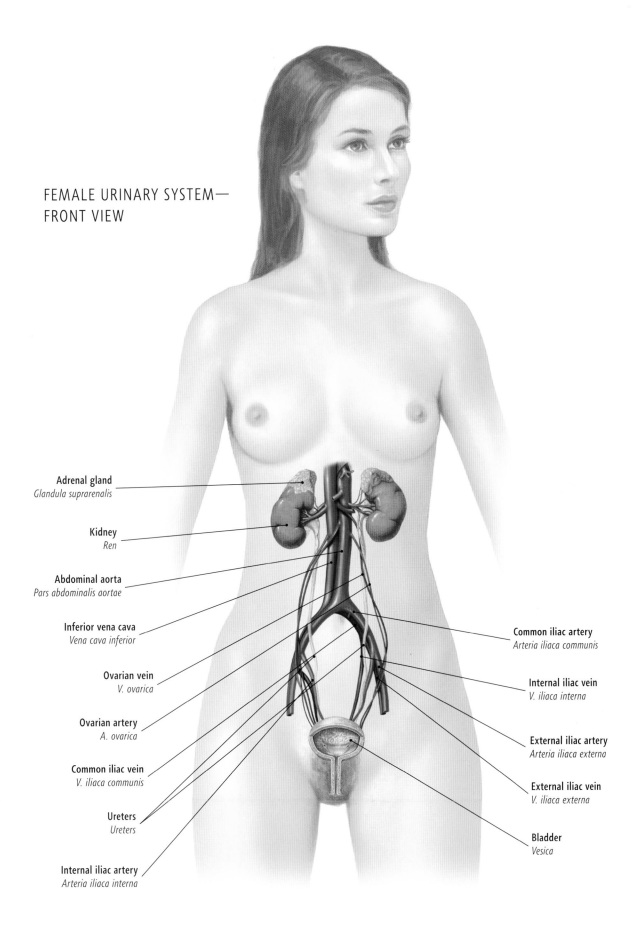

Adrenal gland
Glandula suprarenalis

Kidney
Ren

Abdominal aorta
Pars abdominalis aortae

Inferior vena cava
Vena cava inferior

Ovarian vein
V. ovarica

Ovarian artery
A. ovarica

Common iliac vein
V. iliaca communis

Ureters
Ureters

Internal iliac artery
Arteria iliaca interna

Common iliac artery
Arteria iliaca communis

Internal iliac vein
V. iliaca interna

External iliac artery
Arteria iliaca externa

External iliac vein
V. iliaca externa

Bladder
Vesica

Urinary Tract and Bladder

Abdominal aorta *Pars abdominalis aortae*

Inferior vena cava *Vena cava inferior*

Left ureter *Ureter sinister*

Bladder *Vesica*

Testicular vein *V. testicularis*

Testicular artery *A. testicularis*

Right ureter *Ureter dexter*

Urethra *Urethra*

Common iliac artery *Arteria iliaca communis*

Common iliac vein *V. iliaca communis*

Internal iliac vein *V. iliaca interna*

Internal iliac artery *Arteria iliaca interna*

External urethral orifice *Ostium urethrae externum*

Internal urethral orifice *Ostium urethrae internum*

MALE URETHRA

Bladder *Vesica*

Opening (meatus) of left ureter *Ostium ureteris sinister*

External iliac artery *Arteria iliaca externa*

External iliac vein *V. iliaca externa*

MALE BLADDER

Neck of bladder *Cervix vesicae*

Prostatic utricle *Utriculus prostaticus*

Prostate *Prostata*

Colliculus seminalis *Colliculus seminalis*

Opening of ejaculatory du *Apertura ductus ejaculatorii*

Corpus cavernosum *Corpus cavernosum penis*

Bulbourethral (Cowper's) gl *Glandula bulbourethralis*

Corpus spongiosum *Corpus spongiosum penis*

Bulb of penis *Bulbus penis*

Scrotum *Scrotum*

Urethra *Urethra*

Corona glandis *Corona glandis penis*

Glans of penis *Glans penis*

External urethral orifice *Ostium urethrae externum*

Foreskin *Preputium penis*

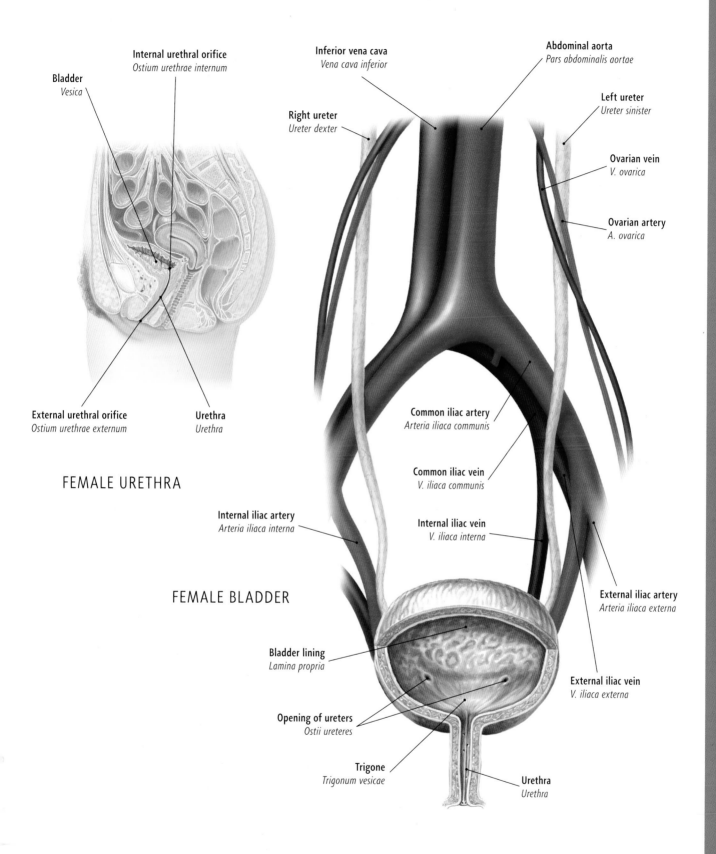

Bladder
Vesica

Internal urethral orifice
Ostium urethrae internum

Inferior vena cava
Vena cava inferior

Abdominal aorta
Pars abdominalis aortae

Right ureter
Ureter dexter

Left ureter
Ureter sinister

Ovarian vein
V. ovarica

Ovarian artery
A. ovarica

External urethral orifice
Ostium urethrae externum

Urethra
Urethra

FEMALE URETHRA

Common iliac artery
Arteria iliaca communis

Common iliac vein
V. iliaca communis

Internal iliac artery
Arteria iliaca interna

Internal iliac vein
V. iliaca interna

FEMALE BLADDER

External iliac artery
Arteria iliaca externa

Bladder lining
Lamina propria

External iliac vein
V. iliaca externa

Opening of ureters
Ostii ureteres

Trigone
Trigonum vesicae

Urethra
Urethra

241

Kidneys

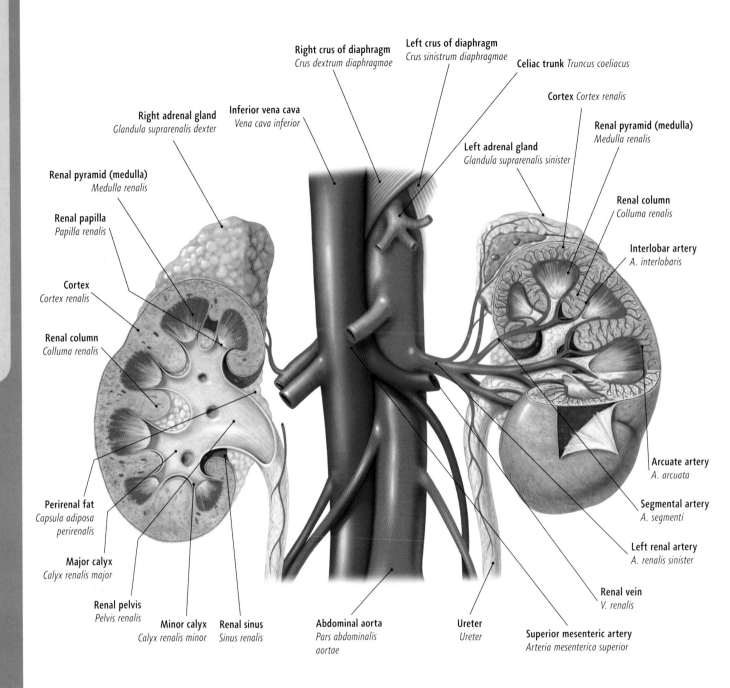

Right crus of diaphragm
Crus dextrum diaphragmae

Left crus of diaphragm
Crus sinistrum diaphragmae

Celiac trunk *Truncus coeliacus*

Cortex *Cortex renalis*

Renal pyramid (medulla)
Medulla renalis

Right adrenal gland
Glandula suprarenalis dexter

Inferior vena cava
Vena cava inferior

Left adrenal gland
Glandula suprarenalis sinister

Renal column
Colluma renalis

Renal pyramid (medulla)
Medulla renalis

Interlobar artery
A. interlobaris

Renal papilla
Papilla renalis

Cortex
Cortex renalis

Renal column
Colluma renalis

Arcuate artery
A. arcuata

Segmental artery
A. segmenti

Perirenal fat
Capsula adiposa perirenalis

Left renal artery
A. renalis sinister

Major calyx
Calyx renalis major

Renal vein
V. renalis

Renal pelvis
Pelvis renalis

Minor calyx
Calyx renalis minor

Renal sinus
Sinus renalis

Abdominal aorta
Pars abdominalis aortae

Ureter
Ureter

Superior mesenteric artery
Arteria mesenterica superior

KIDNEYS AND ADRENAL GLANDS

Urinary pole *Polus urinarius*

Glomerular tuft of capillaries *Rete capillare glomerulare*

Afferent arteriole *Arteriola glomerularis afferens renis*

Interlobular vein *V. interlobularis*

Foot process of podocytes *Cytopodium podocyti*

Efferent arteriole *Arteriola glomerularis efferens renis*

Proximal convoluted tubule *Tubulus proximalis pars contorta*

Basal lamina *Lamina basilis*

Cell body of podocyte *Corpus podocyti*

Parietal layer of Bowman's capsule *Capsula glomerularis*

Peritubular capillaries ~

Interlobular artery *A. interlobularis*

Bowman's space *Spatium capsulare*

Interlobar artery *A. interlobaris*

Basal lamina *Lamina basilis*

Vascular pole *Polus vascularis*

Glomeruli *Glomeruli*

Afferent arteriole *Arteriola afferens*

Endothelial cell *Endotheliocytus*

Connecting tubule *Tubulus reuniens*

Efferent arteriole *Arteriola efferens*

Macula densa *Macula densa*

Arcuate vein *V. arcuata*

Collecting duct *Ductus colligens*

Distal convoluted tubule *Tubulus distalis pars contorta*

Arcuate artery *A. arcuata*

Vasa recta *Vasa recta*

Connecting tubule *Tubulus renalis arcuatus*

Thick ascending limb of loop of Henle (distal straight tubule) *Tubulus distalis pars recta*

Interlobular vein *V. interlobularis*

Medullary plexus of peritubular capillaries *Plexus capillaris interfascicularis*

Thick descending limb of loop of Henle (proximal straight tubule) *Tubulus proximalis pars recta*

Thin descending limb of loop of Henle *Crus descendens attenuatum ansae nephroni*

Thin ascending limb of loop of Henle *Crus ascendens attenuatum ansae nephroni*

KIDNEY NEPHRON

The functional units of the kidneys are microscopic structures called nephrons, of which there are estimated to be about 1.2 million in each kidney. The nephrons filter the blood, producing a liquid (called the filtrate) containing minerals, wastes, and water.

[~] = no direct Latin equivalent

Controlling Fluid Balance

MAINTAINING FLUID BALANCE IN THE BODY

When water levels in the blood drop too low, the hypothalamus instructs the posterior pituitary gland to release antidiuretic hormone (ADH). This makes the kidneys retain water and reabsorb it into the blood, and decreases urine production. When the body has returned to a normal state of hydration, the hypothalamus tells the pituitary to slow ADH secretion, the kidneys keep less water in the blood, and the bladder releases urine again.

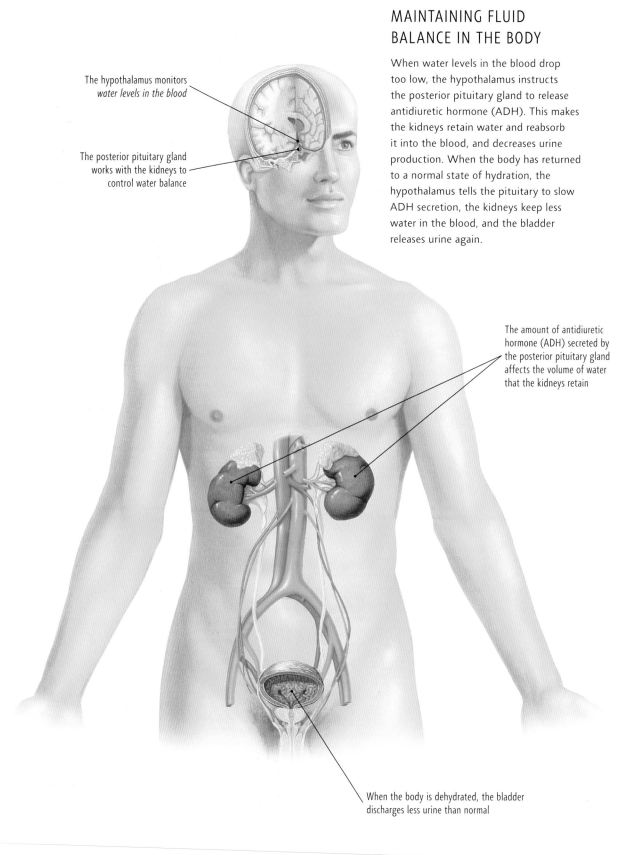

The hypothalamus monitors *water levels in the blood*

The posterior pituitary gland works with the kidneys to control water balance

The amount of antidiuretic hormone (ADH) secreted by the posterior pituitary gland affects the volume of water that the kidneys retain

When the body is dehydrated, the bladder discharges less urine than normal

LOCATION OF THE HYPOTHALAMUS AND POSTERIOR PITUITARY GLAND

Hypothalamus
Hypothalamus

Posterior pituitary gland
Neurohypophysis

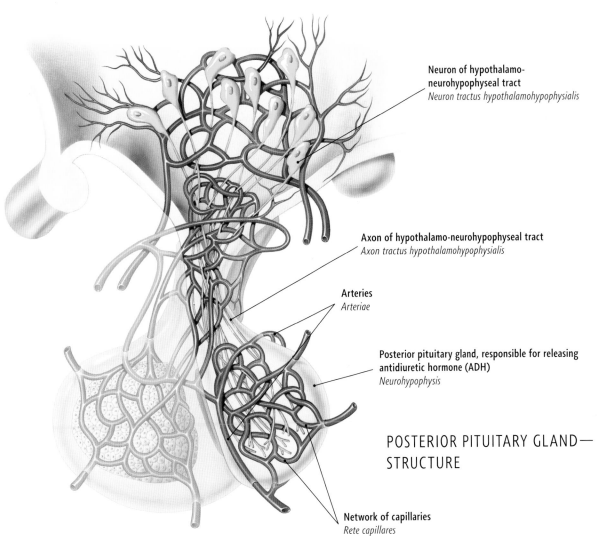

Neuron of hypothalamo-neurohypophyseal tract
Neuron tractus hypothalamohypophysialis

Axon of hypothalamo-neurohypophyseal tract
Axon tractus hypothalamohypophysialis

Arteries
Arteriae

Posterior pituitary gland, responsible for releasing antidiuretic hormone (ADH)
Neurohypophysis

POSTERIOR PITUITARY GLAND— STRUCTURE

Network of capillaries
Rete capillares

[~] = no direct Latin equivalent

The Endocrine System

The Endocrine System

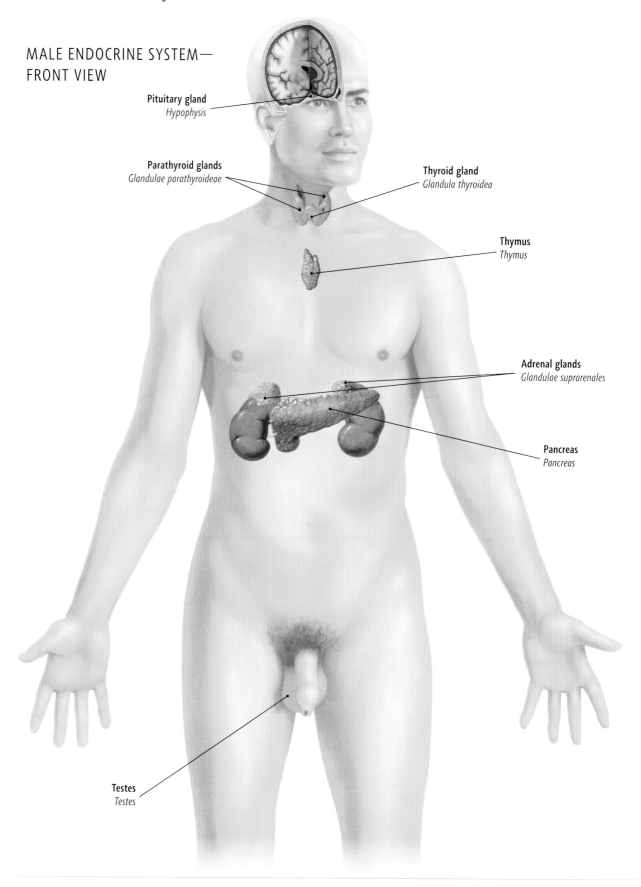

MALE ENDOCRINE SYSTEM—
FRONT VIEW

Pituitary gland
Hypophysis

Parathyroid glands
Glandulae parathyroideae

Thyroid gland
Glandula thyroidea

Thymus
Thymus

Adrenal glands
Glandulae suprarenales

Pancreas
Pancreas

Testes
Testes

FEMALE ENDOCRINE SYSTEM— FRONT VIEW

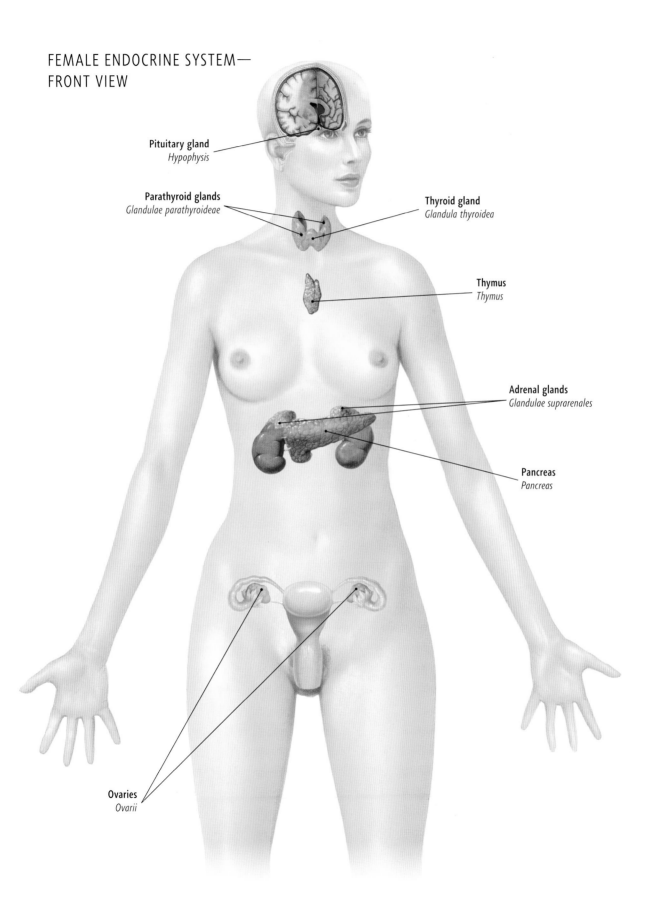

Pituitary gland
Hypophysis

Parathyroid glands
Glandulae parathyroideae

Thyroid gland
Glandula thyroidea

Thymus
Thymus

Adrenal glands
Glandulae suprarenales

Pancreas
Pancreas

Ovaries
Ovarii

Pituitary Gland

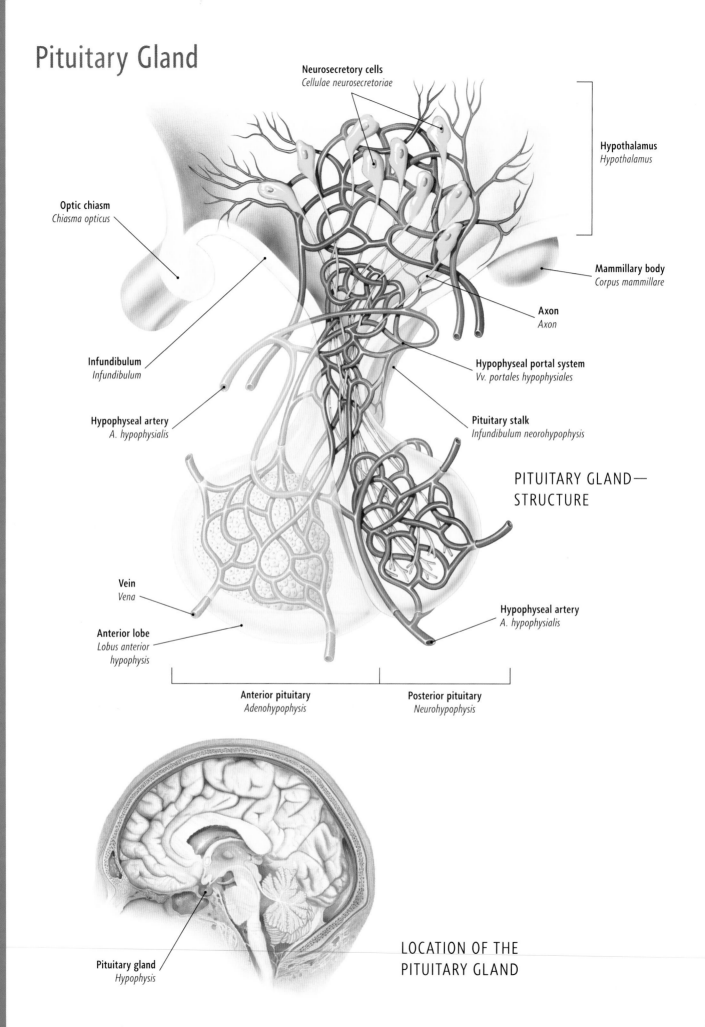

Neurosecretory cells
Cellulae neurosecretoriae

Hypothalamus
Hypothalamus

Optic chiasm
Chiasma opticus

Mammillary body
Corpus mammillare

Axon
Axon

Infundibulum
Infundibulum

Hypophyseal portal system
Vv. portales hypophysiales

Hypophyseal artery
A. hypophysialis

Pituitary stalk
Infundibulum neorohypophysis

PITUITARY GLAND—
STRUCTURE

Vein
Vena

Hypophyseal artery
A. hypophysialis

Anterior lobe
*Lobus anterior
hypophysis*

Anterior pituitary
Adenohypophysis

Posterior pituitary
Neurohypophysis

Pituitary gland
Hypophysis

LOCATION OF THE
PITUITARY GLAND

GLANDS AND ORGANS AFFECTED BY THE PITUITARY GLAND

The pituitary gland exerts its effects on organs and tissues throughout the body by means of organic chemicals called hormones. This illustration shows the organs and tissues affected by the pituitary gland, and the specific hormones involved.

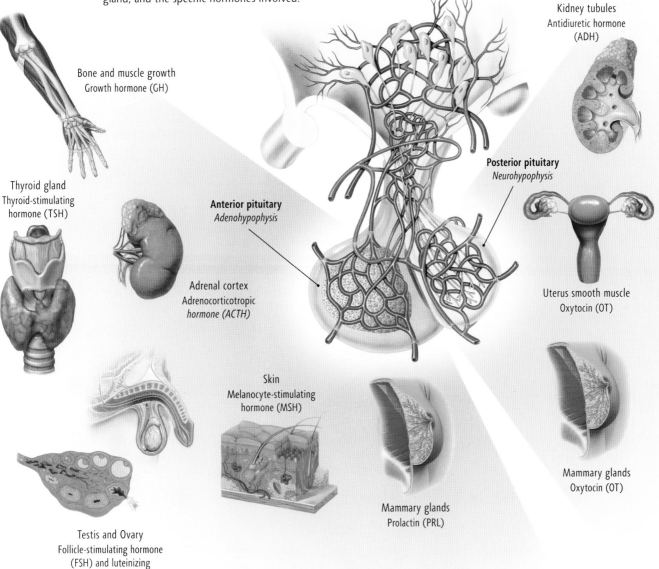

Bone and muscle growth
Growth hormone (GH)

Kidney tubules
Antidiuretic hormone
(ADH)

Thyroid gland
Thyroid-stimulating
hormone (TSH)

Anterior pituitary
Adenohypophysis

Posterior pituitary
Neurohypophysis

Adrenal cortex
Adrenocorticotropic
hormone (ACTH)

Uterus smooth muscle
Oxytocin (OT)

Skin
Melanocyte-stimulating
hormone (MSH)

Mammary glands
Oxytocin (OT)

Testis and Ovary
Follicle-stimulating hormone
(FSH) and luteinizing
hormone (LH)

Mammary glands
Prolactin (PRL)

Endocrine Glands

LOCATION OF THE PINEAL GLAND

The pineal gland is found deep inside the brain. It produces melatonin, thought to be involved in regulating the body's sleep–wake "clock"— melatonin production is highest during a person's normal sleeping hours, and drops off as the body begins to wake.

Corpus callosum
Corpus callosum

Thalamus
Thalamus

Pineal gland
Glandula pinealis

Upper and lower colliculi
Colliculi superior et inferior

LOCATION OF THE THYROID GLAND

The largest of the endocrine glands, the thyroid is situated at the front of the trachea in the neck. It secretes thyroid hormone; the main function of this hormone is to determine the metabolic rate of the body's tissues.

Thyroid gland
Glandula thyroidea

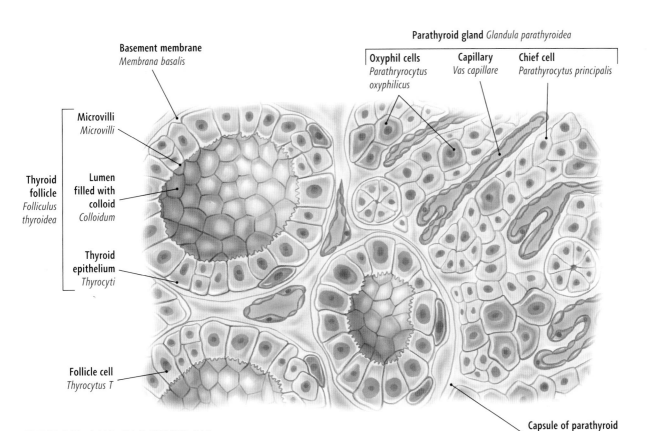

Basement membrane
Membrana basalis

Parathyroid gland *Glandula parathyroidea*

Oxyphil cells
Parathryrocytus oxyphilicus

Capillary
Vas capillare

Chief cell
Parathyrocytus principalis

Microvilli
Microvilli

Thyroid follicle
Folliculus thyroidea

Lumen filled with colloid
Colloidum

Thyroid epithelium
Thyrocyti

Follicle cell
Thyrocytus T

Capsule of parathyroid
Capsula parathyroidea

THYROID AND PARATHYROID GLANDS—MICROSTRUCTURE

Thyroid gland cells are separated from the cells of the parathyroid glands by a dense capsule of fibers. The thyroid gland comprises many follicles, each consisting of thyroid epithelium cells arranged around a cavity (lumen). The parathyroid glands contain two different cells: chief cells and oxyphil cells.

LOCATION OF THE PARATHYROID GLANDS

The parathyroid glands are four (or occasionally three) pea-sized endocrine glands that lie just behind the thyroid gland in the neck. They secrete parathyroid hormone, which controls calcium levels in the blood.

Parathyroid glands
Glandulae parathyroideae

Endocrine Glands

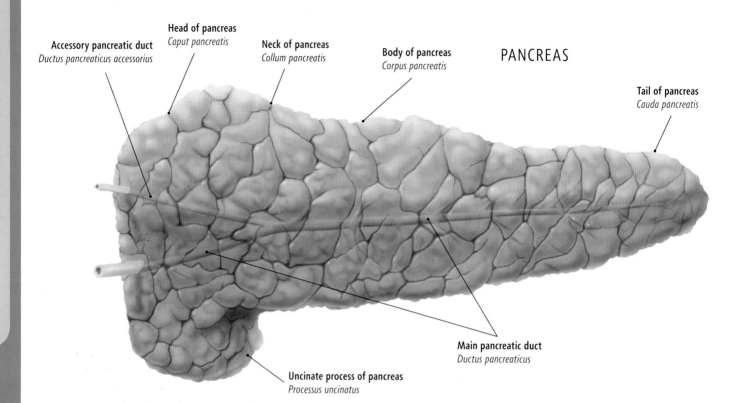

PANCREAS

Accessory pancreatic duct
Ductus pancreaticus accessorius

Head of pancreas
Caput pancreatis

Neck of pancreas
Collum pancreatis

Body of pancreas
Corpus pancreatis

Tail of pancreas
Cauda pancreatis

Main pancreatic duct
Ductus pancreaticus

Uncinate process of pancreas
Processus uncinatus

Insuloacinar portal vessels
~

Beta cells (producing insulin)
Endocrinocyti B

Islet of Langerhans
Insula pancreatica

PANCREAS: ENDOCRINE CELLS

Clusters of hormone-producing endocrine
cells—the islets of Langerhans—are scattered
throughout the pancreas. Alpha cells secrete
glucagon, which elevates blood sugar. Beta cells
secrete insulin, which decreases blood sugar.
Delta cells secrete somatostatin, which can
inhibit the release of both glucagon and insulin.

Delta cells (producing somatostatin)
Endocrinocyti D

Alpha cells (producing glucagon)
Endocrinocyti A

[~] = no direct Latin equivalent

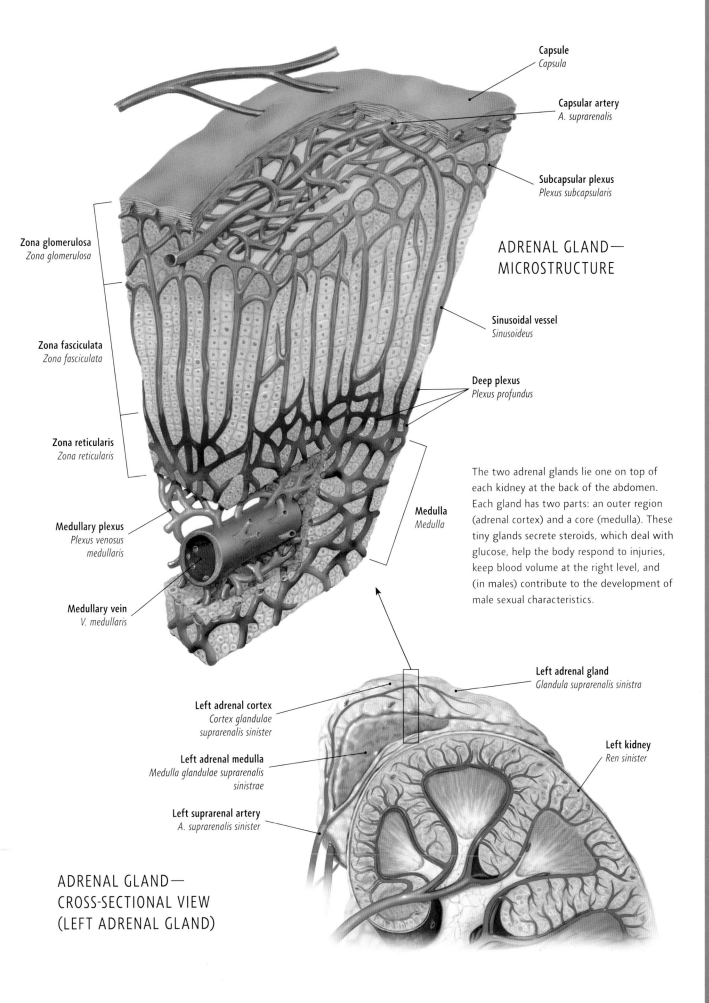

Capsule
Capsula

Capsular artery
A. suprarenalis

Subcapsular plexus
Plexus subcapsularis

ADRENAL GLAND— MICROSTRUCTURE

Zona glomerulosa
Zona glomerulosa

Sinusoidal vessel
Sinusoideus

Zona fasciculata
Zona fasciculata

Deep plexus
Plexus profundus

Zona reticularis
Zona reticularis

Medulla
Medulla

Medullary plexus
Plexus venosus medullaris

The two adrenal glands lie one on top of each kidney at the back of the abdomen. Each gland has two parts: an outer region (adrenal cortex) and a core (medulla). These tiny glands secrete steroids, which deal with glucose, help the body respond to injuries, keep blood volume at the right level, and (in males) contribute to the development of male sexual characteristics.

Medullary vein
V. medullaris

Left adrenal gland
Glandula suprarenalis sinistra

Left adrenal cortex
Cortex glandulae suprarenalis sinister

Left kidney
Ren sinister

Left adrenal medulla
Medulla glandulae suprarenalis sinistrae

Left suprarenal artery
A. suprarenalis sinister

ADRENAL GLAND— CROSS-SECTIONAL VIEW (LEFT ADRENAL GLAND)

255

Male and Female Endocrine Glands

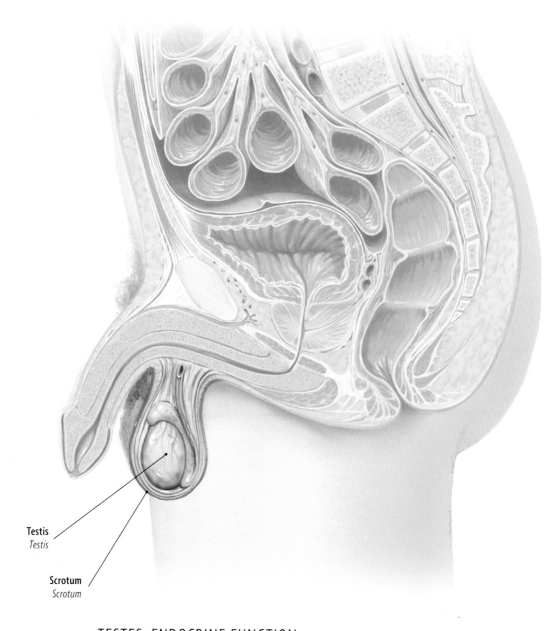

Testis
Testis

Scrotum
Scrotum

TESTES: ENDOCRINE FUNCTION

The testes are two ovoid organs contained in the scrotum, a sac that lies directly behind and beneath the penis. They produce testosterone, which is responsible for the development of secondary sexual characteristics in the male—it stimulates the growth of facial and pubic hair, deepens the voice, and increases muscle tone.

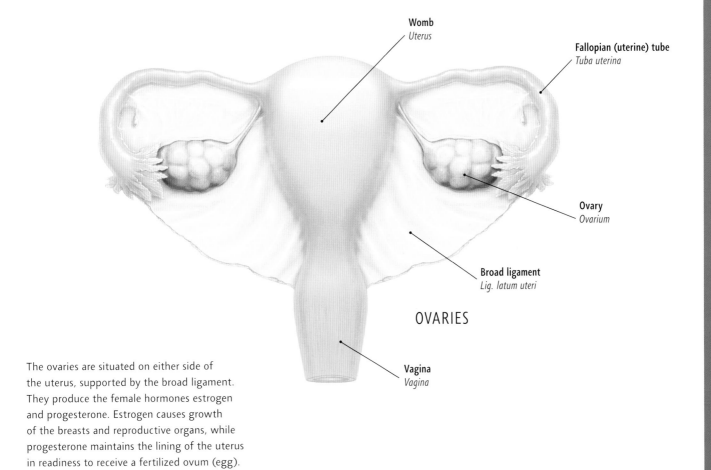

Womb
Uterus

Fallopian (uterine) tube
Tuba uterina

Ovary
Ovarium

Broad ligament
Lig. latum uteri

OVARIES

Vagina
Vagina

The ovaries are situated on either side of
the uterus, supported by the broad ligament.
They produce the female hormones estrogen
and progesterone. Estrogen causes growth
of the breasts and reproductive organs, while
progesterone maintains the lining of the uterus
in readiness to receive a fertilized ovum (egg).

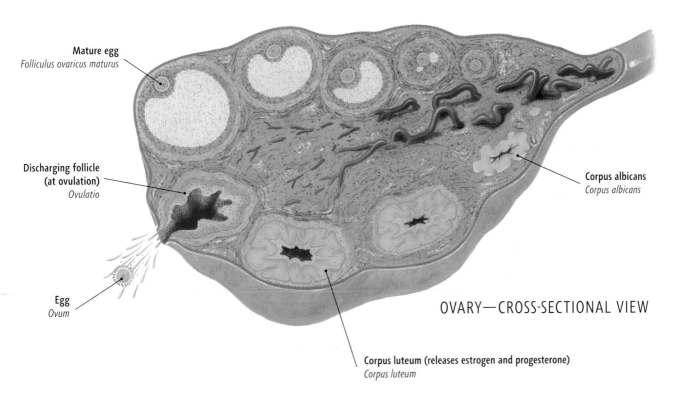

Mature egg
Folliculus ovaricus maturus

Discharging follicle
(at ovulation)
Ovulatio

Corpus albicans
Corpus albicans

Egg
Ovum

OVARY—CROSS-SECTIONAL VIEW

Corpus luteum (releases estrogen and progesterone)
Corpus luteum

[~] = no direct Latin equivalent

The Reproductive System

Male Reproductive System

ORGANS OF MALE REPRODUCTION—
FRONT VIEW

Penis *Penis*

Testis *Testis*

Prostate
Prostata

Penis
Penis

Vas deferens
Ductus deferens

Testis
Testis

Epididymis
Epididymis

Prostate
Prostata

Scrotum
Scrotum

MALE REPRODUCTIVE SYSTEM—
CROSS-SECTIONAL VIEW

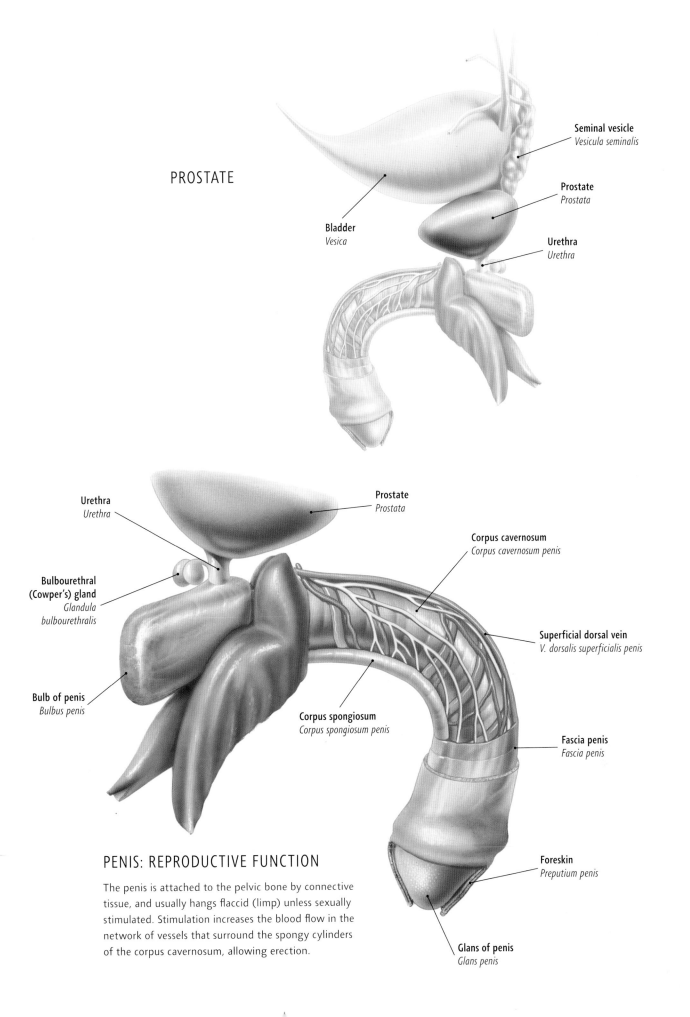

PROSTATE

Seminal vesicle
Vesicula seminalis

Prostate
Prostata

Bladder
Vesica

Urethra
Urethra

Urethra
Urethra

Prostate
Prostata

Corpus cavernosum
Corpus cavernosum penis

**Bulbourethral
(Cowper's) gland**
*Glandula
bulbourethralis*

Superficial dorsal vein
V. dorsalis superficialis penis

Bulb of penis
Bulbus penis

Corpus spongiosum
Corpus spongiosum penis

Fascia penis
Fascia penis

Foreskin
Preputium penis

PENIS: REPRODUCTIVE FUNCTION

The penis is attached to the pelvic bone by connective
tissue, and usually hangs flaccid (limp) unless sexually
stimulated. Stimulation increases the blood flow in the
network of vessels that surround the spongy cylinders
of the corpus cavernosum, allowing erection.

Glans of penis
Glans penis

Male Reproductive System

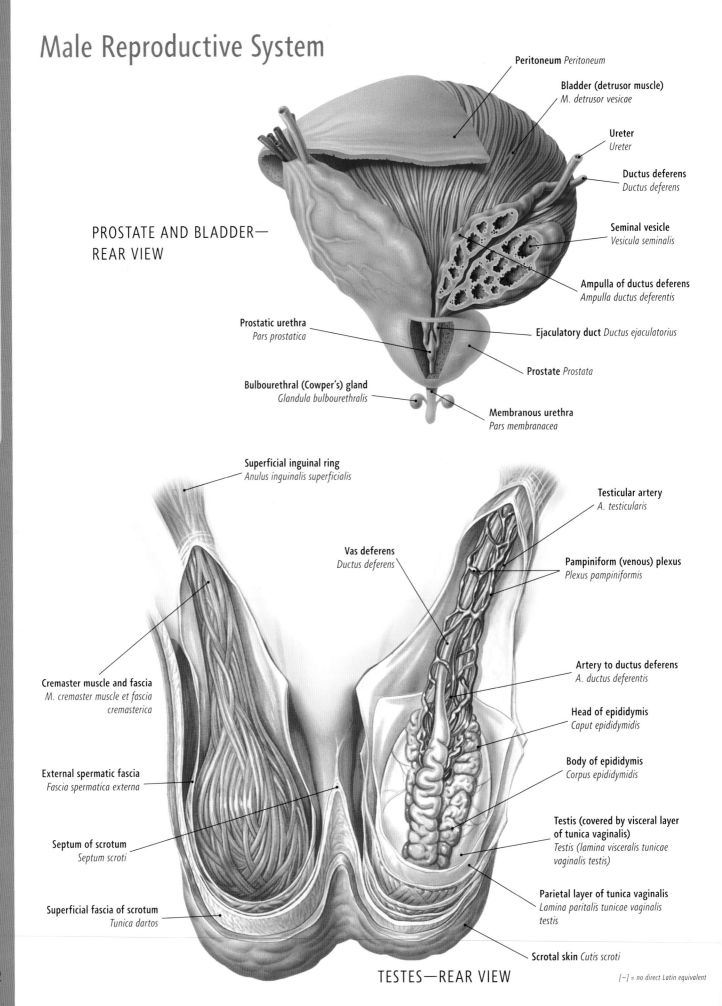

Peritoneum *Peritoneum*

Bladder (detrusor muscle)
M. detrusor vesicae

Ureter
Ureter

Ductus deferens
Ductus deferens

Seminal vesicle
Vesicula seminalis

Ampulla of ductus deferens
Ampulla ductus deferentis

Ejaculatory duct *Ductus ejaculatorius*

Prostate *Prostata*

Membranous urethra
Pars membranacea

PROSTATE AND BLADDER—
REAR VIEW

Prostatic urethra
Pars prostatica

Bulbourethral (Cowper's) gland
Glandula bulbourethralis

Superficial inguinal ring
Anulus inguinalis superficialis

Testicular artery
A. testicularis

Vas deferens
Ductus deferens

Pampiniform (venous) plexus
Plexus pampiniformis

Artery to ductus deferens
A. ductus deferentis

Head of epididymis
Caput epididymidis

Body of epididymis
Corpus epididymidis

Cremaster muscle and fascia
*M. cremaster muscle et fascia
cremasterica*

External spermatic fascia
Fascia spermatica externa

Testis (covered by visceral layer
of tunica vaginalis)
*Testis (lamina visceralis tunicae
vaginalis testis)*

Septum of scrotum
Septum scroti

Parietal layer of tunica vaginalis
*Lamina paritalis tunicae vaginalis
testis*

Superficial fascia of scrotum
Tunica dartos

Scrotal skin *Cutis scroti*

TESTES—REAR VIEW

[~] = no direct Latin equivalent

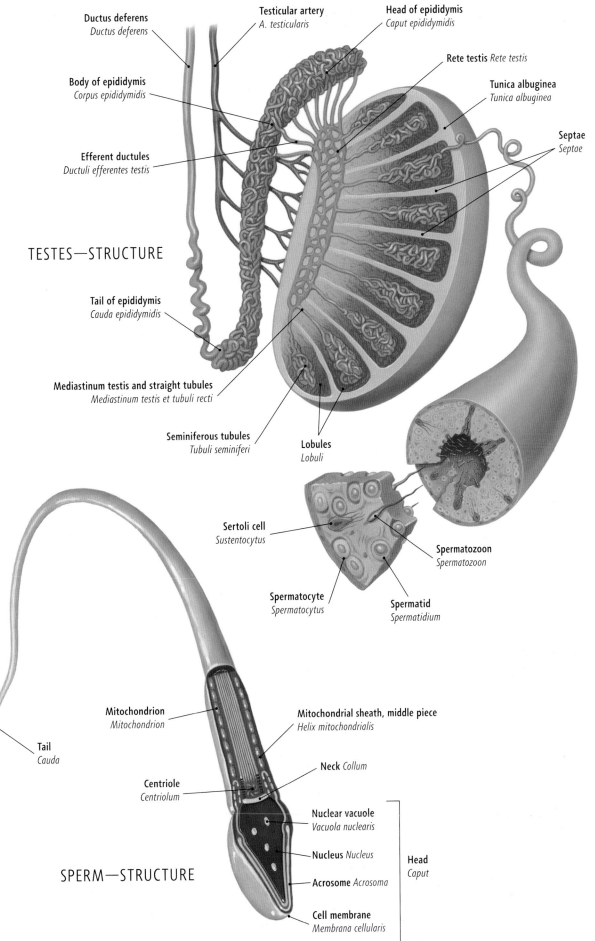

Ductus deferens
Ductus deferens

Testicular artery
A. testicularis

Head of epididymis
Caput epididymidis

Rete testis *Rete testis*

Body of epididymis
Corpus epididymidis

Tunica albuginea
Tunica albuginea

Septae
Septae

Efferent ductules
Ductuli efferentes testis

TESTES—STRUCTURE

Tail of epididymis
Cauda epididymidis

Mediastinum testis and straight tubules
Mediastinum testis et tubuli recti

Seminiferous tubules
Tubuli seminiferi

Lobules
Lobuli

Sertoli cell
Sustentocytus

Spermatozoon
Spermatozoon

Spermatocyte
Spermatocytus

Spermatid
Spermatidium

Mitochondrion
Mitochondrion

Mitochondrial sheath, middle piece
Helix mitochondrialis

Tail
Cauda

Neck *Collum*

Centriole
Centriolum

Nuclear vacuole
Vacuola nuclearis

Nucleus *Nucleus*

Head
Caput

SPERM—STRUCTURE

Acrosome *Acrosoma*

Cell membrane
Membrana cellularis

[~] = no direct Latin equivalent

Female Reproductive System

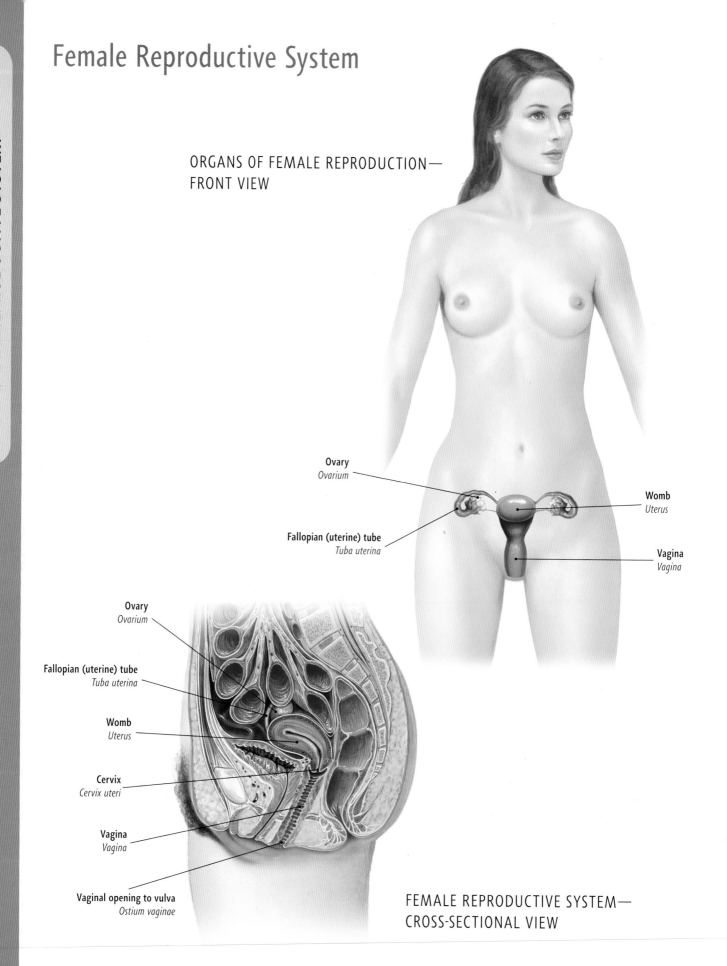

ORGANS OF FEMALE REPRODUCTION—
FRONT VIEW

Ovary
Ovarium

Womb
Uterus

Fallopian (uterine) tube
Tuba uterina

Vagina
Vagina

Ovary
Ovarium

Fallopian (uterine) tube
Tuba uterina

Womb
Uterus

Cervix
Cervix uteri

Vagina
Vagina

Vaginal opening to vulva
Ostium vaginae

FEMALE REPRODUCTIVE SYSTEM—
CROSS-SECTIONAL VIEW

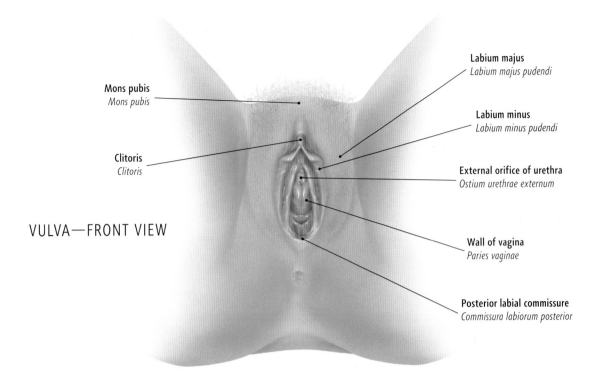

Mons pubis
Mons pubis

Clitoris
Clitoris

Labium majus
Labium majus pudendi

Labium minus
Labium minus pudendi

External orifice of urethra
Ostium urethrae externum

Wall of vagina
Paries vaginae

Posterior labial commissure
Commissura labiorum posterior

VULVA—FRONT VIEW

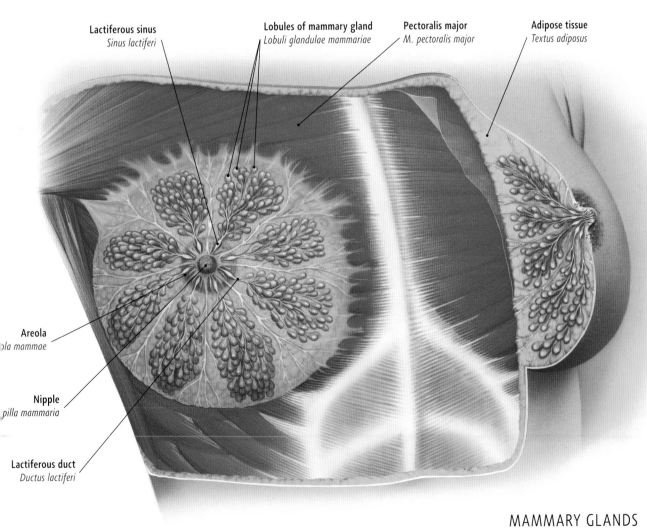

Lactiferous sinus
Sinus lactiferi

Lobules of mammary gland
Lobuli glandulae mammariae

Pectoralis major
M. pectoralis major

Adipose tissue
Textus adiposus

Areola
ola mammae

Nipple
pilla mammaria

Lactiferous duct
Ductus lactiferi

MAMMARY GLANDS

Menstrual Cycle

CYCLE REGULATION

The hypothalamus and the anterior pituitary gland regulate the menstrual cycle. During each cycle the anterior pituitary gland releases follicle-stimulating hormone (FSH) and luteinizing hormone (LH), which trigger follicles (egg sacs) in the ovaries to mature and release estrogen and progesterone.

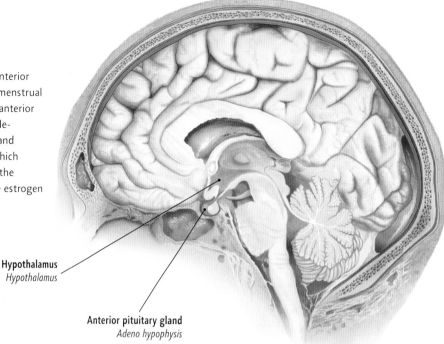

Hypothalamus
Hypothalamus

Anterior pituitary gland
Adeno hypophysis

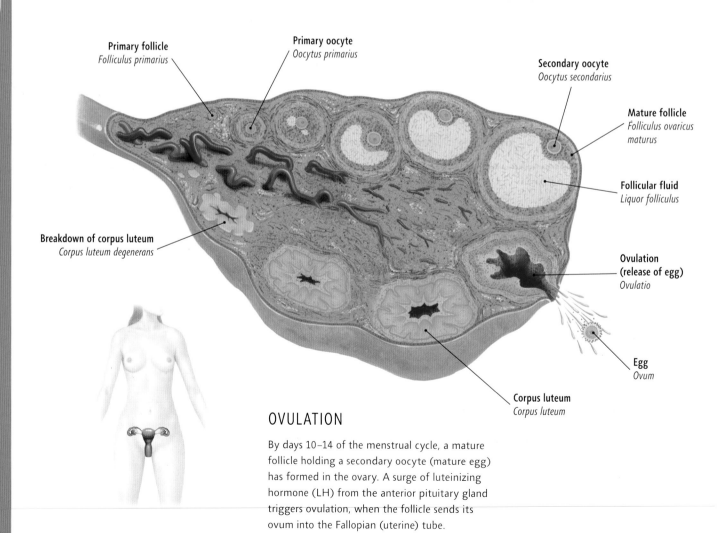

Primary follicle
Folliculus primarius

Primary oocyte
Oocytus primarius

Secondary oocyte
Oocytus secondarius

Mature follicle
Folliculus ovaricus maturus

Follicular fluid
Liquor folliculus

Breakdown of corpus luteum
Corpus luteum degenerans

Ovulation (release of egg)
Ovulatio

Egg
Ovum

Corpus luteum
Corpus luteum

OVULATION

By days 10–14 of the menstrual cycle, a mature follicle holding a secondary oocyte (mature egg) has formed in the ovary. A surge of luteinizing hormone (LH) from the anterior pituitary gland triggers ovulation, when the follicle sends its ovum into the Fallopian (uterine) tube.

a Days 1-6
Menstruation

During menstruation, the lining of the uterus (endometrium) breaks down and is discharged.

b Days 7–13
Proliferative phase

At the start of the proliferative phase, cells begin to repair the lining of the uterus, and follicles in the ovary begin to form an ovum (egg).

Fallopian (uterine) tube
Tuba uterina

Womb
Uterus

Endometrium
Endometrium

Ovary
Ovarium

Egg
Ovum

Menstrual fluid
Liquor mensium

MENSTRUAL CYCLE

Egg
Ovum

Egg
Ovum

Ovary
Ovarium

Womb
Uterus

Ovary
Ovarium

d Days 15–28
Secretory phase

During the secretory phase, the ovum travels along the Fallopian (uterine) tube toward the uterus, and hormones thicken the uterus lining in readiness to support a fertilized ovum. If the ovum is not fertilized, hormone levels fall and blood vessels in the uterus constrict.

c Day 14
Ovulation

Ovulation takes place on around day 14 of the cycle, and the ovary releases its ovum into the Fallopian (uterine) tube.

[~] = no direct Latin equivalent

Conception and Early Pregnancy

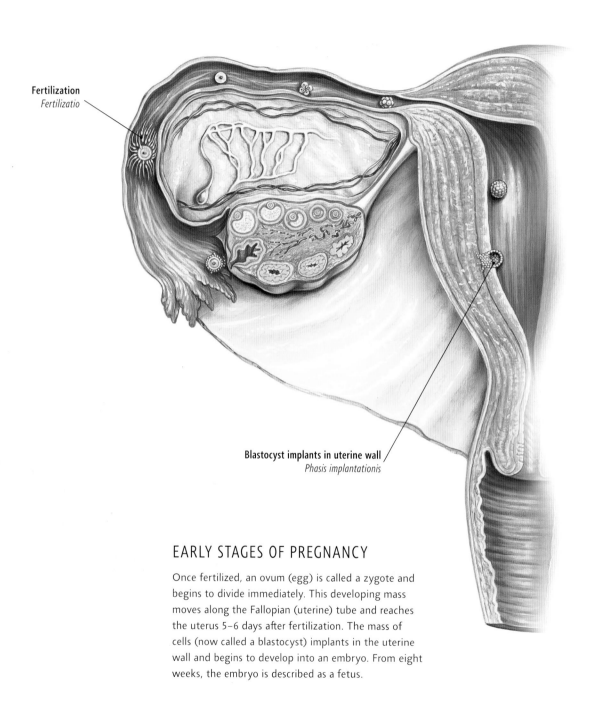

Fertilization
Fertilizatio

Blastocyst implants in uterine wall
Phasis implantationis

EARLY STAGES OF PREGNANCY

Once fertilized, an ovum (egg) is called a zygote and begins to divide immediately. This developing mass moves along the Fallopian (uterine) tube and reaches the uterus 5–6 days after fertilization. The mass of cells (now called a blastocyst) implants in the uterine wall and begins to develop into an embryo. From eight weeks, the embryo is described as a fetus.

[~] = no direct Latin equivalent

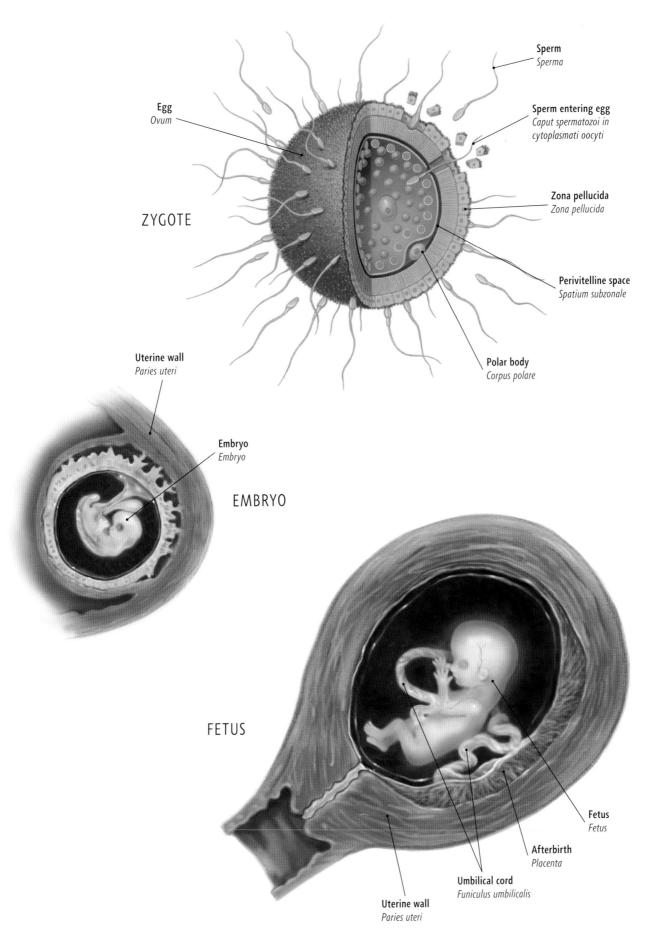

Sperm
Sperma

Egg
Ovum

Sperm entering egg
*Caput spermatozoi in
cytoplasmati oocyti*

ZYGOTE

Zona pellucida
Zona pellucida

Perivitelline space
Spatium subzonale

Polar body
Corpus polare

Uterine wall
Paries uteri

Embryo
Embryo

EMBRYO

FETUS

Fetus
Fetus

Afterbirth
Placenta

Umbilical cord
Funiculus umbilicalis

Uterine wall
Paries uteri

Fetal Development Cycle

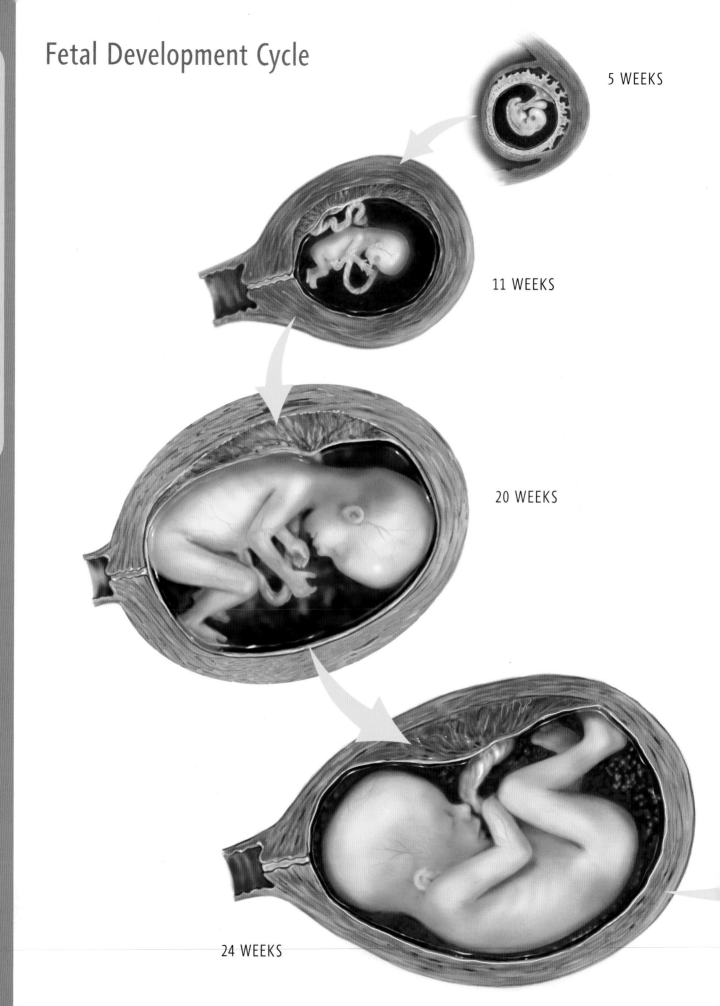

5 WEEKS

11 WEEKS

20 WEEKS

24 WEEKS

FULL TERM

32 WEEKS

Fetal Skull and Bone Development

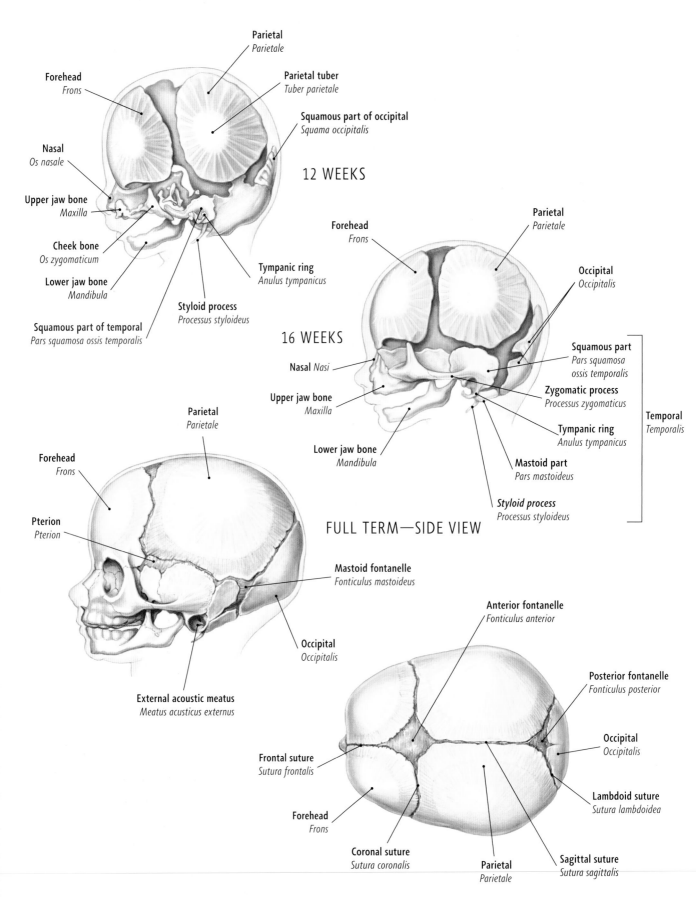

Parietal
Parietale

Forehead
Frons

Parietal tuber
Tuber parietale

Squamous part of occipital
Squama occipitalis

Nasal
Os nasale

12 WEEKS

Upper jaw bone
Maxilla

Cheek bone
Os zygomaticum

Lower jaw bone
Mandibula

Tympanic ring
Anulus tympanicus

Squamous part of temporal
Pars squamosa ossis temporalis

Styloid process
Processus styloideus

Forehead
Frons

Parietal
Parietale

Occipital
Occipitalis

16 WEEKS

Nasal *Nasi*

Squamous part
Pars squamosa ossis temporalis

Upper jaw bone
Maxilla

Zygomatic process
Processus zygomaticus

Temporal
Temporalis

Tympanic ring
Anulus tympanicus

Lower jaw bone
Mandibula

Mastoid part
Pars mastoideus

Styloid process
Processus styloideus

Parietal
Parietale

FULL TERM—SIDE VIEW

Forehead
Frons

Mastoid fontanelle
Fonticulus mastoideus

Pterion
Pterion

Anterior fontanelle
Fonticulus anterior

Occipital
Occipitalis

Posterior fontanelle
Fonticulus posterior

External acoustic meatus
Meatus acusticus externus

Frontal suture
Sutura frontalis

Occipital
Occipitalis

Forehead
Frons

Lambdoid suture
Sutura lambdoidea

Coronal suture
Sutura coronalis

Parietal
Parietale

Sagittal suture
Sutura sagittalis

FULL TERM—VIEW FROM ABOVE

Secondary ossification centers (epiphyses)
Centrum ossificationis secondarium

Epiphyseal (growth) plates
Laminae epiphysiales

Superficial layer of bone
Lamina superficialis ossae

Primary ossification center
Centrum ossificationis primarium

Hyaline cartilage
Cartilago hyalina

Primary ossification center
Centrum ossificationis primarium

Spongy bone
Substantia spongiosa

Marrow cavity
Cavitas medullaris

Compact bone
Substantia compacta

Epiphyseal (growth) plate
Lamina epiphysialis

BONE FORMATION IN CHILDHOOD

During childhood, the long bones—such as those in the arm and leg—start as cartilage "models" that are then gradually converted into bone (ossified). The centers of ossification are the shaft (diaphysis) and regions near the ends of the bone (epiphyses). Between the diaphysis and epiphyses is a growth plate where the increase in bone length takes place.

Fetal Brain Development

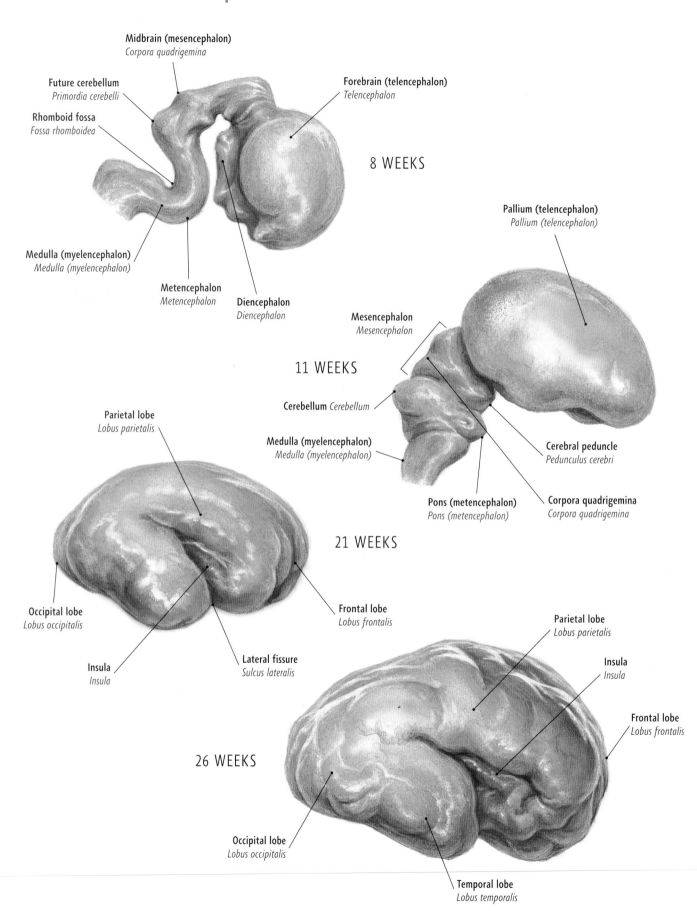

Midbrain (mesencephalon)
Corpora quadrigemina

Future cerebellum
Primordia cerebelli

Rhomboid fossa
Fossa rhomboidea

Forebrain (telencephalon)
Telencephalon

8 WEEKS

Medulla (myelencephalon)
Medulla (myelencephalon)

Metencephalon
Metencephalon

Diencephalon
Diencephalon

Pallium (telencephalon)
Pallium (telencephalon)

Mesencephalon
Mesencephalon

11 WEEKS

Cerebellum *Cerebellum*

Medulla (myelencephalon)
Medulla (myelencephalon)

Cerebral peduncle
Pedunculus cerebri

Corpora quadrigemina
Corpora quadrigemina

Pons (metencephalon)
Pons (metencephalon)

Parietal lobe
Lobus parietalis

21 WEEKS

Occipital lobe
Lobus occipitalis

Insula
Insula

Lateral fissure
Sulcus lateralis

Frontal lobe
Lobus frontalis

Parietal lobe
Lobus parietalis

Insula
Insula

Frontal lobe
Lobus frontalis

26 WEEKS

Occipital lobe
Lobus occipitalis

Temporal lobe
Lobus temporalis

[~] = no direct Latin equivalent

30 WEEKS

Parietal lobe
Lobus parietalis

Central sulcus
Sulcus centralis

Occipital lobe
Lobus occipitalis

Lateral fissure
Sulcus lateralis

Temporal lobe
Lobus temporalis

Orbital surface of frontal lobe
Facies orbitalis lobi frontalis

40 WEEKS

Postcentral sulcus
Sulcus postcentralis

Central sulcus
Sulcus centralis

Precentral sulcus
Sulcus precentralis

Occipital lobe
Lobus occipitalis

Frontal lobe
Lobus frontalis

Temporal lobe
Lobus temporalis

Lateral fissure
Sulcus lateralis

275

Fetal Sex Differentiation

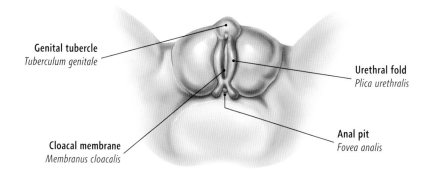

Genital tubercle
Tuberculum genitale

Urethral fold
Plica urethralis

Cloacal membrane
Membranus cloacalis

Anal pit
Fovea analis

UNDIFFERENTIATED (UP TO 12 WEEKS)

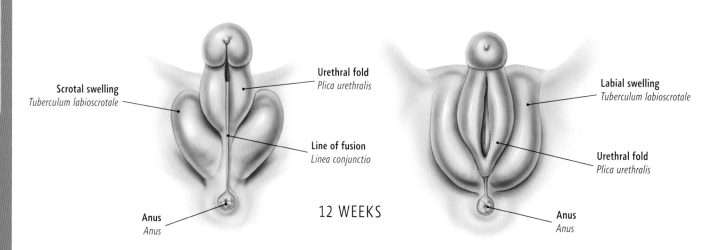

Scrotal swelling
Tuberculum labioscrotale

Urethral fold
Plica urethralis

Line of fusion
Linea conjunctio

Anus
Anus

12 WEEKS

Labial swelling
Tuberculum labioscrotale

Urethral fold
Plica urethralis

Anus
Anus

Male

Female

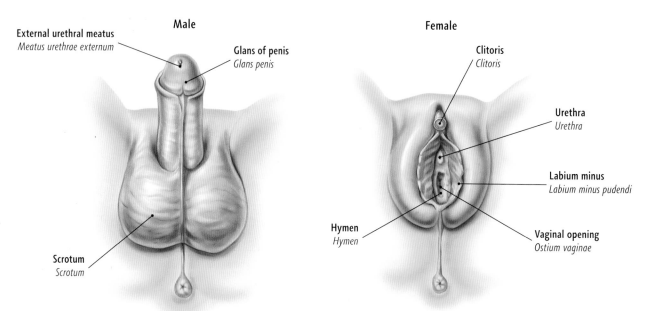

External urethral meatus
Meatus urethrae externum

Glans of penis
Glans penis

Scrotum
Scrotum

Clitoris
Clitoris

Urethra
Urethra

Labium minus
Labium minus pudendi

Hymen
Hymen

Vaginal opening
Ostium vaginae

FULLY DEVELOPED

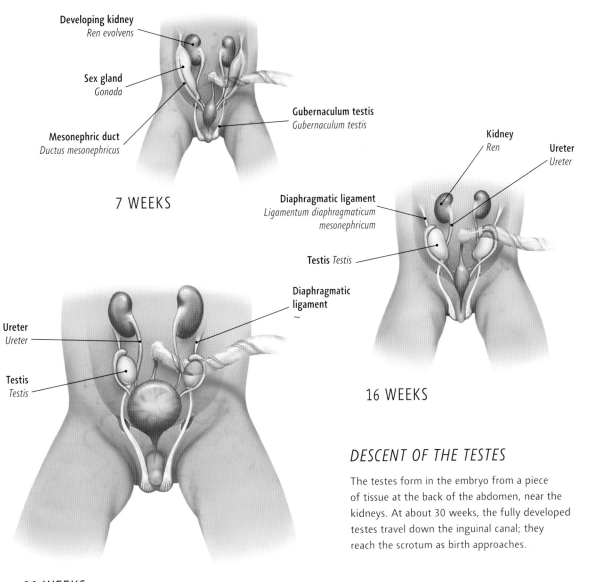

Developing kidney
Ren evolvens

Sex gland
Gonada

Mesonephric duct
Ductus mesonephricus

Gubernaculum testis
Gubernaculum testis

7 WEEKS

Kidney
Ren

Ureter
Ureter

Diaphragmatic ligament
Ligamentum diaphragmaticum mesonephricum

Testis *Testis*

16 WEEKS

Diaphragmatic ligament
~

Ureter
Ureter

Testis
Testis

30 WEEKS

DESCENT OF THE TESTES

The testes form in the embryo from a piece of tissue at the back of the abdomen, near the kidneys. At about 30 weeks, the fully developed testes travel down the inguinal canal; they reach the scrotum as birth approaches.

Ureter
Ureter

Bladder
Vesica

Epididymis
Epididymis

Vas deferens
Ductus deferens

Testis
Testis

FULLY DEVELOPED

[~] = no direct Latin equivalent

Late Pregnancy

FULL TERM

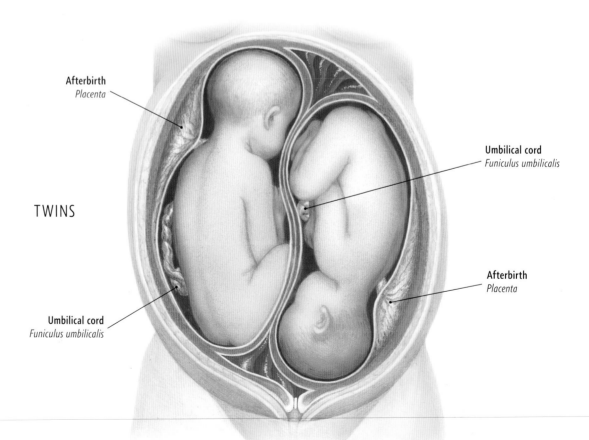

TWINS

Afterbirth
Placenta

Umbilical cord
Funiculus umbilicalis

Afterbirth
Placenta

Umbilical cord
Funiculus umbilicalis

Afterbirth
Placenta

Umbilical cord
Funiculus umbilicalis

LOCATION OF THE PLACENTA

Umbilical vein
V. umbilicalis

Amnion
Amnion

Umbilical cord
Funiculus umbilicalis

PLACENTA—FRONT VIEW

Umbilical artery
A. umbilicalis

Cotyledon (on maternal side)
Cotyledo maternalis

Umbilical vein
V. umbilicalis

Umbilical cord *Funiculus umbilicalis*

Umbilical arteries *Aa. umbilicales*

Area filled with
maternal blood
Spatium intervillosum

Syncytial trophoblast
Syncytiotropoblastus

Afterbirth
Placenta

Chorionic villi
Chorion frondosum

PLACENTA—CROSS-SECTIONAL VIEW

The placenta contains tissue from both the mother
and baby, allowing for the diffusion of nutrients and
oxygen and the removal of fetal waste.

Endometrium
Endometrium

Myometrium
Myometrium

Maternal blood vessels
Vasa sanguinea maternae

[~] = no direct Latin equivalent

Childbirth

Umbilical cord
Funiculus umbilicalis

Head engaged in pelvis
Caput occupatus in pelve

Symphysis pubis of pelvis
Symphysis pubica

Cervix
Cervix

Vagina
Vagina

Cervical canal
Canalis cervicis uteri

PRIOR TO BIRTH

Afterbirth
Placenta

Sacrum
Os sacrum

Dilated cervix
Cervix dilatatus

DILATION

[~] = no direct Latin equivalent

PRESENTATION OF THE HEAD

Afterbirth
Placenta

EXPULSION OF THE PLACENTA

Time of Your Life: Female

At about 10 years of age, girls have a growth spurt, and pubic hair and underarm hair start to grow a year or two later. Soon the reproductive system develops, with the first period arriving around the age of 13. By 18 the body is approaching maturity and from there it continues to change, but not grow. From the late 40s the production of eggs and sex hormones decreases, culminating in menopause at around the age of 50. Without the hormonal effects, the breasts and skin lose firmness, fat distribution changes, bones lose minerals, and height decreases.

BIRTH–6 MONTHS

6–12 MONTHS

20–30 YEARS   30–40 YEARS   40–50 YEARS

1–5 YEARS

6–11 YEARS

12–19 YEARS

50–65 YEARS

65–85 YEARS

85+ YEARS

Time of Your Life: Male

Boys' growth spurt occurs at around 13 or 14 years of age. Muscles begin to bulk up and body hair grows. The testes grow and produce sperm, and the voice deepens. As men mature the body reaches full muscular development, then starts to decline. The skin and muscles become softer, fat may increase, the prostate enlarges, production of male hormones and sperm reduces, and hair loss occurs.

BIRTH–6 MONTHS

6–12 MONTHS

20–30 YEARS

30–40 YEARS

40–50 YEARS

1–5 YEARS

6–11 YEARS

12–19 YEARS

50–65 YEARS

65–85 YEARS

85+ YEARS

Coloring workbook

Muscular System

1. _____
2. _____
3. _____
4. _____
5. _____
6. _____
7. _____
8. _____
9. _____
10. _____
11. _____
12. _____
13. _____

34. _____
33. _____
32. _____
31. _____
30. _____
29. _____
28. _____
27. _____
26. _____
25. _____
24. _____
23. _____
22. _____
21. _____
20. _____
19. _____
18. _____
17. _____
16. _____
15. _____
14. _____

MUSCULAR SYSTEM—
ANTERIOR VIEW

Answers

1. Temporalis, 2. Masseter, 3. Sternohyoid, 4. Sternocleidomastoid, 5. Pectoralis major, 6. Serratus anterior, 7. External abdominal oblique, 8. Brachioradialis, 9. Tensor fasciae latae, 10. Iliopsoas, 11. Pectineus, 12. Lumbricals, 13. Sartorius, 14. Extensor digitorum longus, 15. Soleus, 16. Tibialis anterior, 17. Gastrocnemius, 19. Quadriceps femoris, 20. Adductor magnus, 21. Adductor longus, 22. Flexor digitorum superficialis, 23. Tendon of palmaris longus, 24. Tendon of flexor carpi radialis, 25. Tendon of flexor carpi ulnaris, 26. Rectus abdominis, 27. Triceps brachii, 28. Brachialis, 29. Biceps brachii, 30. Deltoid, 31. Trapezius, 32. Orbicularis oris, 33. Orbicularis oculi, 34. Frontalis

MUSCULAR SYSTEM—
POSTERIOR VIEW

MUSCULAR SYSTEM—
LATERAL VIEW

42. _____

24. _____

23. _____

22. _____

41. _____

21. _____

1. _____

2. _____

3. _____

20. _____

40. _____

39. _____

38. _____

37. _____

36. _____

19. _____

35. _____

18. _____

17. _____

16. _____

34. _____

33. _____

32. _____

15. _____

14. _____

31. _____

30. _____

29. _____

13. _____

4. _____

5. _____

6. _____

7. _____

8. _____

9. _____

28. _____

27. _____

12. _____

11. _____

26. _____

10. _____

25. _____

Answers

1. Teres minor. 2. Teres major. 3. Triceps brachii. 4. Adductor magnus. 5. Vastus lateralis. 6. Long head of biceps femoris. 7. Semitendinosus. 8. Gracilis. 9. Semimembranosus. 10. Soleus. 11. Gastrocnemius. 12. Fibularis (peroneus) longus. 13. Semimembranosus. 14. Gluteus maximus. 15. Flexor carpi ulnaris. 16. Extensor pollicis brevis. 17. Abductor pollicis longus. 18. Latissimus dorsi. 19. External abdominal oblique. 20. Deltoid. 21. Trapezius. 22. Sternocleidomastoid. 23. Occipitalis. 24. Temporalis. 25. Tendo calcaneus (Achilles tendon). 26. Extensor digitorum longus. 27. Tibialis anterior. 28. Iliotibial tract. 29. Lateral head of gastrocnemius. 30. Extensor carpi ulnaris. 31. Quadriceps femoris (vastus lateralis). 32. Extensor digitorum. 33. Tensor fasciae latae. 34. Extensor carpi radialis longus. 35. Brachioradialis. 36. Biceps brachii. 37. Brachialis. 38. Serratus anterior. 39. Lateral head of triceps brachii. 40. Pectoralis major. 41. Levator scapulae. 42. Frontalis

287

Muscles of the Thorax and Abdomen

SUPERFICIAL AND DEEP
MUSCLES OF THE THORAX AND
ABDOMEN—ANTERIOR VIEW

10. _____

1. _____

2. _____

3. _____

4. _____

5. _____

6. _____

7. _____

9. _____

8. _____

Answers

1. Pectoralis major, 2. Pectoralis minor, 3. Internal intercostals, 4. Latissimus dorsi, 5. Internal abdominal oblique,
6. Rectus abdominis, 7. Transversus abdominis, 8. External abdominal oblique, 9. Serratus anterior, 10. Pectoralis major

INTERMEDIATE MUSCLES
OF THE BACK—
POSTERIOR VIEW

DEEP MUSCLES
OF THE BACK—
POSTERIOR VIEW

Muscles of the Upper Limb

1. _____

2. _____

3. _____

4. _____

5. _____

15. _____

6. _____

14. _____

7. _____

13. _____

12. _____

8. _____

9. _____

10. _____

11. _____

DEEP MUSCLES OF
THE UPPER LIMB—
ANTERIOR VIEW

SUPERFICIAL MUSCLES
OF THE UPPER LIMB—
ANTERIOR VIEW

Answers
1. Pectoralis major, 2. Deltoid, 3. Biceps brachii, 4. Brachialis, 5. Triceps brachii, 6. Pronator teres, 7. Brachioradialis, 8. Tendon of flexor carpi radialis, 9. Tendon of palmaris longus, 10. Tendon of flexor carpi ulnaris, 11. Flexor digitorum superficialis, 12. Flexor pollicis longus, 13. Flexor digitorum profundus, 14. Pronator teres, 15. Extensor carpi radialis longus

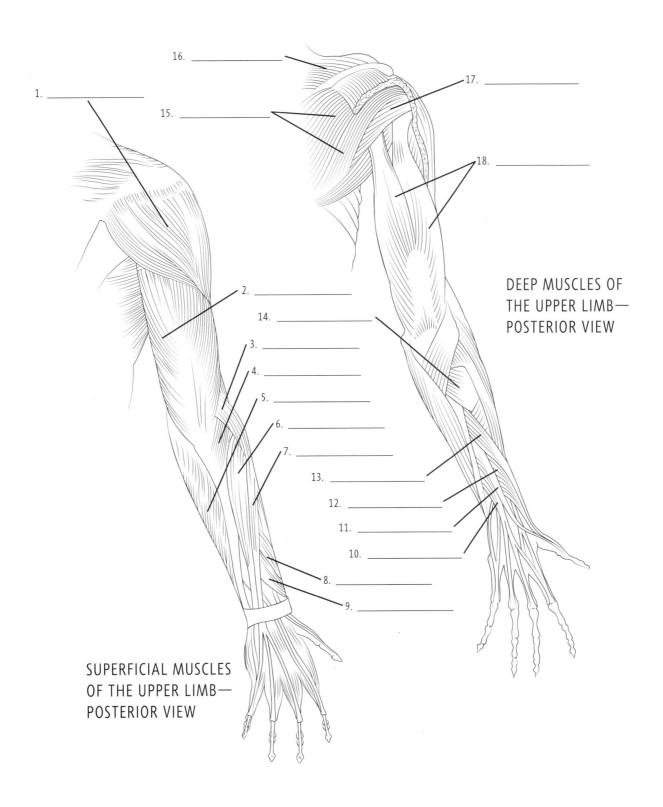

16. _____

17. _____

15. _____

1. _____

18. _____

DEEP MUSCLES OF
THE UPPER LIMB—
POSTERIOR VIEW

2. _____

14. _____

3. _____

4. _____

5. _____

6. _____

7. _____

13. _____

12. _____

11. _____

10. _____

8. _____

9. _____

SUPERFICIAL MUSCLES
OF THE UPPER LIMB—
POSTERIOR VIEW

Answers

1. Deltoid, 2. Long head of triceps brachii, 3. Brachioradialis, 4. Anconeus, 5. Flexor carpi ulnaris, 6. Extensor digiti minimi, 7. Extensor digitorum, 8. Abductor pollicis longus, 9. Extensor pollicis brevis, 10. Extensor indicis, 11. Extensor pollicis longus, 12. Extensor pollicis brevis, 13. Abductor pollicis longus, 14. Supinator, 15. Infraspinatus, 16. Supraspinatus, 17. Teres minor, 18. Triceps brachii

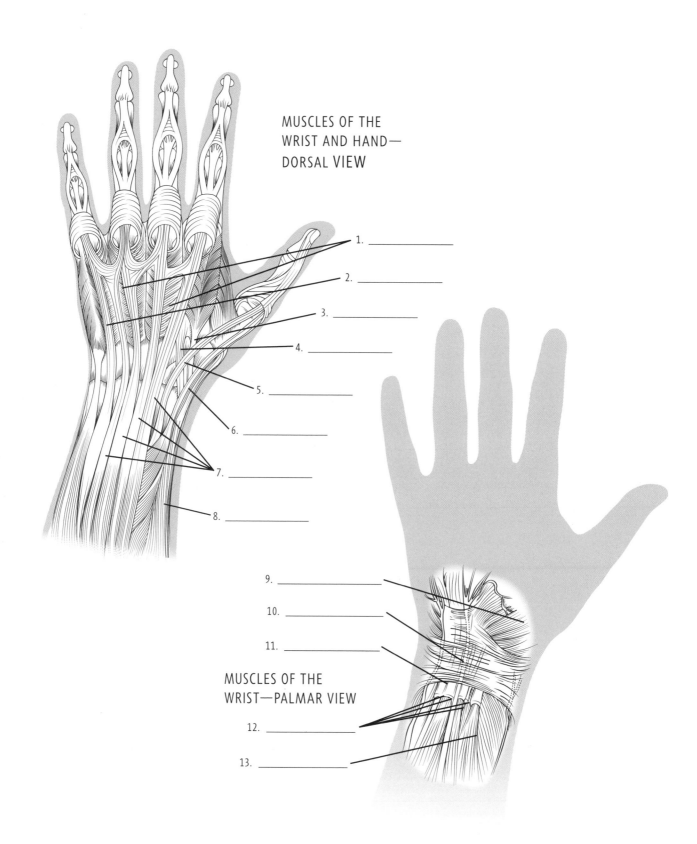

MUSCLES OF THE
WRIST AND HAND—
DORSAL VIEW

1. _____

2. _____

3. _____

4. _____

5. _____

6. _____

7. _____

8. _____

9. _____

10. _____

11. _____

MUSCLES OF THE
WRIST—PALMAR VIEW

12. _____

13. _____

Answers

1. Dorsal interosseous muscles, 2. Extensor digiti minimi, 3. Extensor digitorum, 4. Extensor carpi radialis brevis, 5. Extensor carpi radialis longus, 6. Extensor pollicis brevis, 7. Extensor pollicis longus, 8. Abductor pollicis longus, 9. Thenar muscles, 10. Flexor retinaculum, 11. Tendinous sheath of flexor digitorum superficialis, 12. Flexor digitorum superficialis tendons, 13. Flexor carpi radialis

Muscles of the Lower Limb

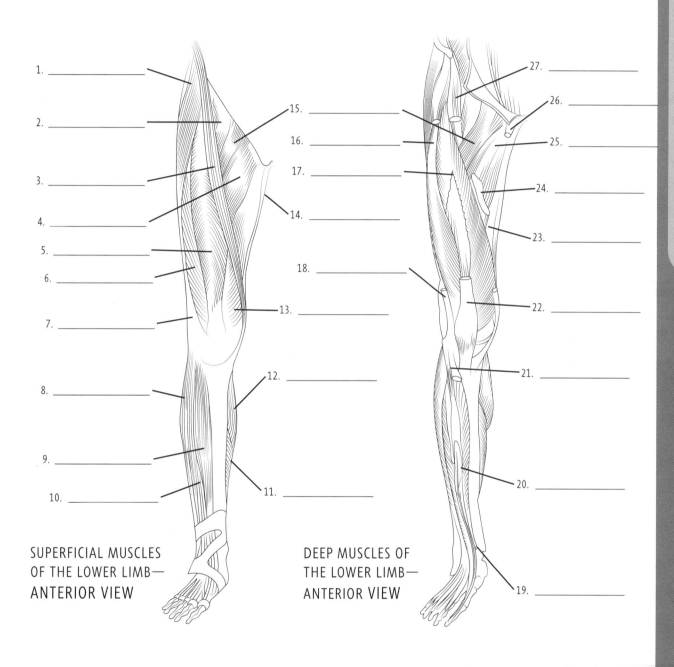

1. _____
2. _____
3. _____
4. _____
5. _____
6. _____
7. _____
8. _____
9. _____
10. _____

15. _____
16. _____
17. _____
14. _____
18. _____
13. _____
12. _____
11. _____

SUPERFICIAL MUSCLES
OF THE LOWER LIMB—
ANTERIOR VIEW

27. _____
26. _____
25. _____
24. _____
23. _____
22. _____
21. _____
20. _____
19. _____

DEEP MUSCLES OF
THE LOWER LIMB—
ANTERIOR VIEW

Answers

Muscles of the Lower Limb

1. _____

2. _____

3. _____

4. _____

5. _____

6. _____

7. _____

8. _____

9. _____

10. _____

11. _____

12. _____

13. _____

14. _____

15. _____

16. _____

17. _____

18. _____

19. _____

20. _____

21. _____

22. _____

SUPERFICIAL MUSCLES
OF THE LOWER LIMB—
POSTERIOR VIEW

DEEP MUSCLES OF
THE LOWER LIMB—
POSTERIOR VIEW

Answers

1. Gluteus medius, 2. Gluteus maximus, 3. Medial head of gastrocnemius, 4. Soleus, 5. Lateral head of gastrocnemius, 6. Gracilis, 7. Semitendinosus, 8. Biceps femoris, 9. Adductor magnus, 10. Piriformis, 11. Superior gemellus, 12. Inferior gemellus, 13. Quadratus femoris, 14. Plantaris, 15. Tibialis posterior, 16. Flexor digitorum longus, 17. Flexor hallucis longus, 18. Fibularis (peroneus) longus, 19. Popliteus, 20. Short head of biceps femoris, 21. Adductor part of adductor magnus, 22. Gluteus minimus

1. _____
2. _____
3. _____
4. _____
5. _____
6. _____
7. _____

MUSCLES OF THE
FOOT—LATERAL VIEW

15. _____
14. _____
13. _____
12. _____

8. _____
9. _____
10. _____
11. _____

16. _____
17. _____
18. _____
19. _____
20. _____
21. _____
22. _____

MUSCLES OF THE FOOT—
POSTEROMEDIAL VIEW

28. _____
27. _____
26. _____
25. _____
24. _____

23. _____

Answers

1. Extensor hallucis longus, 2. Extensor digitorum longus, 3. Superior extensor retinaculum, 4. Tendo calcaneus (Achilles tendon), 5. Tendon sheaths, 6. Superior fibular retinaculum, 7. Inferior fibular retinaculum, 8. Fibularis (peroneus) longus tendon, 9. Extensor digitorum brevis, 10. Fibularis (peroneus) tertius, 11. Fibularis (peroneus) brevis tendon, 12. Extensor hallucis longus tendon, 13. Extensor digitorum brevis tendons, 14. Extensor digitorum longus tendons, 15. Inferior extensor retinaculum, 16. Flexor hallucis longus, 17. Tibialis posterior, 18. Flexor digitorum longus, 19. Tibia, 20. Flexor digitorum longus tendon, 21. Tibialis posterior tendon, 22. Flexor retinaculum, 23. First metatarsal, 24. Calcaneal tuberosity, 25. Tendo calcaneus (Achilles tendon), 26. Flexor hallucis longus tendon, 27. Fibularis (peroneus) longus tendon, 28. Fibularis (peroneus) brevis tendon

295

Skeletal System

SKELETAL SYSTEM—
ANTERIOR VIEW

39. _____
38. _____
37. _____
36. _____
35. _____
34. _____
33. _____
32. _____
31. _____
30. _____
29. _____
28. _____
27. _____
26. _____
25. _____
24. _____
23. _____
22. _____
21. _____
20. _____
19. _____
18. _____

1. _____
2. _____
3. _____
4. _____
5. _____
6. _____
7. _____
8. _____
9. _____
10. _____
11. _____
12. _____
13. _____
14. _____
15. _____
16. _____
17. _____

Answers

1. Frontal bone, 2. Parietal bone, 3. Temporal bone, 4. Maxilla, 5. Cervical vertebra, 6. Costal cartilage, 7. True rib, 8. Thoracic vertebra, 9. False rib, 10. Lumbar vertebra, 11. Transverse process,12. Ilium, 13. Sacrum, 14. Coccyx, 15. Ischium, 16. Pubic symphysis, 17. Tarsal bones, 18. Phalanges, 19. Metatarsal bones, 20. Talus, 21. Fibula, 22. Tibia, 23. Patella, 24. Femur, 25. Pubis, 26. Metacarpal bones, 27. Phalanges, 28. Carpal bones, 29. Ulna, 30. Radius, 31. Twelfth rib (floating rib), 32. Humerus, 33. Sternum, 34. Clavicle, 35. Mandible, 36. Lower teeth, 37. Upper teeth, 38. Anterior nasal aperture (piriform), 39. Orbit

SKELETAL SYSTEM— POSTERIOR VIEW

SKELETAL SYSTEM— LATERAL VIEW

1. _____
2. _____
3. _____
4. _____
5. _____
6. _____
7. _____
8. _____
9. _____
10. _____
11. _____
12. _____
13. _____
14. _____
15. _____
16. _____
17. _____
18. _____
19. _____
20. _____
21. _____
22. _____
23. _____
24. _____
25. _____
26. _____
27. _____
28. _____
29. _____
30. _____
31. _____
32. _____
33. _____
34. _____
35. _____
36. _____
37. _____
38. _____
39. _____
40. _____
41. _____
42. _____
43. _____

Answers

34. Mandible, 35. Zygomatic bone, 36. Metatarsal bones, 37. Phalanges, 38. Navicular, 39. Patella, 40. Ischium, 41. Iliac crest, 42. Intervertebral disk, 43. Humerus
22. Metacarpal bones, 23. Pubis, 24. Phalanges, 25. Sacrum, 26. Ilium, 27. Lumbar vertebra, 28. False rib, 29. True rib, 30. Scapula, 31. Acromion, 32. Spine of the scapula, 33. Clavicle,
11. Carpal bones, 12. Ischial tuberosity, 13. Phalanges, 14. Metatarsal bones, 15. Calcaneus, 16. Talus, 17. Fibula, 18. Tibia, 19. Femoral condyle, 20. Femur, 21. Phalanges,
1. Parietal bone, 2. Occipital bone, 3. Atlas (C1), 4. Axis (C2), 5. Spinous process of thoracic vertebra, 6. Thoracic vertebra, 7. Floating ribs (11 & 12), 8. Ulna, 9. Humerus, 10. Radius,

Vertebral Column

1. _____

2. _____

3. _____

4. _____

5. _____

6. _____

7. _____

8. _____

9. _____

10. _____

11. _____

12. _____

13. _____

14. _____

VERTEBRAL COLUMN—
LATERAL VIEW

VERTEBRAL COLUMN—
POSTERIOR VIEW

Answers

1. Cervical vertebrae (C1–C7), 2. Thoracic vertebrae (T1–T12), 3. Lumbar vertebrae (L1–L5), 4. Sacrum, 5. Coccyx, 6. Cervical region (C1–C7), 7. Thoracic region (T1–T12), 8. Lumbar region (L1–L5), 9. Sacral region (S1–S5), 10. Coccygeal region, 11. Transverse processes, 12. Spinous processes, 13. Axis (C2), 14. Atlas (C1)

Index of English medical terms

Bold numbers indicate chapter names and subject titles. Plain numbers indicate illustration names and labels. *Italicized* numbers indicate references in captions.

Index of Latin medical terms

[m. = musculus]

m. abductor digiti minimi 114
m. abductor pollicis brevis 98, 114
m. abductor pollicis longus 99, 115, 118
m. adductor brevis 120
m. adductor hallucis 125
m. adductor longus 98, 111, 113, 120, 122
m. adductor magnus 98, 99, 113, 120, 121, 122
m. adductor pollicis 114
m. anconeus 115
m. arrector pili 51
m. biceps 102
m. biceps brachii 98, 100, 103, 114, 116, 117, 118
m. biceps femoris (caput breve) 122
m. biceps femoris (caput longum) 122
m. biceps femoris 121
m. bipennatus 102
m. biventer 102
m. brachialis 98, 100, 114, 116, 117, 118
m. brachioradialis 98, 99, 100, 114, 115, 116, 117
m. buccinator 104
m. constrictor pharyngis inferior 109
m. constrictor pharyngis medius 109, 201
m. constrictor pharyngis superior 109, 201
m. cremaster 262
m. cricothyroideus 107, 202, 206
m. cruciatus 102
m. deltoideus 74, 98, 99, 100, 110, 114, 115, 116, 119
m. depressor anguli oris 98, 100, 104
m. depressor labii inferioris 104
m. detrusor vesicae 262
m. extensor carpi radialis brevis 117, 118
m. extensor carpi radialis longus 100, 114, 116, 118
m. extensor carpi ulnaris 100, 116
m. extensor digiti minimi 115, 118
m. extensor digitorum 99, 100, 115, 116, 118
m. extensor digitorum brevis 123
m. extensor digitorum longus 98, 100, 120, 122, 123
m. extensor hallucis longus 98, 120, 123
m. extensor indicis 118
m. extensor pollicis brevis 99, 115, 118
m. extensor pollicis longus 115, 118
m. fibularis (peroneus) brevis 123
m. fibularis (peroneus) longus 98, 99, 100, 120, 121, 122
m. fibularis (peroneus) tertius 123
m. flexor carpi radialis 117
m. flexor carpi ulnaris 99, 100, 115, 116, 117
m. flexor digiti minimi 125
m. flexor digiti minimi brevis 114
m. flexor digitorum brevis 124
m. flexor digitorum longus 121, 123
m. flexor digitorum profundus 114
m. flexor digitorum superficialis 98, 114, 117
m. flexor hallucis brevis 125
m. flexor hallucis longus 121, 123
m. flexor pollicis brevis 114
m. flexor pollicis longus 114
m. fusiformis 102
m. gastrocnemius 98, 120
m. gemellus inferior 110, 121
m. gemellus superior 110, 121
m. gluteus maximus 99, 100, 110, 121, 122
m. gluteus medius 110, 121
m. gluteus minimus 110, 121
m. gracilis 98, 99, 120, 121, 122
m. habenalis (cum intersectiones tendineae) 102
m. habenalis 102
m. iliacus 111, 113
m. iliococcygeus 113
m. iliopsoas 98, 111, 113, 120
m. infraspinatus 103, 110, 115, 119

m. intercostalis externus 112, 199
m. intercostalis internus 112
m. interossei plantares 125
m. interosseus palmaris 114
m. ischiococcygeus 113
m. latissimus dorsi 99, 100, 110
m. levator ani 113, 217
m. levator labii superioris 98, 104
m. levator labii superioris alaeque nasi 104
m. levator palpebrae superioris 106
m. levator scapulae 100, 104, 105, 107, 110
m. longus colli 107
m. masseter 98, 105, 108
m. multicaudalis 102
m. multipennatus 102
m. nasalis 104
m. obliquus externus abdominis 98, 99, 100, 110, 111, 217
m. obliquus inferior 106
m. obliquus internus abdominis 110, 217
m. obliquus superior 106
m. obturatorius internus 113
m. occipitalis 98, 99, 100, 104, 105
m. occipitofrontalis 98, 100, 104, 105
m. opponens digiti minimi 114
m. opponens pollicis 114
m. orbicularis 102
m. orbicularis oculi 98, 100, 104
m. orbicularis oris 98, 100, 104, 109
m. palmaris brevis 114
m. papillaris 187
m. pectineus 98, 111, 113, 120
m. pectoralis major 114
m. pectoralis major 98, 100, 206, 265
m. piriformis 110, 113, 121
m. plantaris 121
m. popliteus 121
m. procerus 104
m. pronator teres 114, 117
m. psoas major 111, 113
m. psoas minor 113
m. pterygoideus lateralis 94, 108
m. pterygoideus medialis 94, 108
m. pubococcygeus 113
m. puborectalis 113
m. quadratus 102
m. quadratus femoris 110, 121
m. quadratus lumborum 112, 199
m. quadriceps 102
m. quadriceps femoris 100, 120, 122
m. radialis 102
m. rectus femoris 98, 120, 122
m. rectus inferior 106
m. rectus lateralis 106
m. rectus medialis 106
m. rectus superior 106
m. rhomboideus major 110
m. rhomboideus minor 110
m. sartorius 98, 100, 122
m. scalenus anterior 104, 107, 206
m. scalenus medius 104, 107
m. scalenus posterior 104
m. semimembranosus 99, 121, 122
m. semispinalis capitis 110
m. semitendinosus 99, 121, 122
m. serratus anterior 98, 100, 111
m. serratus posterior inferior 110
m. soleus 98, 99, 100, 120, 121, 122
m. sphincter ani externus 217, 233
m. sphincter ani internus 217, 233
m. sphincter pyloricus 217, 228
m. spiralis 102
m. splenius capitis 104
m. sternocleidomastoideus 98, 99, 100, 104, 105, 107
m. sternohyoideus 98, 105
m. stylohyoideus 201
m. stylopharyngeus 109, 201

m. supinator 114, 115
m. supraspinatus 103, 110, 115, 119
m. temporalis 98, 99, 100, 105, 108
m. tensor fasciae latae 98
m. teres major 74, 99, 110, 115, 119
m. teres minor 99, 103, 110, 119
m. tibialis anterior 98, 100, 103, 120, 122, 123
m. tibialis posterior 121, 123
m. trachealis 202, 204
m. transversus abdominis 217
m. trapezius 98, 99, 100, 104, 105, 107
m. triangularis 102
m. triceps 102
m. triceps brachii 74, 98, 99, 103, 114, 116, 117, 119
m. triceps surae 120
m. unipennatus 102
m. vastus intermedius 120, 122
m. vastus lateralis 98, 99, 120, 121, 122
m. vastus medialis 98, 120, 122
m. zygomaticus major 98, 100, 104
m. zygomaticus minor 104
macrophagocytus 27, 38, 39
macrophagocytus alveolaris 210
macula densa 243
macula sacculi 157, 159
malleolus lateralis 56, 83, 87
malleolus medialis 83, 87
malleus 65, 156, 157, 158
mandibula 54, 55, 56, 59, 94, 108, 272
manubrium sterni 70, 71
margo anterior 83
margo hepatis inferior 226
margo interosseous 77, 83
margo lateralis scapulae 73, 94
margo medialis 83
margo medialis scapulae 73, 94
margo orbitalis inferior 60
margo superior 172
margo superior scapulae 73, 94
margo supraorbitalis 60
massa lateralis atlantis 68
mastocytus 39
maxilla 54, 58, 59, 60, 94
meatus acusticus externus 58, 156, 158, 272
meatus acusticus internus 59
meatus urethrae externum 276
mediastinum testis et tubuli recti 263
medulla (myelencephalon) 274
medulla 51, 141, 160, 173, 208, 255
medulla glandulae suprarenalis 148
medulla glandulae suprarenalis sinistrae 255
medulla oblongata 128, 140
medulla ossium 57
medulla renalis 242
medulla spinalis 20, 107, 129, 130, 133, 143, 148, 149, 207, 215
megakaryocytus 27
melanocytus 51
membrana basalis 253
membrana cellularis 37, 263
membrana cloacalis 276
membrana interossea 78, 87, 117
membrana nuclearis 25, 129
membrana quadrangularis 202
membrana statoconiorum 159
membrana synovialis 74, 119
membrana tectoria 158
membrana thyrohyoida 202
membrana tympanica 65, 158
membrana vestibularis 157
membrum inferius 19
membrum superius 19
meninges 133
meniscus lateralis 84
meniscus medialis 84
mesencephalon 138, 141, 274
mesenterium 218, 234

metencephalon 274
microvilli 24, 253
mitochondrion 24, 25, 129, 263
mm. ciliares 153, 154
mm. hypothenares 114
mm. infrahyoidei 107
mm. intercostales 217
mm. intercostales externi 110
mm. intercostales interni 199
mm. interossei dorsales 118
mm. lumbricales 124
mm. lumbricales 98, 114
mm. quadratus plantae 124
mm. recti abdomines 98, 111
mm. scaleni anterior et medius 100
mm. thenares 114
monocytus 27, 170
mons pubis 265
mucocytus 225
musculi compartimenti femoris posterius 121, 122
musculi erector spinae 110
musculi interossei dorsales 125
musculus palmaris longus 117
myocyti leves 235
myofibra 101
myofibrilla 101
myometrium 279
myosinum 101

N

[n. = nervus]

n. alveolaris 223
n. auricularis posterior 146
n. axillaris 128, 147
n. cervicalis 128
n. cervicalis C1 141
n. cochlearis 157, 158
n. cutaneus femoris lateralis 128, 147
n. digitalis 128
n. facialis (VII) 139, 140
n. femoralis 128, 147
n. fibularis communis 128, 147
n. fibularis profundus 128, 147
n. fibularis superficialis 128, 147
n. glossopharyngeus (IX) 139, 140
n. hypoglossus (XII) 139, 140
n. intercostalis 128
n. ischiadicus 128, 147
n. lingualis 224
n. medianus 128, 146, 147
n. musculocutaneus 147
n. obturatorius 122, 128, 147
n. oculomotorius (III) 139, 140
n. olfactorius (I) 139
n. olfactorius (I) 163
n. opticus (II) 106, 155, 185
n. opticus (II) 139, 140
n. periphericus 143
n. phrenicus 112, 199
n. radialis 118, 128, 147
n. saphenus 122, 128
n. tibialis posterior 128, 147
n. trigeminus (V) 139
n. trochlearis (IV) 139, 140, 141
n. ulnaris 128, 146, 147
n. vagus (X) 139, 140
n. vestibulocochlearis (VIII) 139, 140
nervus abducens (VI) 139, 140
nervus accessorius (XI) 139, 140, 141
nervus coccygeus 143
neurofibra 158, 159, 161
neurohypophysis 245, 250, 251
neuron mitrale 163

neuron tractus hypothalamohypophysialis 245
neurosoma 25, 129
neutrophilus 27
nn. digitales palmares communes 146, 147
nn. spinales C1–C8 143
nn. spinales L1–L5 143
nn. spinales S1–S5 143
nn. spinales T1–T12 143
nodi anteriores 168
nodi axillares 168
nodi axillarum apicales 168
nodi buccinatorii 168
nodi cervicales 168
nodi cubitales 168
nodi iliaci communes 168
nodi iliaci externi 168
nodi iliaci interni 168
nodi inguinales superficiales 168
nodi intercostales 168
nodi laterales 168
nodi mastoidei 168
nodi mediastinales posteriores 168
nodi parasternales 168
nodi parotidei 168
nodi poplitei 168
nodi sacrales 168
nodulus lymphoideus 235
nodus interruptionis myelini 142
nucleolus 24, 25, 129
nucleus anterior thalami 162
nucleus caudatus 131, 138
nucleus endotheliocyti 26
nucleus endotheliocytus 177

O

occipitalis 272
oculus 148, 149
oesophagus 107, 112, 199, 201, 202, 207, 230, 231
olecranon 76, 77, 93, 94, 99, 115, 116, 117
omentum majus 216, 217
omentum minus 215
oocytus primarius 266
oocytus secondarius 266
orbita 54
organa genitalia 148, 149
organa olfactoria 160
organum spirale 157
origo extensor communis 117
os capitatum 78
os coccygis 54, 55, 56, 67, 80, 81, 95
os cranii 50
os cuboideum 56, 86
os cuneiforme intermedium 56
os cuneiforme laterale 56
os cuneiforme mediale 56
os ethmoidale 58, 64
os frontale 54, 56, 58, 59, 60, 63, 64
os hamatum 78
os ilium 54, 55, 56, 80, 81, 95, 217
os ischii 54, 56, 80, 81, 95
os lacrimale 58
os lunatum 78
os metacarpi I 79
os metacarpi II 79
os metacarpi III 79
os metacarpi pollicis 92
os metacarpus 54
os metatarsi 54, 55
os metatarsi I 123
os nasale 272
os nasale 58, 59, 60
os naviculare 56
os occipitale 55, 56, 58, 59, 61, 62, 63
os palatinum 62

os parietale 54, 55, 56, 58, 59, 60, 61, 63
os pisiforme 78
os pubis 54, 56, 81, 95, 217
os sacrum 54, 55, 56, 69, 81, 95, 280
os scaphoideum 78, 92
os sphenoidale 56, 162
os temporale 54, 56, 60, 61, 64, 65, 157
os trapezium 78, 92
os trapezoideum 78
os triquetrum 78
os zygomaticum 55, 58, 60, 62, 272
ossa carpalia 54, 55, 72, 79, 92
ossa cuneiformia 86
ossa metacarpalia 55, 72, 78
ossa metatarsalia 56, 82, 86
ossa tarsalia 54, 82
ossiculae 157, 158
osteonum 63
ostii ureteres 241
ostium ureteris sinister 240
ostium urethrae externum 240, 241, 265
ostium vaginae 276
ovarii 249, 256, 264, 267
ovulatio 257, 266
ovum 256, 267, 269

P

palatum molle 201, 220
palatum osseum (processus palatinus maxilla) 59
pallium (telencephalon) 274
pancreas 148, 149, 192, 214, 219, 248, 249
panniculus adiposus 46
papilla dermis 46, 51
papilla duodeni major 217
papilla filiformes 161, 221
papilla filiformis 160
papilla foliatae 161, 221
papilla fungiformis 160, 161, 221
papilla lacrimalis superior 152
papilla mammaria 265
papilla renalis 242
papilla vallata 160, 161, 221
parathryrocytus oxyphilicus 253
parathyrocytus principalis 253
paries arteriae 178
paries intestinus tenuis 235
paries posterior pharyngis 220
paries uteri 269
paries uteri 269
paries vaginae 265
parietale 272
pars abdominalis aortae 112, 192, 199, 215, 216, 217, 238, 239, 240, 241, 242
pars addcutorius musculi adductorius magnus 121
pars ascendens aortae 187, 190, 191, 207
pars descendens aortae 176, 180, 186, 187, 207
pars descendens m. trapezii 110
pars flaccida 156
pars laryngea pharyngis 201
pars mastoideus 272
pars medialis musculi adductorius magnus 121
pars membranacea 262
pars meningea durae matris cranialis 133
pars nasalis pharyngis 200, 201, 202
pars oralis pharyngis 201, 202
pars periostea durae matris cranialis 133
pars petrosa ossis temporalis 59
pars prostatica 262
pars squamosa ossis temporalis 58, 272
pars tensa 156
pars transversa m. trapezii 110
pars tympanica ossis temporalis 58, 62
patella 54, 56, 82, 84, 85, 95

ACKNOWLEDGMENTS

The publisher would like to thank Professor Ian Whitmore for his work on the Latin terms.

The Latin anatomical terms used in this book are based on *Terminologia Anatomica* (2011, Georg Thieme Verlag), which represents the international standard on anatomical terminology developed by the Federative Committee on Anatomical Terminology (FCAT) and the International Federation of Associations of Anatomists (IFAA) in 1998.